MATHEM
FOR LEAVIN

C000072077

N

Ɛ

2

MATHEMATICS REVISION FOR LEAVING CERTIFICATE PAPER 2

HIGHER LEVEL

George Humphrey

Gill & Macmillan

Gill & Macmillan Ltd
Hume Avenue
Park West
Dublin 12
with associated companies throughout the world
www.gillmacmillan.ie

0 7171 3038 X

Typeset by Mathematical Composition Setters Ltd, Salisbury, Wiltshire
Printed by ColourBooks Ltd, Dublin

*The paper used in this book is made from the wood pulp of managed forests.
For every tree felled, at least one tree is planted, thereby renewing
natural resources.*

CONTENTS

PREFACE

This book was written to help you revise for the Leaving Certificate Higher Level Mathematics Examination, Paper 2. It has been developed to help you to achieve the best result you can in the examination. Unlike a textbook, this book has been organised to make your revision easier.

Throughout your course you can use the book to:

- remind you of what you have been taught
- help you with your homework
- do some extra practice at the kind of questions you will meet in the examination
- sort out things you did not quite follow in class
- focus on the essential points in each topic
- organise your revision and preparation for the actual examination.

To make the best use of this book, attempt to solve the problems yourself before looking at the solutions given. Re-do any questions you answer incorrectly. Get into the habit of making your own notes as you work throughout the book and use these notes in later revision sessions.

I would like to thank Michael Dunne, Maryfield College, who read the entire manuscript and made many valuable suggestions which I have included in the final text. I would also like to thank Jane Finucane, second year student, Trinity College, Dublin, who also read the entire manuscript and greatly reduced my errors!

I also wish to express my thanks to the staff at Gill & Macmillan for their advice, guidance and untiring assistance in the preparation and presentation of the text.

George Humphrey
St Andrew's College
Booterstown Avenue
Blackrock
Co. Dublin
December 1996

GUIDELINES ON DOING THE EXAM

Each question carries a total of 50 marks. Therefore, you should not spend more than 25 minutes answering any one question. Attempt each part of each question as there is an **'attempt mark'** given for each part which is normally worth one-third of the marks. Marks may be lost if all your work is not shown. If you use a calculator, show the results of each stage of the calculation. Do what the question asks and always write any formula that you use. Give clear reasons for your answers if asked. Make sure you understand the words *solve, verify, evaluate, show, prove, plot, investigate, hence, calculate.* Be familiar with the relevant pages of the mathematical tables, in particular, pages 6, 7, 9, 41 and 42. Drawing diagrams can help you in obtaining a solution but do not answer questions from the diagram where the use of a formula would be expected. It is good practice to make the units on both axes the same and is essential when drawing circles.

Marking Scheme
There is an attempt to divide each question into 3 parts:

(a) Straightforward, testing only one or two basic concepts and carrying a total of 10 marks.
(b) More difficult but still straightforward and carrying a total of 20 marks.
(c) Much more challenging and may have several parts, all related to the one situation and carrying a total of 20 marks.

Structure of the Examination
Paper 2
Time: $2\frac{1}{2}$ hours   Marks: 300
Section A: Attempt any 5 questions from a choice of 7

Q1	The Circle
Q2	Vectors
Q3	The Line and Transformation Geometry
Q4, 5	Trigonometry
Q6, 7	Permutations, Combinations, Probability, Statistics and Difference Equations

Section B: Attempt any 1 question from a choice of 4

Q8	Further Calculus and Series
Q9	Further Probability and Statistics
Q10	Groups
Q11	Further Geometry

1. THE CIRCLE

Equation of a Circle

> **Note:** Two quantities are needed to find the equation of a circle:
>
>   **1.** Centre   **2.** Radius
>
>> The equation of a circle, centre $(0, 0)$ and radius r, is:
>> $$x^2 + y^2 = r^2$$
>
>> The equation of a circle, centre (h, k) and radius r, is:
>> $$(x - h)^2 + (y - k)^2 = r^2$$

Note: A diagram is a very effective way to see what is going on. When drawing a circle always make sure the scales are the same on both the X and Y axes.

Points Inside, On or Outside a Circle

If the coordinates of a point satisfy the equation of a circle, then that point is **on** the circle. Otherwise, the point is either **inside** or **outside** the circle.

The following method is used to decide whether a point is inside, on or outside a circle.

> **1.** Substitute the coordinates of the given point into the equation of the circle.
> **2.** One of the following three situations will arise:
>
>   **(i)**   LHS < RHS,   the point is **inside** the circle
>
>   **(ii)** LHS = RHS,   the point is **on** the circle
>
>   **(iii)** LHS > RHS,   the point is **outside** the circle

Note: Another way of determining if a point is inside, on or outside a circle is to find the distance between the centre of a circle and the given point and compare this distance to the radius.

Equation of a Tangent to a Circle at a Given Point

A tangent is perpendicular to the radius that joins the centre of a circle to the point of tangency. This fact is used to find the slope of the tangent when a point on the circle is given. In the diagram on the right, the radius R is perpendicular to the tangent T at the point of tangency p.

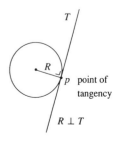

$R \perp T$

The equation of a tangent to a circle at a given point is found with the following steps.

Step 1: Find the slope of the radius to the point of tangency.

Step 2: Turn this slope upside down and change its sign.

This gives the slope of the tangent.

Step 3: Use the coordinates of the point of contact and the slope of the tangent at this point in the formula:

$$(y - y_1) = m(x - x_1)$$

This gives the equation of the tangent.

Note: The perpendicular distance from the centre of the circle to the tangent is equal to the radius.

Circle Intersecting the Axes

To find where a circle intersects the axes, we use the following.

The circle intersects the X axis at $y = 0$.

The circle intersects the Y axis at $x = 0$.

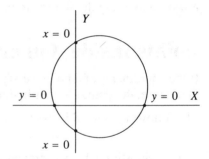

Intersection of a Line and a Circle

To find the points where a line and a circle meet, the 'method of substitution' between their equations is used. The method involves the following three steps.

1. Get x or y on its own from the line.

(Look carefully and select, if possible, the variable which will make the working easier.)

2. Substitute for this same variable into the equation of the circle and solve the resultant quadratic equation.

3. Substitute **separately** the value(s) obtained in Step 2 into the linear equation in Step 1 to find the corresponding value(s) of the other variable.

Note: If there is only one **point of intersection** between a line and a circle, then the line is a **tangent** to the circle.

Transformations on Circles

Under a central symmetry, axial symmetry, translation or rotation, a circle will keep the **same** radius. Hence, all that is needed is to find the image of the centre under the particular transformation. The equation of a circle under a transformation is found with the following steps.

---

1. Find the **centre** and **radius** of the given circle.

2. Find the **image** of the centre under the given transformation.

3. Use this new centre and the radius of the original circle in the equation:

$$(x - h)^2 + (y - k)^2 = r^2$$

to find the equation of the circle.

Touching Circles

To investigate whether two circles touch, or intersect, we compare the distance between their centres to the sum or difference of their radii.

Consider two circles of radius r_1 and r_2 $(r_1 > r_2)$, and let d be the distance between their centres.

(i) Circles touch externally	**(ii)** Circles touch internally
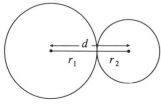	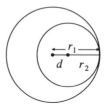
$d = r_1 + r_2$	$d = r_1 - r_2$
(iii) Circles do not touch	**(iv)** Circles intersect at two distinct points
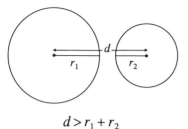	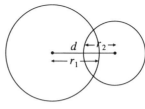
$d > r_1 + r_2$	$d < r_1 + r_2$

The General Equation of a Circle

The general equation of a circle is written as:

$$x^2 + y^2 + 2gx + 2fy + c = 0$$

When the equation of a circle is given in this form, we use the following method to find its centre and radius.

1. Make sure every term is on the left-hand side and the coefficients of x^2 and y^2 are equal to 1.

2. Centre $= (-g, -f) = (-\frac{1}{2}$ coefficient of x, $-\frac{1}{2}$ coefficient of y)

3. Radius $= \sqrt{g^2 + f^2 - c}$

Note: If $c = 0$, then the circle passes through the origin $(0, 0)$.

Touching the Axes

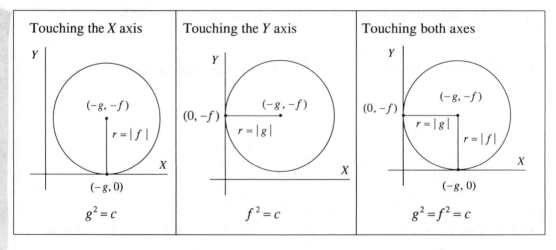

Touching the X axis	Touching the Y axis	Touching both axes
$(-g, -f)$ $r = |f|$ $(-g, 0)$ $g^2 = c$	$(0, -f)$ $(-g, -f)$ $r = |g|$ $f^2 = c$	$(0, -f)$ $(-g, -f)$ $r = |g|$ $r = |f|$ $(-g, 0)$ $g^2 = f^2 = c$

Centre on an Axis

Centre on the X axis, $f = 0$	Centre on the Y axis, $g = 0$
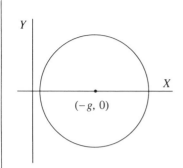	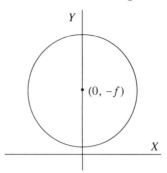
Equation: $x^2 + y^2 + 2gx + c = 0$	Equation: $x^2 + y^2 + 2fy + c = 0$

Finding Equations of Circles Given Different Types of Information

Note: If the centre and radius are given, or can be found, then using $(x - h)^2 + (y - k)^2 = r^2$ is best.

Type 1. Given three points on the circle.

Method 1:

Let the equation of the circle be $x^2 + y^2 + 2gx + 2fy + c = 0$.

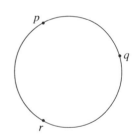

(i)   Substitute each point into this equation.

(ii) This gives three equations in three unknowns: g, f and c.

(iii) Solve these equations for g, f and c.

(iv) Put these values back into the equation.

Method 2:

Let the three points be p, q and r.

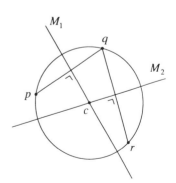

(i)   Find the equations of the perpendicular bisectors M_1 and M_2 of the chords $[pq]$ and $[qr]$, respectively.

(The perpendicular bisector of a chord passes through the centre)

(ii) The centre of the circle is $c = M_1 \cap M_2$.

(Solve the equations of M_1 and M_2 simultaneously)

(iii) The radius is the distance from c to p, q or r.

(iv) Use the formula: $(x - h)^2 + (y - k)^2 = r^2$.

Type 2. Given two points on the circle and the equation of a line containing the centre.

Let the equation of the circle be $x^2 + y^2 + 2gx + 2fy + c = 0$.

(i) Substitute both points into this equation.

(ii) Substitute $(-g, -f)$ into the equation of the given line.

(iii) This gives three equations in three unknowns: g, f and c.

(iv) Solve these equations for g, f and c.

(v) Put these values back into the equation.

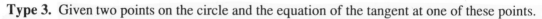

Type 3. Given two points on the circle and the equation of the tangent at one of these points.

(i) Find the equation of L, the line perpendicular to the tangent T passing through the given point of contact. This line will contain the centre c.

(ii) Find the equation of M, the perpendicular bisector of $[pq]$. This line will also contain the centre c.

(iii) Find the centre c, the point of intersection of L and M, by solving the equations of L and M simultaneously.

(iv) Find the radius r, the distance from c to p or q.

(v) Use the formula: $(x - h)^2 + (y - k)^2 = r^2$.

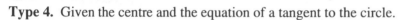

Type 4. Given the centre and the equation of a tangent to the circle.

We have the centre and require the radius. We use the fact that:

> radius = perpendicular distance from centre to the tangent

Having found the radius we use the formula: $(x - h)^2 + (y - k)^2 = r^2$.

Type 5. Often we have to use geometrical facts concerning a circle.

(i) Angle in a semicircle is a right angle.

This enables us to use Pythagoras' Theorem:

$$|pq|^2 + |qr|^2 = |pr|^2$$

where c is the centre of the circle.

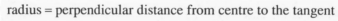

(ii) Radius perpendicular to a chord.

A radius (or part of a radius) that is perpendicular to a chord bisects that chord. This also enables us to use Pythagoras' Theorem:

$$d^2 + x^2 = r^2$$

Thus, knowing two of d, x and r, we can find the third.

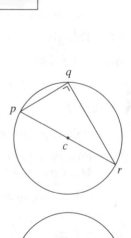

Common Chord and Common Tangent

> If $S_1 = 0$ and $S_2 = 0$ are the equations of two circles in standard form, then
> $S_1 - S_2 = 0$ is the equation of the common chord or common tangent of the two circles.

(i) Common chord

$$S_1 - S_2 = 0$$

Two points of intersection

(ii) Common tangent

$$S_1 - S_2 = 0$$

One point of intersection

Note: To find the equation of the common chord, or common tangent, of two circles, $S_1 = 0$ and $S_2 = 0$, the coefficients of x^2 and y^2 must be the same for both circles.

Parametric Equation of a Circle

We can represent the equation of a circle with x and y written as trigonometric functions of the parameter θ.

> $$x = h + r \sin \theta, \qquad y = k + r \cos \theta$$
>
> are the parametric equations of the circle
>
> $$(x - h)^2 + (y - k)^2 = r^2$$

We can also represent the equation of a circle with x and y written as algebraic functions of the parameter t. For example,

$$x = \frac{1 - t^2}{1 + t^2}, \qquad y = \frac{2t}{1 + t^2}$$

Example

Find the Cartesian equations of each of the following circles whose parametric equations are:

(i) $x = \sin\theta - 2, \; y = \cos\theta + 1$

(ii) $x = 4\cos\theta, \; y = 2 + 4\sin\theta$

(iii) $x = -2 + \frac{1}{3}\sin\theta, \; y = 1 + \frac{1}{3}\cos\theta$

(iv) $x = 5 + \frac{\sqrt{3}}{2}\cos\theta, \; y = -3 + \frac{\sqrt{3}}{2}\sin\theta$

(v) $x = \dfrac{6t}{t^2 + 1}, \; y = \dfrac{3(t^2 - 1)}{t^2 + 1}$

(vi) $x = (t + 1), \; y = \pm\sqrt{15 - t^2 - 2t}$

Solution:

We use the fact that $\sin^2\theta + \cos^2\theta = 1$.

(i) $\qquad x = \sin\theta - 2 \qquad\qquad\qquad y = \cos\theta + 1$

$\Rightarrow \quad (x + 2) = \sin\theta \qquad\quad$ and $\qquad (y - 1) = \cos\theta$

$\Rightarrow \qquad\qquad (x + 2)^2 + (y - 1)^2 = \sin^2\theta + \cos^2\theta$

$\Rightarrow \quad x^2 + 4x + 4 + y^2 - 2y + 1 = 1$

$\Rightarrow \qquad\quad x^2 + y^2 + 4x - 2y + 4 = 0$

(ii) $\quad x = 4\cos\theta \qquad\qquad\qquad y = 2 + 4\sin\theta$

$\Rightarrow \quad x = 4\cos\theta \qquad$ and $\qquad (y - 2) = 4\sin\theta$

$\Rightarrow \qquad\quad x^2 + (y - 2)^2 = (4\cos\theta)^2 + (4\sin\theta)^2$

$\Rightarrow \qquad\quad x^2 + y^2 - 4y + 4 = 16\cos^2\theta + 16\sin^2\theta$

$\Rightarrow \qquad\quad x^2 + y^2 - 4y + 4 = 16(\cos^2\theta + \sin^2\theta)$

$\Rightarrow \qquad\quad x^2 + y^2 - 4y + 4 = 16$

$\Rightarrow \qquad\quad x^2 + y^2 - 4y - 12 = 0$

(iii) $\qquad x = -2 + \frac{1}{3}\sin\theta \qquad\qquad\qquad y = 1 + \frac{1}{3}\cos\theta$

$\Rightarrow \qquad\quad 3x = -6 + \sin\theta \qquad$ and $\qquad\quad 3y = 3 + \cos\theta$

$\Rightarrow \quad (3x + 6) = \sin\theta \qquad$ and $\qquad (3y - 3) = \cos\theta$

$\Rightarrow \qquad\qquad\qquad (3x + 6)^2 + (3y - 3)^2 = \sin^2\theta + \cos^2\theta$

$\Rightarrow \quad 9x^2 + 36x + 36 + 9y^2 - 18y + 9 = 1$

$\Rightarrow \qquad\quad 9x^2 + 9y^2 + 36x - 18y + 44 = 0$

(iv) $\qquad x = 5 + \frac{\sqrt{3}}{2} \cos\theta \qquad\qquad\qquad y = -3 + \frac{\sqrt{3}}{2} \sin\theta$

$\Longrightarrow \qquad 2x = 10 + \sqrt{3}\cos\theta \qquad$ and $\qquad 2y = -6 + \sqrt{3}\sin\theta$

$\Longrightarrow \quad (2x - 10) = \sqrt{3}\cos\theta \qquad$ and $\qquad (2y + 6) = \sqrt{3}\sin\theta$

$\Longrightarrow \qquad\qquad (2x - 10)^2 + (2y + 6)^2 = (\sqrt{3}\cos\theta)^2 + (\sqrt{3}\sin\theta)^2$

$\Longrightarrow \quad 4x^2 - 40x + 100 + 4y^2 + 24y + 36 = 3\cos^2\theta + 3\sin^2\theta$

$\Longrightarrow \quad 4x^2 - 40x + 100 + 4y^2 + 24y + 36 = 3(\cos^2\theta + \sin^2\theta)$

$\Longrightarrow \quad 4x^2 - 40x + 100 + 4y^2 + 24y + 36 = 3$

$\Longrightarrow \qquad 4x^2 + 4y^2 - 40x + 24y + 133 = 0$

(v) $\quad x = \dfrac{6t}{t^2 + 1}, \qquad y = \dfrac{3(t^2 - 1)}{t^2 + 1}$

$\Longrightarrow \quad x^2 + y^2 = \left(\dfrac{6t}{t^2 + 1}\right)^2 + \left(\dfrac{3(t^2 - 1)}{t^2 + 1}\right)^2$

$\qquad\qquad = \dfrac{36t^2}{t^4 + 2t^2 + 1} + \dfrac{9t^4 - 18t^2 + 9}{t^4 + 2t^2 + 1}$

$\qquad\qquad = \dfrac{9t^4 + 18t^2 + 9}{t^4 + 2t^2 + 1} = \dfrac{9(t^4 + 2t^2 + 1)}{(t^4 + 2t^2 + 1)} = 9$

Thus, $\quad x^2 + y^2 = 9$

(vi) $\quad x = (t + 1), \qquad y = \pm\sqrt{15 - t^2 - 2t}$

$\Longrightarrow \quad x^2 + y^2 = (t + 1)^2 + (\pm\sqrt{15 - t^2 - 2t})^2$

$\qquad\qquad = t^2 + 2t + 1 + 15 - t^2 - 2t = 16$

Thus, $\quad x^2 + y^2 = 16$

Example

Find the centre and radius of each of the following circles.

(i) $\quad x^2 + y^2 = 8x + 9$ $\qquad\qquad$ **(ii)** $\quad x(x - 4) = y(6 - y) - 3$

(iii) $\quad 2x^2 + 2y^2 - 6x + 2y - 5 = 0$ $\qquad$ **(iv)** $\quad (x - 1)(x - 3) + (y - 2)(y + 4) = 1$

Solution:

First write the equation of each circle in the form: $x^2 + y^2 + 2gx + 2fy + c = 0$, where:

centre $= (-g, -f)$, $\qquad\qquad\qquad\qquad$ radius $= \sqrt{g^2 + f^2 - c}$

(i)
$$x^2 + y^2 = 8x + 9$$
$$x^2 + y^2 - 8x + 0y - 9 = 0$$

centre $= (4, 0)$

radius $= \sqrt{(4)^2 + (0)^2 + 9}$

$\qquad = \sqrt{16 + 9} = \sqrt{25} = 5$

(ii)
$$x(x - 4) = y(6 - y) - 3$$
$$x^2 - 4x = 6y - y^2 - 3$$
$$x^2 + y^2 - 4x - 6x + 3 = 0$$

centre $= (2, 3)$

radius $= \sqrt{2^2 + 3^2 - 3}$

$\qquad = \sqrt{4 + 9 - 3} = \sqrt{10}$

(iii)
$$2x^2 + 2y^2 - 6x + 2y - 5 = 0$$
$$x^2 + y^2 - 3x + y - \tfrac{5}{2} = 0$$

centre $= (\tfrac{3}{2}, -\tfrac{1}{2})$

radius $= \sqrt{(\tfrac{3}{2})^2 + (-\tfrac{1}{2})^2 + \tfrac{5}{2}}$

$\qquad = \sqrt{\tfrac{9}{4} + \tfrac{1}{4} + \tfrac{5}{2}} = \sqrt{5}$

(iv)
$$(x - 1)(x - 3) + (y - 2)(y + 4) = 1$$
$$x^2 - 4x + 3 + y^2 + 2y - 8 = 1$$
$$x^2 + y^2 - 4x + 2y - 6 = 0$$

centre $= (2, -1)$

radius $= \sqrt{2^2 + (-1)^2 + 6}$

$\qquad = \sqrt{4 + 1 + 6} = \sqrt{11}$

If the locus of a set of points is of the form $x^2 + y^2 + 2gx + 2fy + c = 0$, then the locus is a circle and we can find its centre and radius.

Example

$p\,(3, -1)$, $q\,(3, -4)$ and $r\,(x, y)$ are points such that $2|qr| = |pr|$.

Verify that r is on a circle. Find the centre and radius-length of the circle.

Solution:

$p(3, -1)$, $q(3, -4)$ and $r(x, y)$

$$2|qr| = |pr|$$
$$2\sqrt{(x - 3)^2 + (y + 4)^2} = \sqrt{(x - 3)^2 + (y + 1)^2}$$
$$\left(2\sqrt{(x - 3)^2 + (y + 4)^2}\right)^2 = \left(\sqrt{(x - 3)^2 + (y + 1)^2}\right)^2$$
$$4[(x - 3)^2 + (y + 4)^2] = (x - 3)^2 + (y + 1)^2$$
$$4x^2 - 24x + 36 + 4y^2 + 32y + 64 = x^2 - 6x + 9 + y^2 + 2y + 1$$
$$3x^2 + 3y^2 - 18x + 30y + 90 = 0$$
$$x^2 + y^2 - 6x + 10y + 30 = 0$$

$(g = -3, f = 5, c = 30)$

This is a circle as the coefficients of x^2 and y^2 are equal and there is no xy term.

Also, $r = \sqrt{g^2 + f^2 - c} = \sqrt{(-3)^2 + (5)^2 - 30} = \sqrt{9 + 25 - 30} = \sqrt{4} = 2$ and is real.

Thus, centre $= (3, -5)$ and radius $= 2$

Example

$p\,(0, -2)$ and $q\,(-2, -6)$ are points of a circle centre $c(k, -2k)$.

Find k and write the equation of the circle.

Solution:

$$|cp| = |cq| \qquad \text{(as both must equal the radius)}$$

$$\implies \sqrt{(k-0)^2 + (-2k+2)^2} = \sqrt{(k+2)^2 + (-2k+6)^2}$$

$$\implies k^2 + 4k^2 - 8k + 4 = k^2 + 4k + 4 + 4k^2 - 24k + 36$$

$$\implies -8k + 4 = 40 - 20k$$

$$\implies 12k = 36$$

$$\implies k = 3$$

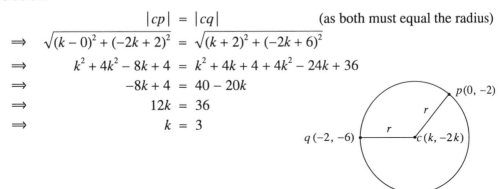

Centre of circle $= (k, -2k) = (3, -6)$ and radius $= |cp| = \sqrt{(3-0)^2 + (-6+2)^2} = 5$

Equation of circle: centre $(3, -6)$, radius 5

$$(x-3)^2 + (y+6)^2 = 5^2$$

$$x^2 - 6x + 9 + y^2 + 12y + 36 = 25$$

$$x^2 + y^2 - 6x + 12y + 20 = 0$$

Example

$p\,(2, 6)$ and $q\,(-4, -2)$ are two points. Show that the locus of a point $r(x, y)$ such that $|\angle prq| = 90°$ is a circle. Write down its centre and radius.

Solution:

Given: $rp \perp rq$

$\therefore$ (slope of rp).(slope of rq) $= -1$

$$\implies \frac{y-6}{x-2} \cdot \frac{y+2}{x+4} = -1$$

$$\implies \frac{y^2 - 4y - 12}{x^2 + 2x - 8} = -1$$

$$\implies y^2 - 4y - 12 = -x^2 - 2x + 8$$

$$\implies x^2 + y^2 + 2x - 4y - 20 = 0 \qquad (g = 1, f = -2, c = -20)$$

This is a circle as the coefficients of x^2 and y^2 are equal and there is no xy term.

Also, $r = \sqrt{g^2 + f^2 - c} = \sqrt{(1)^2 + (-2)^2 + 20} = \sqrt{1 + 4 + 20} = \sqrt{25} = 5$ and is real.

Thus, centre $= (-1, 2)$ and radius $= 5$.

Note: This question could have been solved by finding the midpoint of [pq], the centre of the circumcentre of $\triangle pqr$, and then finding the radius or using Pythagoras' Theorem: $|rp|^2 + |rq|^2 = |pq|^2$.

Example

$x^2 + y^2 - 6x + 4y - 12 = 0$ is the equation of a circle C.

Determine whether each of the points $(7, -3)$, $(-1, -5)$ and $(9, 2)$ is inside, on or outside c.

Solution:

$C: x^2 + y^2 - 6x + 4y - 12 = 0$

$(7, -3)$: $(7)^2 + (-3)^2 - 6(7) + 4(-3) - 12$
$= 49 + 9 - 42 - 12 - 12 = -8 < 0$ $\therefore$ $(7, -3)$ is inside C

$(-1, -5)$: $(-1)^2 + (-5)^2 - 6(-1) + 4(-5) - 12$
$= 1 + 25 + 6 - 20 - 12 = 0$ $\therefore$ $(-1, -5)$ is on C

$(9, 2)$: $(9)^2 + (2)^2 - 6(9) + 4(2) - 12$
$= 81 + 4 - 54 + 8 - 12 = 27 > 0$ $\therefore$ $(9, 2)$ is outside C

Example

$a(3, 5)$ and $b(-1, -1)$ are the end points of a diameter of a circle K.

(i)   Find the centre and radius length of K.

(ii)   Find the equation of K.

(iii) K intersects the X axis at p and q, $p < q$. Find the coordinates of p and q.

Solution:

(i)   Centre

The centre is the midpoint of [ab]: $a(3, 5)$, $b(-1, -1)$.

Thus, the centre of K is $(1, 2)$.

Radius

The radius is the distance from $(1, 2)$ to $(3, 5)$ or $(-1, -1)$.

Thus, radius $= \sqrt{(3 - 1)^2 + (5 - 2)^2} = \sqrt{2^2 + 3^2} = \sqrt{13}$

(ii)   Equation of K:

Centre $(1, 2)$, radius $\sqrt{13}$

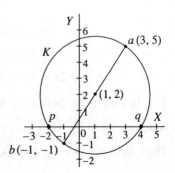

$$(x - 1)^2 + (y - 2)^2 = (\sqrt{13})^2$$
$$x^2 - 2x + 1 + y^2 - 4y + 4 = 13$$
$$x^2 + y^2 - 2x - 4y - 8 = 0$$

12

(iii) Coordinates of p and q

On the X axis, $y = 0$.

$\therefore \quad x^2 - 2x - 8 = 0$ (put in $y = 0$)

$(x + 2)(x - 4) = 0$

$x = -2$ or $x = 4$

Thus, the coordinates of where K intersects the X axis are $p(-2, 0)$ and $q(4, 0)$.

Example

State the centre and radius of the circle $C: x^2 + y^2 - 4x - 6y - 12 = 0$.

Show that the point $p(5, 7)$ is on C and find the equation of the tangent T to C at p.

Find the equation of K, the image of C under an axial symmetry in T.

Solution

$\quad C: x^2 + y^2 - 4x - 6y - 12 = 0$

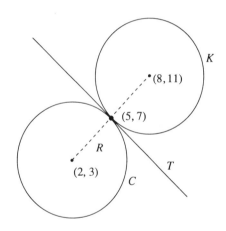

$\quad$ centre $= (2, 3)$

$\quad$ radius $= \sqrt{2^2 + 3^2 + 12} = \sqrt{25} = 5$

$\quad (5, 7) : (5)^2 + (7)^2 - 4(5) - 6(7) - 12$

$\qquad\quad = 25 + 49 - 20 - 42 - 12 = 0$

$\therefore \quad p(5, 7)$ is on the circle C.

Slope of radius $R = \dfrac{7 - 3}{5 - 2} = \dfrac{4}{3}$

$\therefore \quad$ slope of $T = -\frac{3}{4}$

Equation of T: slope $-\frac{3}{4}$, point $(5, 7)$

$\qquad (y - 7) = -\frac{3}{4}(x - 5)$

$\qquad 4y - 28 = -3x + 15$

$\quad 3x + 4y - 43 = 0$

The centre of K is the image of $(2, 3)$ under a central symmetry in $(5, 7)$.

$\qquad (2, 3) \longrightarrow (5, 7) \longrightarrow (8, 11)$

Thus, the centre of K is $(8, 11)$.

Equation of K: centre $(8, 11)$, radius 5 (same as C, radius does not change).

$\qquad\quad (x - 8)^2 + (y - 11)^2 = 5^2$

$\quad x^2 - 16x + 64 + y^2 - 22y + 121 = 25$

$\qquad x^2 + y^2 - 16x - 22y + 160 = 0$

Example

$S_1: x^2 + y^2 + 4x + 2y - 4 = 0$ is the equation of a circle. Find the equations of the circles, S_2 and S_3, both with centre $(-5, 3)$, such that

S_1 touches S_2 internally and S_1 touches S_3 externally.

Solution:

Draw a diagram:

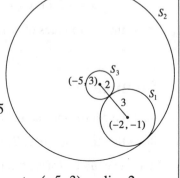

$\quad S_1: x^2 + y^2 + 4x + 2y - 4 = 0$

Centre of $S_1 = (-2, -1)$, radius of $S_1 = \sqrt{4 + 1 + 4} = \sqrt{9} = 3$

Distance from $(-5, 3)$ to $(-2, -1) = \sqrt{(-5 + 2)^2 + (3 + 1)^2} = 5$

Thus, the radius of $S_2 = 2 + 3 + 3 = 8$

and the radius of $S_3 = 5 - 3 = 2$

Equation of S_2: centre $(-5, 3)$, radius 8

$$(x + 5)^2 + (y - 3)^2 = 8^2$$
$$x^2 + 10x + 25 + y^2 - 6y + 9 = 64$$
$$x^2 + y^2 + 10x - 6y - 30 = 0$$

Equation of S_3: centre $(-5, 3)$, radius 2

$$(x + 5)^2 + (y - 3)^2 = 2^2$$
$$x^2 + 10x + 25 + y^2 - 6y + 9 = 4$$
$$x^2 + y^2 + 10x - 6y + 30 = 0$$

Example

S_1 and S_2 are two circles which touch externally.

The centre of S_1 is $(13, 3)$ and the equation of S_2 is $x^2 + y^2 - 2x + 4y - 11 = 0$.

Find the equation of:

(i) S_1 **(ii)** the common tangent T at the point of contact.

Solution:

Draw a diagram:

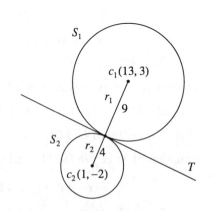

(i) $S_2: x^2 + y^2 - 2x + 4y - 11 = 0$.

Centre of $S_2 = c_2(1, -2)$ and radius of $S_2 = r_2 = \sqrt{1^2 + (-2)^2 + 11} = 4$

Distance between centres =
$|c_1 c_2| = \sqrt{(13 - 1)^2 + (3 + 2)^2} = 13$

As circles touch externally,

$$r_1 + r_2 = |c_1 c_2|$$
$$\Rightarrow \quad r_1 + 4 = 13$$
$$\Rightarrow \quad\quad r_1 = 9$$

Thus, the radius r_1 of S_1 is 9.

14

Equation of S_1:

$$(x - 13)^2 + (y - 3)^2 = 9^2$$
$$x^2 - 26x + 169 + y^2 - 6y + 9 = 81$$
$$x^2 + y^2 - 26x - 6y + 97 = 0$$

(ii) Equation of tangent T:

$$S_1 - S_2 = 0$$
$$\implies (x^2 + y^2 - 26x - 6y + 97) - (x^2 + y^2 - 2x + 4y - 11) = 0$$
$$\implies x^2 + y^2 - 26x - 6y + 97 - x^2 - y^2 + 2x - 4y + 11 = 0$$
$$\implies \qquad\qquad\qquad -24x - 10y + 108 = 0$$
$$\implies \qquad\qquad\qquad 12x + 5y - 54 = 0$$

Example

S is the circle $x^2 + y^2 - 8x + 4y - 5 = 0$.

A circle K touches S internally and passes through c, the centre of S. If $3x - 4y + 5 = 0$ is the tangent common to both circles, find the equation of K.

H is the image of K under the central symmetry in c. Find the equation of H and of the common tangent to H and S.

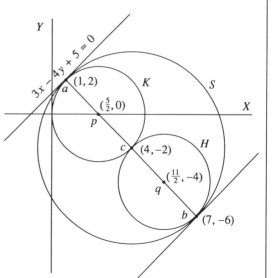

Solution:

$$x^2 + y^2 - 8x + 4y - 5 = 0$$

Centre c is $(4, -2)$.

$$\text{radius} = \sqrt{4^2 + (-2)^2 + 5} = 5$$

We need to find the point of contact a between the tangent and the circles S and K.

$$3x - 4y + 5 = 0$$
$$3x = 4y - 5$$
$$x = \left(\frac{4y - 5}{3}\right)$$

$$x^2 + y^2 - 8x + 4y - 5 = 0$$

$$\left(\frac{4y - 5}{3}\right)^2 + y^2 - 8\left(\frac{4y - 5}{3}\right) + 4y - 5 = 0$$

$$\left(\frac{16y^2 - 40y + 25}{9}\right) + y^2 - \left(\frac{32y - 40}{3}\right) + 4y - 5 = 0$$

15

$$16y^2 - 40y + 25 + 9y^2 - 96y + 120 + 36y - 45 = 0$$
$$25y^2 - 100y + 100 = 0$$
$$y^2 - 4y + 4 = 0$$
$$(y - 2)(y - 2) = 0$$
$$y = 2$$

When $y = 2$,

$$x = \frac{4(2) - 5}{3} = \frac{8 - 5}{3} = \frac{3}{3} = 1$$

Thus, the point of contact is $a(1, 2)$.

The centre of K is the midpoint of $a(1, 2)$ and $c(4, -2) = p(\frac{5}{2}, 0)$.

Radius of $K = \frac{1}{2}$ radius of $S = \frac{1}{2}(5) = \frac{5}{2}$

$\therefore$ K is

$$(x - \tfrac{5}{2})^2 + y^2 = (\tfrac{5}{2})^2$$
$$x^2 - 5x + \tfrac{25}{4} + y^2 = \tfrac{25}{4} \qquad \text{i.e. } K\colon x^2 + y^2 - 5x = 0$$

q is the centre of the circle H.

q is the image of $p(\frac{5}{2}, 0)$ under a central symmetry in $c(4, -2)$.

Thus, q is $(\frac{11}{2}, -4)$. The radius of H is also $\frac{5}{2}$.

$\therefore$ H is $(x - \frac{11}{2})^2 + (y + 4)^2 = (\frac{5}{2})^2$

i.e. $x^2 - 11x + \frac{121}{4} + y^2 + 8y + 16 = \frac{25}{4}$

i.e. $x^2 + y^2 - 11x + 8y + 40 = 0$

The point of contact b between H and S is the image of $a(1, 2)$ under a central symmetry in $c(4, -2)$.

$$a(1, 2) \rightarrow c(4, -2) \rightarrow b(7, -6)$$

Thus, b is $(7, -6)$.

The common tangent at b is parallel to the tangent at a.

The slope of $3x - 4y + 5 = 0$ is $\frac{3}{4}$.
Thus, we have a slope $\frac{3}{4}$ and a point $(7, -6)$

$$(y + 6) = \tfrac{3}{4}(x - 7)$$
$$\Rightarrow \qquad 4y + 24 = 3x - 21$$
$$\Rightarrow \quad 3x - 4y - 45 = 0$$

Thus, the common tangent to H and S is $3x - 4y - 45 = 0$

Example

$S: x^2 + y^2 - 16y + 32 = 0$ and $K: x^2 + y^2 - 18x + 2y + 32 = 0$ are two circles.

Show that the circles touch externally and find their point of contact.

Solution:

$S: x^2 + y^2 + 0x - 16y + 32 = 0$

centre $= (0, 8) = c_1$

radius $= \sqrt{0^2 + 8^2 - 32}$

$\qquad = \sqrt{64 - 32} = \sqrt{32} = 4\sqrt{2}$

$K: x^2 + y^2 - 18x + 2y + 32 = 0$

centre $= (9, -1) = c_2$

radius $= \sqrt{9^2 + (-1)^2 - 32}$

$\qquad = \sqrt{81 + 1 - 32} = \sqrt{50} = 5\sqrt{2}$

$r_1 + r_2 = 4\sqrt{2} + 5\sqrt{2} = 9\sqrt{2}$

distance between centres $=$

$\sqrt{(9 - 0)^2 + (-1 - 8)^2} = \sqrt{81 + 81} = \sqrt{162} = 9\sqrt{2}$

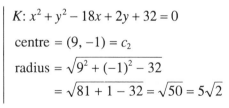

Thus, the circles touch externally, as $r_1 + r_2 = |c_1 c_2|$.

To determine the point of contact, divide the line segment joining the centres in the ratio 4:5.

Let the point of contact be (x, y).

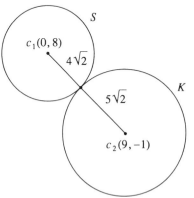

Method 1:

$\dfrac{x - 0}{9 - x} = \dfrac{4}{5}$

$\qquad 5x = 36 - 4x$

$\qquad 9x = 36$

$\qquad x = 4$

$\dfrac{y - 8}{-1 - y} = \dfrac{4}{5}$

$5y - 40 = -4 - 4x$

$\qquad 9y = 36$

$\qquad y = 4$

Thus, the point of contact is $(4, 4)$.

Method 2: Using the formula,

$$(x, y) = \left(\frac{mx_2 + nx_1}{m + n}, \frac{my_2 + nx_1}{m + n} \right)$$

$$= \left(\frac{4(9) + 5(0)}{4 + 5}, \frac{4(-1) + 5(8)}{4 + 5} \right)$$

$$= \left(\frac{36}{9}, \frac{36}{9} \right) = (4, 4)$$

Thus, the point of contact is $(4, 4)$.

Example

If the circles $S_1: x^2 + y^2 + 4x + 6y + c = 0$ and $S_2: x^2 + y^2 - 6x - 4y + 11 = 0$ touch externally, find the value of c.

Solution:

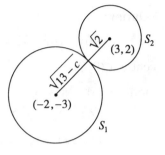

$$S_1: x^2 + y^2 + 4x + 6y + c = 0$$

Centre $= (-2, -3)$, radius $= \sqrt{(-2)^2 + (-3)^2 - c} = \sqrt{13 - c} = r_1$

$$S_2: x^2 + y^2 - 6x - 4y + 11 = 0$$

Centre $= (3, 2)$, radius $= \sqrt{3^2 + 2^2 - 11} = \sqrt{2} = r_2$

Distance between centres $= \sqrt{(3 + 2)^2 + (2 + 3)^2} = \sqrt{50} = 5\sqrt{2}$

Touch externally: thus,

$$r_1 + r_2 = \text{distance between centres}$$
$$\sqrt{13 - c} + \sqrt{2} = 5\sqrt{2}$$
$$\sqrt{13 - c} = 4\sqrt{2}$$
$$13 - c = 32 \quad \text{(square both sides)}$$
$$-c = 19$$
$$c = -19$$

Alternatively,

$$r_1 + \sqrt{2} = 5\sqrt{2}$$
$$r_1 = 4\sqrt{2}$$

We now have the centre and radius of S_1 and can evaluate c.

Equation of S_1:

Centre $(-2, -3)$, radius $= 4\sqrt{2}$

$$(x + 2)^2 + (y + 3)^2 = (4\sqrt{2})^2$$
$$x^2 + y^2 + 4x + 6y - 19 = 0$$

By comparing to $x^2 + y^2 + 4x + 6y + c = 0$, we can see that $c = -19$.

Example

Find the equation of the circle which touches the X axis at $p(4, 0)$, has its centre in the first quadrant and cuts the Y axis at points which are 6 units apart.

Solution:

Draw a diagram.

The X axis is a tangent. The centre is $(4, k)$.

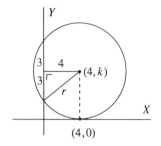

Using Pythagoras' Theorem,

$$r^2 = 3^2 + 4^2 = 9 + 16 = 25$$

Thus, the radius is 5.

From the diagram, $k = 5$ (same as the radius)

Equation of the circle: centre $(4, 5)$, radius 5

$$(x - 4)^2 + (y - 5)^2 = 5^2$$
$$x^2 - 8x + 16 + y^2 - 10y + 25 = 25$$
$$x^2 + y^2 - 8x - 10y + 16 = 0$$

Example

A circle S has centre $(-2, 3)$ and makes a chord 8 units along the X axis.

Find the equation of S.

Solution:

Draw a diagram.

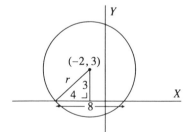

centre $= (-2, 3) = (h, k)$

We need to find the radius r.

From the centre of the circle, drop a perpendicular of length 3 onto the chord. This bisects the chord.

Join the centre to one end of the chord and use Pythagoras' Theorem:

$$r^2 = 3^2 + 4^2 = 9 + 16 = 25 \implies r = 5$$

Equation:

$$(x - h)^2 + (y - k)^2 = r^2$$
$$\implies \quad (x + 2)^2 + (y - 3)^2 = 5^2$$
$$\implies \quad x^2 + 4x + 4 + y^2 - 6y + 9 = 25$$
$$\implies \quad x^2 + y^2 + 4x - 6y - 12 = 0$$

Example

Prove that the line $2x - y + 2 = 0$ intersects the circle $x^2 + y^2 - x - y - 2 = 0$ and find the length of the chord which the line makes with the circle.

Solution:

$$2x - y + 2 = 0$$
$$\Rightarrow \qquad -y = -2x - 2$$
$$\Rightarrow \qquad y = (2x + 2)$$

$$x^2 + y^2 - x - y - 2 = 0$$
$$x^2 + (2x + 2)^2 - x - (2x + 2) - 2 = 0$$
$$x^2 + 4x^2 + 8x + 4 - x - 2x - 2 - 2 = 0$$
$$5x^2 - 5x = 0$$
$$x^2 - x = 0$$
$$x(x - 1) = 0$$
$$x = 0 \text{ or } x = 1$$

$x = 0 : y = 2x + 2 = 0 + 2 = 2$

$x = 1 : y = 2x + 2 = 2 + 2 = 4$

Thus, the points of intersection of the line and the circle are $(0, 2)$ and $(1, 4)$.

$\therefore$ the line forms a chord of the circle.

length of chord $= \sqrt{(1 - 0)^2 + (4 - 2)^2} = \sqrt{1^2 + 2^2} = \sqrt{1 + 4} = \sqrt{5}$

Example

Find the equations of the two circles which contain the points $(0, 3)$ and $(0, -2)$ and with radius $\sqrt{12\frac{1}{2}}$.

Solution:

Method 1:

Midpoint of chord $(0, 3)$ to $(0, -2)$ is $(0, \frac{1}{2})$.

Length of chord is 5.

Thus, half the length of this chord is $2\frac{1}{2}$.

Using Pythagoras' Theorem,

$$x^2 + (2\tfrac{1}{2})^2 = r^2 = 12\tfrac{1}{2}$$
$$x^2 + \tfrac{25}{4} = \tfrac{25}{2}$$
$$x^2 = \tfrac{25}{4}$$
$$x = \pm \tfrac{5}{2}$$

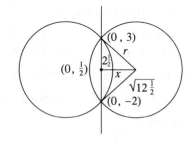

Using a translation from $(0, \frac{1}{2})$, parallel to the X axis, the centres of the circles are $(2\frac{1}{2}, \frac{1}{2})$ and $(-2\frac{1}{2}, \frac{1}{2})$.

Equations:

$$(x - 2\tfrac{1}{2})^2 + (y - \tfrac{1}{2})^2 = 12\tfrac{1}{2} \quad \text{or} \quad (x + 2\tfrac{1}{2})^2 + (y - \tfrac{1}{2})^2 = 12\tfrac{1}{2}$$

i.e.

$$x^2 + y^2 - 5x - y - 6 = 0 \quad \text{or} \quad x^2 + y^2 + 5x - y - 6 = 0$$

Method 2:

Let the equation of the circle be

$$x^2 + y^2 + 2gx + 2fy + c = 0$$

$(0, 3)$ on the circle: $\quad 0 + 9 + 0 + 6f + c = = 0 \Longrightarrow \quad 6f + c = -9 \quad$ ①

$(0, -2)$ on the circle: $\quad 0 + 4 + 0 - 4f + c = = 0 \Longrightarrow \quad -4f + c = -4 \quad$ ②

Solving simultaneously ① and ② gives $f = -\tfrac{1}{2}$, $c = -6$

$$\text{radius} = \sqrt{12\tfrac{1}{2}}$$

$$\sqrt{g^2 + f^2 - c} = \sqrt{12\tfrac{1}{2}}$$

Thus,

$$\Longrightarrow \quad \sqrt{g^2 + (-\tfrac{1}{2})^2 + 6} = \sqrt{12\tfrac{1}{2}} \quad (\text{put in } f = -\tfrac{1}{2}, c = -6)$$

$$\Longrightarrow \quad g^2 + 6\tfrac{1}{4} = 12\tfrac{1}{2}$$

$$\Longrightarrow \quad g^2 = 6\tfrac{1}{4}$$

$$g = \pm 2\tfrac{1}{2}$$

Equations:

$g = 2\tfrac{1}{2}, \; f = -\tfrac{1}{2}, c = -6 \; : \; x^2 + y^2 + 5x - y - 6 = 0$

$g = -2\tfrac{1}{2}, f = -\tfrac{1}{2}, c = -6 \; : \; x^2 + y^2 - 5x - y - 6 = 0$

(same as before)

Example

(i)   Show that the line $3x - 4y + 10 = 0$ is a tangent to the circle $y^2 = x(10 - x)$

(ii) Investigate if the line $x + 3y + 16 = 0$ is a tangent to the circle
$y^2 + 2y - 3 = x(12 - x)$.

Solution:

First write both equations of the circles in the form $x^2 + y^2 + 2gx + 2fy + c = 0$.

In both cases, we compare the length of the radius to the distance from the centre of the circle to the line.

(i)
$$y^2 = x(10 - x)$$
$$\Rightarrow \qquad y^2 = 10x - x^2$$
$$\Rightarrow \quad x^2 + y^2 - 10x + 0y = 0$$

centre $= (5, 0)$

radius $= \sqrt{5^2 + 0} = 5$

Distance from $(5, 0)$ to $3x - 4y + 10 = 0$ is

$$\frac{|3(5) - 4(0) + 10|}{\sqrt{3^2 + 4^2}}$$

$$= \frac{|15 + 10|}{\sqrt{25}} = \frac{25}{5} = 5 = \text{radius}$$

$\therefore$ line is a tangent

(ii)
$$y^2 + 2y - 3 = x(12 - x)$$
$$\Rightarrow \qquad y^2 + 2y - 3 = 12x - x^2$$
$$\Rightarrow \quad x^2 + y^2 - 12x + 2y - 3 = 0$$

centre $= (6, -1)$

radius $= \sqrt{6^2 + (-1)^2 + 3} = \sqrt{40} = 2\sqrt{10}$

Distance from $(6, -1)$ to $x + 3y + 16 = 0$ is

$$\frac{|6 + 3(-1) + 16|}{\sqrt{1^2 + 3^2}}$$

$$= \frac{|6 - 3 + 16|}{\sqrt{10}} = \frac{19}{\sqrt{10}} = \frac{19\sqrt{10}}{10}$$

$$= 1.9\sqrt{10} \neq \text{radius}$$

$\therefore$ line is not a tangent

Example

Find the equation of the circle C with centre $(3, 2)$ which touches the X axis at one point only.

T is a tangent to C and is parallel to the Y axis.

Find the two possible equations for T.

Solution:

Draw a diagram.

The centre $= (3, 2) = (h, k)$.

C touches the X axis at $(3, 0)$.

Radius = distance from $(3, 2)$ to $(3, 0) = 2$.

$h = 3, \quad k = 2, \quad r = 2$

$$(x - h)^2 + (y - k)^2 = r^2$$
$$(x - 3)^2 + (y - 2)^2 = 2^2$$

$C: x^2 + y^2 - 6x - 4y + 9 = 0$

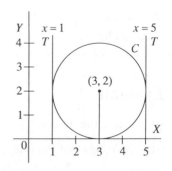

From the diagram the two tangents to C which are parallel to the Y axis are

$x = 1 \qquad$ and $\qquad x = 5$

Example

A line containing $p(5, 6)$ touches the circle $x^2 + y^2 - 4x - 4y + 4 = 0$ at k.

Calculate $|pk|$.

Solution:

Draw a diagram.

$$x^2 + y^2 - 4x - 4y + 4 = 0$$

Centre $= (2, 2)$, call this c.

Radius $= \sqrt{2^2 + 2^2 - 4} = \sqrt{4} = 2.$

$$|pc| = \sqrt{(5 - 2)^2 + (6 - 2)^2} = \sqrt{25} = 5$$

Using Pythagoras' Theorem,

$$|pk|^2 + |kc|^2 = |pc|^2$$
$$\Rightarrow \quad |pk|^2 + 2^2 = 5^2$$
$$\Rightarrow \quad |pk|^2 + 4 = 25$$
$$\Rightarrow \quad |pk|^2 = 21$$
$$\Rightarrow \quad |pk| = \sqrt{21}$$

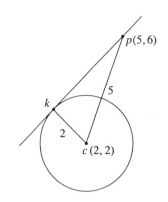

Example

Find the equation of the circle whose centre is $(1, -4)$ and which touches the line $2x + 3y - 6 = 0$.

Solution:

We have the centre and we need the radius. We use the following fact.

Distance from the centre $(1, -4)$ to the line $2x + 3y - 6 = 0$ is equal to the radius.

$$\text{radius} = \frac{|2(1) + 3(-4) - 6|}{\sqrt{2^2 + 3^2}}$$

$$= \frac{|2 - 12 - 6|}{\sqrt{13}} = \frac{|-16|}{\sqrt{13}} = \frac{16}{\sqrt{13}}$$

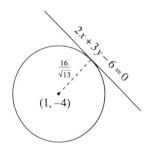

Equation:

$$(x - 1)^2 + (y + 4)^2 = \left(\frac{16}{\sqrt{13}}\right)^2$$

$$x^2 - 2x + 1 + y^2 + 8y + 16 = \frac{256}{13}$$

$$13x^2 - 26x + 13 + 13y^2 + 104y + 208 = 256$$

$$13x^2 + 13y^2 - 26x + 104y - 35 = 0$$

Example

Find two values of k for which the line $8x + 3y + k = 0$ is a tangent to the circle $x^2 + y^2 + 4x - 3y - 12 = 0$.

Solution:

$x^2 + y^2 + 4x - 3y - 12 = 0$

centre $= (-2, \frac{3}{2})$, radius $= \sqrt{(-2)^2 + (\frac{3}{2})^2 + 12} = \sqrt{\dfrac{73}{4}} = \dfrac{\sqrt{73}}{2}$

As $8x + 3y + k = 0$ is a tangent to the circle, the perpendicular distance from the centre of the circle $(-2, \frac{3}{2})$ to the line is equal to the radius $\dfrac{\sqrt{73}}{2}$.

$$\frac{|8(-2) + 3(\frac{3}{2}) + k|}{\sqrt{64 + 9}} = \frac{\sqrt{73}}{2}$$

$$\frac{|k - 11\frac{1}{2}|}{\sqrt{73}} = \frac{\sqrt{73}}{2}$$

$$2|k - 11\tfrac{1}{2}| = \sqrt{73} \cdot \sqrt{73}$$

$$|2k - 23| = 73$$

$\Longrightarrow \qquad 2k - 23 = 73 \quad$ or $\quad 2k - 23 = -73$

$\qquad\qquad\quad 2k = 96 \quad$ or $\qquad\quad 2k = -50$

$\qquad\qquad\quad\; k = 48 \quad$ or $\qquad\qquad\; k = -25$

Example

Find the condition that the line $y = mx + c$ is a tangent to the circle $x^2 + y^2 = a^2$.

Solution:

$\quad x^2 + y^2 = a^2$

Centre $= (0, 0)$ and radius $= a$.

If $y = mx + c$ is a tangent, then the distance from the centre of the circle $(0, 0)$ to the line will equal the radius a.

Thus,

$$\frac{|m(0) - (0) + c|}{\sqrt{m^2 + (-1)^2}} = a \qquad\qquad \begin{array}{l} \text{if } y = mx + c, \text{ then} \\ mx - y + c = 0 \end{array}$$

$$\frac{|c|}{\sqrt{m^2 + 1}} = a$$

$$|c| = a\sqrt{m^2 + 1}$$

$$c = \pm a\sqrt{m^2 + 1} \quad \text{(this is the condition)}$$

24

Example

$L: 3x - 2y - 8 = 0$ is a line and $S: x^2 + y^2 + 2x - 2y - 11 = 0$ is a circle.

Verify that L is a tangent to S and find the coordinates of the point of contact.

Solution:

As we need the point of contact, we use an algebraic approach.

$$3x - 2y - 8 = 0$$
$$\Rightarrow \qquad 3x = 2y + 8$$
$$\Rightarrow \qquad x = \frac{2y + 8}{3}$$

$\left(\text{Put this into the equation of the circle.}\right)$

$$x^2 + y^2 + 2x - 2y - 11 = 0$$

$$\left(\frac{2y + 8}{3}\right)^2 + y^2 + 2\left(\frac{2y + 8}{3}\right) - 2y - 11 = 0$$

$$\frac{4y^2 + 32y + 64}{9} + y^2 + \frac{4y + 16}{3} - 2y - 11 = 0$$

$$4y^2 + 32y + 64 + 9y^2 + 12y + 48 - 18y - 99 = 0$$
$$\text{(multiply across by 9)}$$
$$13y^2 + 26y + 13 = 0$$
$$y^2 + 2y + 1 = 0$$
$$(y + 1)(y + 1) = 0$$
$$y = -1$$

When $y = -1$,

$$x = \frac{2(-1) + 8}{3} = \frac{6}{3} = 2$$

Thus, the coordinates of the point of contact are $(2, -1)$.

As there is only one point of contact, the line L is a tangent to the circle S.

Example

Find the equations of the two tangents from the point $(7, -1)$ to the circle $x^2 + y^2 - 8x + 4y + 12 = 0$.

Solution:

Draw a diagram.

We have a point $(7, -1)$ and we need the slopes of the two tangents.

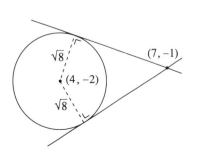

Equation:

$$(y + 1) = m(x - 7)$$
$$y + 1 = mx - 7m$$
$$mx - y + (-7m - 1) = 0$$

Centre of circle $= (4, -2)$.　　Radius $= \sqrt{16 + 4 - 12} = \sqrt{8}$.

25

The distance from the centre of the circle $(4, -2)$ to the tangents is equal to the radius $\sqrt{8}$.

Thus,

$$\frac{|m(4) - (-2) + (-7m - 1)|}{\sqrt{m^2 + (-1)^2}} = \sqrt{8}$$

$$\Rightarrow \qquad \frac{|1 - 3m|}{\sqrt{m^2 + 1}} = \sqrt{8}$$

$$\Rightarrow \qquad \frac{1 - 6m + 9m^2}{m^2 + 1} = 8 \quad \text{(square both sides)}$$

$$\Rightarrow \qquad 1 - 6m + 9m^2 = 8m^2 + 8$$

$$\Rightarrow \qquad m^2 - 6m - 7 = 0$$

$$\Rightarrow \qquad (m + 1)(m - 7) = 0$$

$$\Rightarrow \qquad m = -1 \quad \text{or} \quad m = 7$$

Equations of the tangents:

slope $= -1$, point $= (7, -1)$	slope $= 7$, point $= (7, -1)$
$(y + 1) = -1(x - 7)$	$(y + 1) = 7(x - 7)$
$y + 1 = -x + 7$	$y + 1 = 7x - 49$
$x + y - 6 = 0$	$7x - y - 50 = 0$

Example

Find the equations of the tangents to the circle $x^2 + y^2 - 5x - y + 4 = 0$ which have slope 3.

Solution:

$$x^2 + y^2 - 5x - y + 4 = 0$$

Centre $= (\frac{5}{2}, \frac{1}{2})$, Radius $= \sqrt{(\frac{5}{2})^2 + (\frac{1}{2})^2 - 4} = \sqrt{\frac{5}{2}}$

Any line of slope 3 will be of the form

$$y = 3x + k \quad \text{or} \quad 3x - y + k = 0$$

The distance from the centre of the circle $(\frac{5}{2}, \frac{1}{2})$ to the tangent $3x - y + k = 0$ will equal the radius $\sqrt{\frac{5}{2}}$.

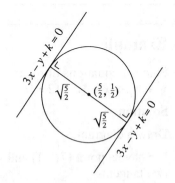

Thus,

$$\frac{|3(\frac{5}{2}) - (\frac{1}{2}) + k|}{\sqrt{3^2 + (-1)^2}} = \sqrt{\frac{5}{2}}$$

$$\Rightarrow \quad \frac{|k + 7|}{\sqrt{10}} = \sqrt{\frac{5}{2}}$$

$$\Rightarrow \quad \frac{k^2 + 14k + 49}{10} = \frac{5}{2} \quad \text{(squaring both sides)}$$

$$\Rightarrow \quad 2k^2 + 28k + 98 = 50$$

$$\Rightarrow \quad 2k^2 + 28k + 48 = 0$$

$$\Rightarrow \quad k^2 + 14k + 24 = 0$$

$$\Rightarrow \quad (k + 2)(k + 12) = 0$$

$$\Rightarrow \quad k = -2 \quad \text{or} \quad k = -12$$

Thus, the equations of the tangents are $3x - y - 2 = 0$ and $3x - y - 12 = 0$.

Example

$p(1, 1)$, $q(6, 2)$ and $r(4, -1)$ are the vertices of Δpqr.

Find the equation of the circle that circumscribes (passes through each vertex) Δpqr.

Solution:

We are given three points of the circumference of the circle.

Let the equation of the circle be $x^2 + y^2 + 2gx + 2fy + c = 0$.

We need the values of g, f and c.

$(1, 1)$ on the circle $\Rightarrow$	$1 + 1 + 2g + 2f + c = 0 \Rightarrow$	$2g + 2f + c = -2$ ①
$(6, 2)$ on the circle $\Rightarrow$	$36 + 4 + 12g + 4f + c = 0 \Rightarrow$	$12g + 4f + c = -40$ ②
$(4, -1)$ on the circle $\Rightarrow$	$16 + 1 + 8g - 2f + c = 0 \Rightarrow$	$8g - 2f + c = -17$ ③

We now solve between ①, ② and ③.

$$\begin{array}{ll} 12g + 4f + c = -40 & ② \\ 2g + 2f + c = -2 & ① \\ \hline 10g + 2f \quad = -38 & ④ \text{ (subtract)} \end{array} \qquad \begin{array}{ll} 12g + 4f + c = -40 & ② \\ 8g - 2f + c = -17 & ③ \\ \hline 4g + 6f \quad = -23 & ⑤ \text{ (subtract)} \end{array}$$

We now solve between ④ and ⑤.

$30g + 6f = -114$	④ × 3	$10g + 2f = -38$	④
$4g + 6f = -23$	⑤	$10(-\frac{7}{2}) + 2f = -38$	

$$26g \quad = -91 \quad \text{(subtract)}$$
$$g \quad = -\frac{91}{26} = -\frac{7}{2}$$

Put this into ④ or ⑤.

$$-35 + 2f = -38$$
$$2f = -3$$
$$f = -\frac{3}{2}$$

Put $g = -\frac{7}{2}, f = -\frac{3}{2}$ into ①, ② or ③ to find c.

$$2g + 2f + c = -2 \quad ①$$
$$2(-\frac{7}{2}) + 2(-\frac{3}{2}) + c = -2$$
$$-7 - 3 + c = -2$$
$$c = 8$$

The equation of the circle is

$$x^2 + y^2 + 2gx + 2fy + c = 0$$
$$x^2 + y^2 + 2(-\frac{7}{2})x + 2(-\frac{3}{2})y + 8 = 0$$
$$x^2 + y^2 - 7x - 3y + 8 = 0$$

Example

Find the equation of the circle which contains the points $(4, 3)$, $(1, -1)$ and has its centre on the line $2x + 3y - 8 = 0$.

Solution:

Let the equation of the circle be $x^2 + y^2 + 2gx + 2fy + c = 0$. Its centre is $(-g, -f)$.

We need the values of g, f and c.

$(4, 3)$ on the circle $\implies 16 + 9 + 8g + 6f + c = 0 \implies 8g + 6f + c = -25$ ①

$(1, -1)$ on the circle $\implies 1 + 1 + 2g - 2f + c = 0 \implies 2g - 2f + c = -2$ ②

Centre $(-g, -f)$ is on the line $2x + 3y - 8 = 0$

$\implies -2g - 3f - 8 = 0 \implies 2g + 3f = -8$ ③

Solving between ①, ② and ③ gives $g = -\frac{5}{2}, f = -1$ and $c = 1$.

The equation of the circle is

$$x^2 + y^2 + 2gx + 2fy + c = 0$$
$$\implies x^2 + y^2 - 5x - 2y + 1 = 0$$

Example

Find the equations of the two circles which contain the points $(-2, 4)$ and $(5,3)$ and have a radius 5.

Solution:

Let the circle be $x^2 + y^2 + 2gx + 2fy + c = 0$.

We need the values of g, f and c.

$(-2, 4)$ is on the circle $\implies$ $4 + 16 - 4g + 8f + c = 0$ $\implies$ $-4g + 8f + c = -20$ ①

$(5, 3)$ is on the circle $\implies$ $25 + 9 + 10g + 6f + c = 0$ $\implies$ $10g + 6f + c = -34$ ②

The radius of the circle is 5

$\implies$ $\sqrt{g^2 + f^2 - c} = 5$

$\implies$ $g^2 + f^2 - c = 25$ (square both sides) ③

We now have to solve between equations ①, ② and ③ with the following steps:

1. From ① and ② eliminate c and then express f in terms of g.

2. From ① or ② get c on its own in terms of f and g, and then substitute for f the expression obtained in step 1.

(we now have f and c in terms of g.)

3. Substitute these expressions into ③, solve for g and then solve for f and c.

1.
$$-4g + 8f + c = -20 \quad ①$$
$$10g + 6f + c = -34 \quad ②$$

$$\overline{-14g + 2f \ = \ 14} \quad \text{(subtract)}$$
$\implies \quad 2f \ = \ 14 + 14g$
$\implies \quad f \ = \ 7 + 7g$

2.
$$-4g + 8f + c \ = -20 \quad ①$$
$\implies \quad c = -20 + 4g - 8f$
$\implies \quad c = -20 + 4g - 8(7 + 7g)$

[replace f with $(7 + 7g)$]

$\implies \quad c = -76 - 52g$

3.
$$g^2 + f^2 - c = 25 \quad ③$$
$\implies \quad g^2 + (7 + 7g)^2 - (-76 - 52g) = 25 \quad [f = (7 + 7g) \text{ and } c = (-76 - 52g)]$
$\implies \quad g^2 + 49 + 98g + 49g^2 + 76 + 52g = 25$
$\implies \quad 50g^2 + 150g + 100 = 0$
$\implies \quad g^2 + 3g + 2 = 0$
$\implies \quad (g + 1)(g + 2) = 0$
$\implies \quad g = -1 \text{ or } g = -2$

Case 1: $g = -1$
$f = 7 + 7g = 7 - 7 = 0$
$c = -76 - 52g = -76 + 52 = -24$
$\therefore \quad g = -1, f = 0$ and $c = -24$

Case 2: $g = -2$
$f = 7 + 7g = 7 - 14 = -7$
$c = -76 - 52g = -76 + 104 = 28$
$\therefore \quad g = -2, f = -7, c = 28$

The equation of the circle is $x^2 + y^2 + 2gx + 2fy + c = 0$.

Thus, one circle is

$$x^2 + y^2 - 2x - 24 = 0$$

and the other circle is

$$x^2 + y^2 - 4x - 14y + 28 = 0$$

Example

Find the equations of the circles which touch both axes, which contain the point $(3, 6)$ and whose centre lies in the first quadrant.

Solution:

Let the equation of the circle be $x^2 + y^2 + 2gx + 2fy + c = 0$.

As the centre lies in the first quadrant, both g and f are negative.

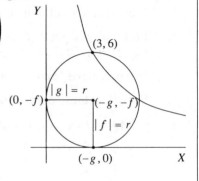

$$g = f \quad \text{①} \quad \left(\begin{array}{l} \text{as centre lies on the line } y = x \\ \text{because circle touches both axes} \end{array} \right)$$

$$|g| = r \quad (\text{or } |f| = r)$$
$$\Rightarrow \quad |g| = \sqrt{g^2 + f^2 - c}$$
$$\Rightarrow \quad g^2 = g^2 + f^2 - c$$
$$\Rightarrow \quad g^2 = g^2 + g^2 - c \quad (\text{as } g = f)$$
$$\Rightarrow \quad g^2 = c \quad \text{②}$$

$(3, 6)$ is on the circle:

$$9 + 36 + 6g + 12f + c = 0$$
$$\Rightarrow \quad 9 + 36 + 6g + 12g + g^2 = 0 \quad (\text{put in } f = g \text{ and } c = g^2)$$
$$\Rightarrow \quad g^2 + 18g + 45 = 0$$
$$\Rightarrow \quad (g + 3)(g + 15) = 0$$
$$\Rightarrow \quad g = -3 \text{ or } g = -15$$

Case 1: $g = -3$, $f = -3$, $c = 9$

$$x^2 + y^2 + 2(-3)x + 2(-3)y + 9 = 0$$
$$x^2 + y^2 - 6x - 6y + 9 = 0$$

Case 2: $g = -15$, $f = -15$, $c = 225$

$$x^2 + y^2 + 2(-15)x + 2(-15)y + 225 = 0$$
$$x^2 + y^2 - 30x - 30y + 225 = 0$$

2. VECTORS

A vector is a displacement (movement) over a certain distance and in a certain direction. It has both magnitude and direction but no unique position.

The diagram on the right shows the vector $\vec{ab}$.

Its length or modulus is denoted by $|\vec{ab}|$.

Equal vectors have three common characteristics:

1. Same length   2. Parallel   3. Same direction

To get the inverse of a vector, simply change its direction.

The inverse of $\vec{ab}$ is written $-\vec{ab}$ or $\vec{ba}$ (change the order of the letters).

A vector can be multiplied by a scalar (number). If a vector is multiplied by a scalar, its size is changed. If the scalar is **negative**, the direction of the vector is also changed. However, the new vector will always remain parallel to the original vector.

Triangle Law

Vectors are added using the triangle law. The **order** in which vectors are added (or subtracted) is not important.

A very useful result is to look for **linkage**:

e.g. $\vec{ab} + \vec{bc} = \vec{ac}$

(Join the starting point to the finishing point.)

If the letter at the end of the first vector is equal to the letter at the start of the second vector, the result of adding the two vectors is straightforward to write down. Simply write the letter at the start of the first vector followed by the letter at the end of the second vector together and put an arrow over them.

e.g. $\vec{pq} + \vec{qr} = \vec{pr}$ $\vec{xy} - \vec{zy} = \vec{xy} + \vec{yz} = \vec{xz}$

$-\vec{pm} + \vec{qm} = \vec{mp} + \vec{qm} = \vec{qm} + \vec{mp} = \vec{qp}$

(change order of addition)   (change sign and swop order of the letters)

Any number of vectors can be added in this way. The resultant vector joins the **start** of the **first** vector to the **end** of the **last** vector,

i.e., $\vec{ab} + \vec{bc} + \vec{cd} + \vec{de} + \vec{ef} = \vec{af}$

Using a diagram:

Notice that the arrows all **follow** each other. The result is found simply by joining the start to the finish.

(Notice the linkage of the vectors.)

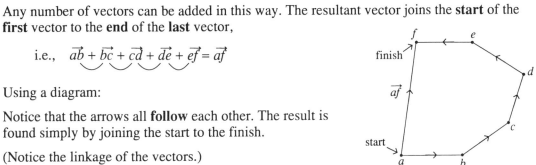

31

A vector which starts and finishes at the same point is called the **null**, or **zero**, vector.
It is denoted by $\vec{o}$. It has no size or direction.

A vector which starts from the origin to any point p in the plane is called a **position** vector,
e.g. $\vec{op}$. A position vector is usually indicated by its end point only,

e.g. $\quad \vec{op} = \vec{p}, \quad \vec{oq} = \vec{q}, \quad \vec{ro} = -\vec{or} = -\vec{r}$

A two-letter vector can be represented as a combination of two single-letter vectors using the
following result:

$$\boxed{\vec{pq} = \vec{q} - \vec{p}} \qquad \overrightarrow{(\text{second letter}} - \overrightarrow{\text{first letter})}$$

Midpoint

If m is the midpoint of $[ab]$,

then

$$\vec{m} = \tfrac{1}{2}\vec{a} + \tfrac{1}{2}\vec{b}$$

Collinear Points

If a, b and c are collinear points,

then

$$\vec{ac} = k\vec{ab}, k \in \mathbf{R} \quad \text{and} \quad \frac{|\vec{ac}|}{|\vec{ab}|} = k$$

Parallel Vectors

If $\vec{p} = h\vec{a} + k\vec{b}$ and $\vec{q} = m\vec{a} + n\vec{b}$, $h, k, m, n \in \mathbf{R}$ and $\vec{p} \parallel \vec{q}$, then the following ratio holds:

$$|\vec{p}| : |\vec{q}| = \text{ratio of coefficients of } \vec{a} = \text{ratio of coefficients of } \vec{b}$$

i.e.

$$\frac{|\vec{p}|}{|\vec{q}|} = \frac{h}{m} = \frac{k}{n}$$

Centroid of a Triangle

A median of a triangle is a line segment from a vertex to the midpoint of the opposite side.

The three medians of a triangle meet at a point called the centroid g in the diagram.

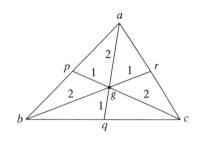

g divides each median in the ratio $2:1$,

i.e.

$$|ag| : |gq| = |bg| : |gr| = |cg| : |gp| = 2:1$$

Medians of a triangle and where they meet, the centroid, occur frequently when writing vectors in terms of other vectors.

Perpendicular Unit Vectors $\vec{i}$ and $\vec{j}$

The **length** of the vector $a\vec{i} + b\vec{j}$ is the distance from the origin to the point (a, b).

It is denoted by

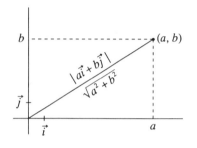

$$\left| a\vec{i} + b\vec{j} \right|$$

and given by

$$\sqrt{a^2 + b^2}$$

Note: Before getting the length of a vector, make sure it is written in the form $a\vec{i} + b\vec{j}$.

Unit Vector

If $\vec{x}$ is any vector, then $\dfrac{\vec{x}}{|\vec{x}|}$ is a vector parallel to $\vec{x}$ but of length one.

Vector Equations Involving $\vec{i}$ and $\vec{j}$

> If two vectors are equal, then
>
> their $\vec{i}$ parts are equal and their $\vec{j}$ parts are equal.

For example, if $a\vec{i} + b\vec{j} = c\vec{i} + d\vec{j}$, then $a = c$ and $b = d$.

Vector equations involving $\vec{\imath}$ and $\vec{\jmath}$ are solved with the following steps:

1. Remove the brackets.
2. Let the $\vec{\imath}$ parts equal the $\vec{\imath}$ parts and the $\vec{\jmath}$ parts equal the $\vec{\jmath}$ parts.
3. Solve these resultant equations.

Note: If one side of the equation does not contain an $\vec{\imath}$ part or a $\vec{\jmath}$ part, add in $0\vec{\imath}$ or $0\vec{\jmath}$, respectively.

Dot Product (or scalar product)

If $\vec{a}$ and $\vec{b}$ are two vectors, their dot product is defined as

$\vec{a} \cdot \vec{b} = |\vec{a}||\vec{b}| \cos \theta$

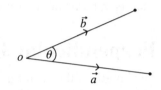

Properties of the Dot Product

1. If two vectors, $\vec{a}$ and $\vec{b}$, are perpendicular, their dot product is zero.

   $\vec{a} \cdot \vec{b} = |\vec{a}||\vec{b}| \cos 90° = 0$ (because $\cos 90° = 0$)

   In particular,

   $$\vec{\imath} \cdot \vec{\jmath} = 0 = \vec{\jmath} \cdot \vec{\imath}$$

2. If two vectors, $\vec{a}$ and $\vec{b}$, are parallel, their dot product is $|\vec{a}||\vec{b}|$.

   $\vec{a} \cdot \vec{b} = |\vec{a}||\vec{b}| \cos 0° = |\vec{a}||\vec{b}|$ (because $\cos 0° = 1$)

3. The dot product of $\vec{a}$ with $\vec{a}$ is $|\vec{a}|^2$.

   $\vec{a} \cdot \vec{a} = |\vec{a}||\vec{a}| \cos 0° = |\vec{a}||\vec{a}| = |\vec{a}|^2$.

   In particular,

   $$\vec{\imath} \cdot \vec{\imath} = 1 = \vec{\jmath} \cdot \vec{\jmath}$$

4. $\vec{a} \cdot \vec{b} = \vec{b} \cdot \vec{a}$.
5. $\vec{a} \cdot (\vec{b} + \vec{c}) = \vec{a} \cdot \vec{b} + \vec{a} \cdot \vec{c}$.
6. If $\vec{a} = p\vec{\imath} + q\vec{\jmath}$ and $\vec{b} = r\vec{\imath} + s\vec{\jmath}$, then $\vec{a} \cdot \vec{b} = pr + qs$.

   Multiply the $\vec{\imath}$ coefficients, multiply the $\vec{\jmath}$ coefficients and add these results.

   e.g. If $\vec{a} = 3\vec{\imath} - 2\vec{\jmath}$ and $\vec{b} = 5\vec{\imath} + \vec{\jmath}$, then

   $\vec{a} \cdot \vec{b} = (3)(5) + (-2)(1) = 15 - 2 = 13$

Angle between Two Vectors

Given that

$$\vec{a}.\vec{b} = |\vec{a}||\vec{b}|\cos\theta$$

$$\Rightarrow \quad \cos\theta = \frac{\vec{a}.\vec{b}}{|\vec{a}||\vec{b}|}$$

$$\boxed{\theta = \cos^{-1}\frac{\vec{a}.\vec{b}}{|\vec{a}||\vec{b}|}}$$

Related Perpendicular Vector $r^{\perp}$

If

$$\vec{r} = a\vec{i} + b\vec{j},$$

then,

$$\vec{r}^{\perp} = -b\vec{i} + a\vec{j}$$

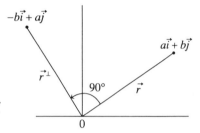

In short: Swop the coefficients and **then** change the sign of the coefficient of $\vec{i}$.

$\vec{r}^{\perp}$ is obtained by rotating $\vec{r}$ anticlockwise, about the origin, through 90°.

Note: $|\vec{r}| = |\vec{r}^{\perp}|$.

Example

oab is a triangle, where o is the origin and m is the midpoint of $[ab]$.

Prove (i) $\vec{ab} = \vec{b} - \vec{a}$

  (ii) $\vec{m} = \frac{1}{2}\vec{a} + \frac{1}{2}\vec{b}$.

Solution:

(i) Using the Triangle Law:

$$\vec{ab} = \vec{ao} + \vec{ob}$$
$$\vec{ab} = -\vec{oa} + \vec{ob}$$
$$\vec{ab} = -\vec{a} + \vec{b}$$
$$\vec{ab} = \vec{b} - \vec{a}$$

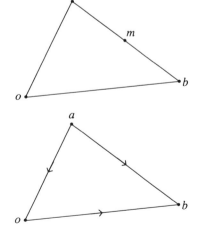

(ii) Using the Triangle Law:

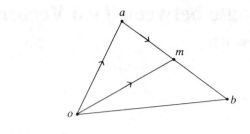

$$\vec{om} = \vec{oa} + \vec{am}$$
$$\vec{m} = \vec{a} + \tfrac{1}{2}\vec{ab}$$
$$\vec{m} = \vec{a} + \tfrac{1}{2}(\vec{b} - \vec{a})$$
$$\vec{m} = \vec{a} + \tfrac{1}{2}\vec{b} - \tfrac{1}{2}\vec{a}$$
$$\vec{m} = \tfrac{1}{2}\vec{a} + \tfrac{1}{2}\vec{b}$$

Example

abc is a triangle and o is the origin.

p, q and r are the midpoints of the sides as shown in the diagram and g is the centroid.

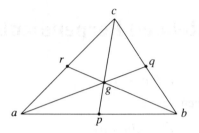

Verify:

(i) $\vec{p} + \vec{q} + \vec{r} = \vec{a} + \vec{b} + \vec{c}$

(ii) $g = \tfrac{1}{3}\vec{a} + \tfrac{1}{3}\vec{b} + \tfrac{1}{3}\vec{c}$.

Solution:

(i) As p, q and r are the midpoints of the sides of the triangle,

$$\vec{p} = \tfrac{1}{2}\vec{a} + \tfrac{1}{2}\vec{b}, \qquad \vec{q} = \tfrac{1}{2}\vec{b} + \tfrac{1}{2}\vec{c}, \qquad \vec{r} = \tfrac{1}{2}\vec{a} + \tfrac{1}{2}\vec{c}$$

Thus,

$$\vec{p} + \vec{q} + \vec{r} = \tfrac{1}{2}\vec{a} + \tfrac{1}{2}\vec{b} + \tfrac{1}{2}\vec{b} + \tfrac{1}{2}\vec{c} + \tfrac{1}{2}\vec{a} + \tfrac{1}{2}\vec{c}$$
$$= \vec{a} + \vec{b} + \vec{c}$$

(ii) Using the Triangle Law:

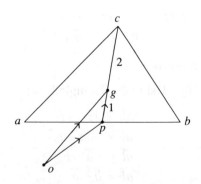

$$\vec{og} = \vec{op} + \vec{pg}$$
$$\vec{g} = \vec{p} + \tfrac{1}{3}\vec{pc} \qquad \text{(as } g \text{ is the centroid)}$$
$$\vec{g} = \tfrac{1}{2}\vec{a} + \tfrac{1}{2}\vec{b} + \tfrac{1}{3}(\vec{c} - \vec{p})$$
$$\vec{g} = \tfrac{1}{2}\vec{a} + \tfrac{1}{2}\vec{b} + \tfrac{1}{3}\vec{c} - \tfrac{1}{3}\vec{p}$$
$$\vec{g} = \tfrac{1}{2}\vec{a} + \tfrac{1}{2}\vec{b} + \tfrac{1}{3}\vec{c} - \tfrac{1}{3}(\tfrac{1}{2}\vec{a} + \tfrac{1}{2}\vec{b})$$
$$\vec{g} = \tfrac{1}{2}\vec{a} + \tfrac{1}{2}\vec{b} + \tfrac{1}{3}\vec{c} - \tfrac{1}{6}\vec{a} - \tfrac{1}{6}\vec{b}$$
$$\vec{g} = \tfrac{1}{3}\vec{a} + \tfrac{1}{3}\vec{b} + \tfrac{1}{3}\vec{c}$$

Example

In the diagram, *oabc* is a parallelogram.

p is a point on *oa* such that $|op|:|pa| = 2:3$

[*bp*] is produced to *r* such that $|bp| = |pr|$.

Taking $\vec{o}$ as the origin,

(i) express $\vec{bp}$ in terms of $\vec{a}$ and $\vec{c}$

(ii) find the values of *h* and *k* given $\vec{r} = h\vec{a} + k\vec{c}$, *h* and *k* being scalars.

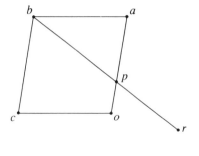

Solution:

(i) $\vec{bp} = \vec{ba} + \vec{ap}$ [Triangle Law]

$\quad = \vec{co} + \frac{3}{5}\vec{ao}$

$\quad = -\vec{oc} - \frac{3}{5}\vec{oa}$

$\quad = -\vec{c} - \frac{3}{5}\vec{a}$

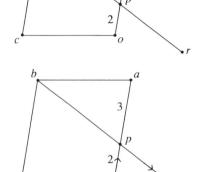

(ii) $\vec{or} = \vec{op} + \vec{pr}$ [Triangle Law]

$\quad \vec{r} = \frac{2}{5}\vec{oa} + \vec{bp}$ $\quad [\vec{bp} = \vec{pr}]$

$\quad \vec{r} = \frac{2}{5}\vec{a} - \vec{c} - \frac{3}{5}\vec{a}$ [from (i)]

$\quad \vec{r} = -\frac{1}{5}\vec{a} - \vec{c}$

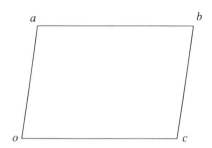

Comparing:

$\qquad \vec{r} = h\vec{a} + k\vec{c} = -\frac{1}{5}\vec{a} - \vec{c}$

$\Rightarrow \quad h = -\frac{1}{5}$ $\quad$ and $\quad k = -1$

Example

oabc is a parallelogram where *o* is the origin.

Write each of the following in terms of $\vec{a}$ and *c*:

(i) $\vec{ab}$ $\qquad$ **(ii)** $2\vec{cb}$ $\qquad$ **(iii)** $\vec{bc}$

(iv) $\vec{b}$ $\qquad$ **(v)** $-\vec{ca}$

(vi) express $\vec{ac} - \vec{cb}$ in terms of $\vec{a}$, $\vec{b}$ and $\vec{c}$

(vii) identify the point *k* such that

$\qquad (\vec{ob} - \vec{ab}) - \vec{ca} = \vec{ok}$

Solution:

(i) $\vec{ab} = \vec{oc} = \vec{c}$ (ii) $2\vec{cb} = 2\vec{oa} = 2\vec{a}$ (iii) $\vec{bc} = \vec{ao} = -\vec{oa} = -\vec{a}$

(iv) $\vec{b} = \vec{ob}$

     Using the Triangle Law:
$$\vec{ob} = \vec{oa} + \vec{ab} = \vec{a} + \vec{c}$$
   or $\vec{ob} = \vec{oc} + \vec{cb} = \vec{c} + \vec{a}$

(v) $-\vec{ca} = \vec{ac} = \vec{c} - \vec{a}$

     (writing a two-letter vector as single vectors)
     Or using the Triangle Law:
$$\vec{ac} = \vec{ab} + \vec{bc} = \vec{oc} + \vec{ao}$$
$$= \vec{oc} - \vec{oa} = \vec{c} - \vec{a}$$

(vi) $\vec{ac} - \vec{cb}$
$$= \vec{ac} + \vec{bc}$$
$$= (\vec{c} - \vec{a}) + (\vec{c} - \vec{b})$$
$$= \vec{c} - \vec{a} + \vec{c} - \vec{b}$$
$$= -\vec{a} - \vec{b} + 2\vec{c}$$

(vii) $(\vec{ob} - \vec{ab}) - \vec{ca} = \vec{ok}$
$$\vec{ob} - \vec{ab} - \vec{ca}$$
$$= \vec{ob} + \vec{ba} + \vec{ac}$$
$$= \vec{b} + (\vec{a} - \vec{b}) + (\vec{c} - \vec{a})$$
$$= \vec{b} + \vec{a} - \vec{b} + \vec{c} - \vec{a} = \vec{c} = \vec{oc}$$
$$\therefore \quad \vec{oc} = \vec{ok}$$
$$\therefore \quad k \text{ is the point } c$$
$$\left[\begin{array}{c} \text{or using the idea of linkage} \\ \vec{ob} + \vec{ba} + \vec{ac} = \vec{oc} = \vec{ok} \end{array} \right]$$

Example

oab is a triangle, o is the origin.

p, q are points on $[oa]$ and $[ab]$, respectively, such that

$$|op| : |pa| = 2:1 \quad \text{and} \quad |bq| : |qa| = 2:3$$

Express   (i) $\vec{bq}$, (ii) $\vec{oq}$ and (iii) $\vec{qp}$ in terms of $\vec{a}$ and $\vec{b}$.

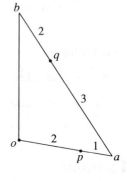

Solution:

(i) $\vec{bq} = \frac{2}{5}\vec{ba} = \frac{2}{5}(\vec{a} - \vec{b}) = \frac{2}{5}\vec{a} - \frac{2}{5}\vec{b}$

(ii) $\vec{oq} = \vec{ob} + \vec{bq}$ [Triangle Law]
$$= \vec{b} + \frac{2}{5}\vec{a} - \frac{2}{5}\vec{b} \quad \text{(from part (i))}$$
$$= \frac{2}{5}\vec{a} + \frac{3}{5}\vec{b}$$

(iii) $\overrightarrow{qp} = \overrightarrow{qa} + \overrightarrow{ap}$ [Triangle Law]

$$= \tfrac{3}{5}\overrightarrow{ba} + \tfrac{1}{3}\overrightarrow{ao}$$

$$= \tfrac{3}{5}(\overrightarrow{a} - \overrightarrow{b}) - \tfrac{1}{3}\overrightarrow{oa}$$

$$= \tfrac{3}{5}\overrightarrow{a} - \tfrac{3}{5}\overrightarrow{b} - \tfrac{1}{3}\overrightarrow{a}$$

$$= \tfrac{4}{15}\overrightarrow{a} - \tfrac{3}{5}\overrightarrow{b}$$

Example

$opqr$ is a parallelogram, where o is the origin, y is the midpoint of $[qr]$ and x is the point of intersection of $[oq]$ and $[py]$.

Express in terms of $\overrightarrow{p}$ and $\overrightarrow{r}$,

(i) $\overrightarrow{y}$ **(ii)** $\overrightarrow{px}$.

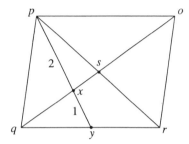

Solution:

(i) $\overrightarrow{y} = \overrightarrow{oy}$

$$= \overrightarrow{or} + \overrightarrow{ry} \text{[Triangle Law]}$$

$$= \overrightarrow{r} + \tfrac{1}{2}\overrightarrow{p} [\overrightarrow{ry} = \tfrac{1}{2}\overrightarrow{op} = \tfrac{1}{2}\overrightarrow{p}]$$

(ii) $\overrightarrow{px} = \tfrac{2}{3}\overrightarrow{py}$ [x is the centroid of Δpqr, $\therefore |px| = \tfrac{2}{3}|py|$]

$$= \tfrac{2}{3}(\overrightarrow{y} - \overrightarrow{p})   [\overrightarrow{py} = \overrightarrow{y} - \overrightarrow{p}]$$

$$= \tfrac{2}{3}\overrightarrow{y} - \tfrac{2}{3}\overrightarrow{p}$$

$$= \tfrac{2}{3}(\overrightarrow{r} + \tfrac{1}{2}\overrightarrow{p}) - \tfrac{2}{3}\overrightarrow{p} \text{[from (i) above]}$$

$$= \tfrac{2}{3}\overrightarrow{r} + \tfrac{1}{3}\overrightarrow{p} - \tfrac{2}{3}\overrightarrow{p}$$

$$= \tfrac{2}{3}\overrightarrow{r} - \tfrac{1}{3}\overrightarrow{p}$$

Example

p, q, r, s are the midpoints of the sides of a quadrilateral $abcd$.

Prove by vector methods that $pqrs$ is a parallelogram.

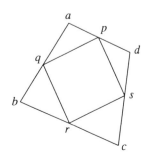

Solution:

$$\vec{p} = \tfrac{1}{2}\vec{a} + \tfrac{1}{2}\vec{d}, \qquad \vec{q} = \tfrac{1}{2}\vec{a} + \tfrac{1}{2}\vec{b}$$
$$\vec{r} = \tfrac{1}{2}\vec{b} + \tfrac{1}{2}\vec{c}, \qquad \vec{s} = \tfrac{1}{2}\vec{c} + \tfrac{1}{2}\vec{d}$$

$$\vec{pq} = \vec{q} - \vec{p} = \tfrac{1}{2}\vec{a} + \tfrac{1}{2}\vec{b} - \tfrac{1}{2}\vec{a} - \tfrac{1}{2}\vec{d} = \tfrac{1}{2}\vec{b} - \tfrac{1}{2}\vec{d}$$
$$\vec{sr} = \vec{r} - \vec{s} = \tfrac{1}{2}\vec{b} + \tfrac{1}{2}\vec{c} - \tfrac{1}{2}\vec{c} - \tfrac{1}{2}\vec{d} = \tfrac{1}{2}\vec{b} - \tfrac{1}{2}\vec{d}$$

Thus,

$$\vec{pq} \parallel \vec{sr} \text{ and } |\vec{pq}| = |\vec{sr}|$$

∴   *pqrs* is a parallelogram.

Example

o is the origin, $\vec{a} = 2\vec{i} + 2\vec{j}$, $\vec{b} = 4\vec{i} + 4\vec{j}$.

If $\vec{r} = \tfrac{1}{2}(\vec{a} + \vec{b}) + t(\vec{b} - \vec{a})^{\perp}$, $t \in \mathbf{R}$, express $\vec{r}$ in terms of $\vec{i}$, $\vec{j}$ and *t*.

Show that *r* lies on the perpendicular bisector of [*ab*] for all $t \in \mathbf{R}$, i.e. show that

$|\vec{ra}| = |\vec{rb}|$ and verify that $\left| \dfrac{\vec{ra}}{|\vec{ra}|} \right| = 1.$

Solution:

$$\vec{r} = \tfrac{1}{2}(\vec{a} + \vec{b}) + t(\vec{b} - \vec{a})^{\perp}$$
$$\vec{r} = \tfrac{1}{2}(6\vec{i} + 6\vec{j}) + t(-2\vec{i} + 2\vec{j})$$
$$\vec{r} = 3\vec{i} + 3\vec{j} - 2t\vec{i} + 2t\vec{j}$$
$$\vec{r} = (3 - 2t)\vec{i} + (3 + 2t)\vec{j}$$

$$\vec{a} + \vec{b} = 2\vec{i} + 2\vec{j} + 4\vec{i} + 4\vec{j} = 6\vec{i} + 6\vec{j}$$
$$\vec{b} - \vec{a} = 4\vec{i} + 4\vec{j} - 2\vec{i} - 2\vec{j} = 2\vec{i} + 2\vec{j}$$
$$\therefore \quad (\vec{b} - \vec{a})^{\perp} = -2\vec{i} + 2\vec{j}$$

$$\begin{aligned}
|\vec{ra}| = |\vec{a} - \vec{r}| &= |(2\vec{i} + 2\vec{j}) - [(3 - 2t)\vec{i} + (3 + 2t)\vec{j}]| \\
&= |2\vec{i} + 2\vec{j} - 3\vec{i} + 2t\vec{i} - 3\vec{j} - 2t\vec{j}| \\
&= |(2t - 1)\vec{i} + (-2t - 1)\vec{j}| \\
&= \sqrt{(2t - 1)^2 + (-2t - 1)^2} = \sqrt{4t^2 - 4t + 1 + 4t^2 + 4t + 1} = \sqrt{8t^2 + 2}
\end{aligned}$$

$$\begin{aligned}
|\vec{rb}| = |\vec{b} - \vec{r}| &= |(4\vec{i} + 4\vec{j}) - [(3 - 2t)\vec{i} + (3 + 2t)\vec{j}]| \\
&= |4\vec{i} + 4\vec{j} - 3\vec{i} + 2t\vec{i} - 3\vec{j} - 2t\vec{j}| \\
&= |(2t + 1)\vec{i} + (-2t + 1)\vec{j}| \\
&= \sqrt{(2t + 1)^2 + (-2t + 1)^2} = \sqrt{4t^2 + 4t + 1 + 4t^2 - 4t + 1} = \sqrt{8t^2 + 2}
\end{aligned}$$

Thus, $|\overrightarrow{ra}| = |\overrightarrow{rb}|$,

$\therefore$ r lies on the perpendicular bisector of [ab].

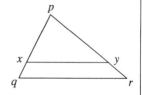

$$\overrightarrow{ra} = (2t - 1)\vec{i} + (-2t - 1)\vec{j} \quad \text{and} \quad |\overrightarrow{ra}| = \sqrt{8t^2 + 2}$$

Thus,

$$\frac{\overrightarrow{ra}}{|\overrightarrow{ra}|} = \frac{(2t - 1)\vec{i} + (-2t - 1)\vec{j}}{\sqrt{8t^2 + 2}} = \frac{(2t - 1)}{\sqrt{8t^2 + 2}}\vec{i} + \frac{(-2t - 1)}{\sqrt{8t^2 + 2}}\vec{j}$$

$$\therefore \left|\frac{\overrightarrow{ra}}{|\overrightarrow{ra}|}\right| = \sqrt{\left(\frac{2t - 1}{\sqrt{8t^2 + 2}}\right)^2 + \left(\frac{-2t - 1}{\sqrt{8t^2 + 2}}\right)^2}$$

$$= \sqrt{\frac{4t^2 - 4t + 1}{8t^2 + 2} + \frac{4t^2 + 4t + 1}{8t^2 + 2}}$$

$$= \sqrt{\frac{8t^2 + 2}{8t^2 + 2}} = \sqrt{1} = 1$$

Example

(i) In $\triangle pqr$,

$$|px| : |xq| = 3 : 1 = |py| : |yr|$$

Using vector methods, prove $\overrightarrow{xy} \parallel \overrightarrow{qr}$.

(ii) $\vec{a} = (1 - k)\vec{p} + \vec{q}, \qquad \vec{b} = -3\vec{p} + (k + 1)\vec{q}$.

If $\vec{a} \parallel \vec{b}$, find two possible values of k.

Solution:

(i)

$$\overrightarrow{xy} = \overrightarrow{xp} + \overrightarrow{py} \quad \text{(Triangle Law)}$$

$$= \tfrac{3}{4}\overrightarrow{qp} + \tfrac{3}{4}\overrightarrow{pr}$$

$$= \tfrac{3}{4}(\overrightarrow{qp} + \overrightarrow{pr})$$

$$\overrightarrow{xy} = \tfrac{3}{4}\overrightarrow{qr}$$

Thus, $\overrightarrow{xy} \parallel \overrightarrow{qr}$ as $\overrightarrow{xy} = k\overrightarrow{qr}$, $k \in \mathbf{R}$.

(ii) $\vec{a} = (1-k)\vec{p} + \vec{q}, \qquad \vec{b} = -3\vec{p} + (k+1)\vec{q}$

As $\vec{a} \parallel \vec{b}$, the following ratios are equal:

ratio of coefficients of $\vec{p}$ = ratio of coefficients of $\vec{q}$

$$\Rightarrow \quad \frac{1-k}{-3} = \frac{1}{k+1}$$

$$\Rightarrow \quad 1 - k^2 = -3$$

$$\Rightarrow \quad -k^2 = -4$$

$$\Rightarrow \quad k^2 = 4$$

$$\Rightarrow \quad k = \pm 2$$

Example

In triangle oab, o is the origin, c is the midpoint of $[ob]$ and $|\vec{ap}| : |\vec{pc}| = 3:1$.

Express in terms of $\vec{a}$ and $\vec{c}$:

(i) $\vec{ac}$ **(ii)** $\vec{cp}$ **(iii)** $\vec{p}$.

Taking $\vec{q} = k\vec{p}$, $k \in \mathbf{R}$, find $\vec{bq}$ and $\vec{qa}$ in terms of $\vec{a}$, $\vec{c}$ and k.

Hence, find the ratio $|\vec{bq}| : |\vec{qa}|$.

Solution:

(i) $\vec{ac} = \vec{c} - \vec{a}.$

(ii) $\vec{cp} = \tfrac{1}{4}\vec{ca} = \tfrac{1}{4}(\vec{a} - \vec{c}) = \tfrac{1}{4}\vec{a} - \tfrac{1}{4}\vec{c}.$

(iii) $\vec{p} = \vec{op} = \vec{oc} + \vec{cp} = \vec{c} + \tfrac{1}{4}\vec{a} - \tfrac{1}{4}\vec{c} = \tfrac{1}{4}\vec{a} + \tfrac{3}{4}\vec{c}$

$$\vec{q} = k\vec{p}$$

$$
\begin{aligned}
\vec{bq} &= \vec{q} - \vec{b} \\
&= k\vec{p} - 2\vec{c} \\
&= k(\tfrac{1}{4}\vec{a} + \tfrac{3}{4}\vec{c}) - 2\vec{c} \\
&= \tfrac{1}{4}k\vec{a} + \tfrac{3}{4}k\vec{c} - 2\vec{c} \\
&= \tfrac{1}{4}k\vec{a} + (\tfrac{3}{4}k - 2)\vec{c}
\end{aligned}
$$

$$
\begin{aligned}
\vec{qa} &= \vec{a} - \vec{q} \\
&= \vec{a} - k\vec{p} \\
&= \vec{a} - k(\tfrac{1}{4}\vec{a} + \tfrac{3}{4}\vec{c}) \\
&= \vec{a} - \tfrac{1}{4}k\vec{a} - \tfrac{3}{4}k\vec{c} \\
&= (1 - \tfrac{1}{4}k)\vec{a} - \tfrac{3}{4}k\vec{c}
\end{aligned}
$$

As $\vec{bq} \parallel \vec{qa}$, the following ratios hold,

$|\vec{bq}| : |\vec{qa}|$ = ratio of coefficients of $\vec{a}$ = ratio of coefficients of $\vec{c}$

$$\Rightarrow \quad \frac{\frac{1}{4}k}{1 - \frac{1}{4}k} = \frac{\frac{3}{4}k - 2}{-\frac{3}{4}k}$$

$$\Rightarrow \quad \frac{k}{4 - k} = \frac{3k - 8}{-3k} \quad \left(\begin{array}{l} \text{Multiply the top and bottom} \\ \text{of each fraction by 4} \end{array} \right)$$

$$\Rightarrow \quad -3k^2 = 12k - 32 - 3k^2 + 8k$$

$$\Rightarrow \quad 20k = 32$$

$$\Rightarrow \quad k = \frac{32}{20} = \frac{8}{5}$$

$$\frac{|\vec{bq}|}{|\vec{qa}|} = \frac{\frac{1}{4}k}{1 - \frac{1}{4}k} = \frac{\frac{1}{4}\left(\frac{8}{5}\right)}{1 - \frac{1}{4}\left(\frac{8}{5}\right)} = \frac{\frac{2}{5}}{1 - \frac{2}{5}} = \frac{2}{5 - 2} = \frac{2}{3}$$

Thus,

$$|\vec{bq}| : |\vec{qa}| = 2 : 3$$

Example

(i) $\vec{a} = 4\vec{i} - 3\vec{j}, \qquad \vec{b} = 5(\vec{i} + \vec{j}).$

If $\vec{a} + t\vec{b} = k\vec{i}$, $t, k \in R$, find the value of t and the value of k.

(ii) $\vec{r} = 7\vec{i} - 4\vec{j}.$

If $m\vec{r} + n\vec{r}^{\perp} = 5\vec{i} - 40\vec{j}$, find the value of m and the value of n, $m, n \in R$.

(iii) $\vec{a} = 2\vec{i} - 3\vec{j}, \qquad \vec{ab} = -3\vec{i} + 7\vec{j}.$

If $p\vec{a} + q\vec{b} = 7\vec{i} - 18\vec{j}$, find the value of p and the value of q, $p, q \in R$.

(iv) Solve for x,

$$x(x\vec{i} - 6\vec{j}) + x(4\vec{i} + x\vec{j}) - 5\vec{j} = 5(\vec{i} - 2x\vec{j})$$

(v) $\vec{k} = 4\vec{i} - 3\vec{j}$ and $\vec{m} = -2\vec{i} + 5\vec{j}.$

If $\vec{p} = \vec{k} + \alpha\vec{km}$, $\alpha \in R$, and p is a point on the $\vec{j}$ axis, calculate the value of α.

Solution:

(i) $\vec{a} = 4\vec{i} - 3\vec{j}, \qquad \vec{b} = 5(\vec{i} + \vec{j}) = 5\vec{i} + 5\vec{j}$

$$\vec{a} + t\vec{b} = k\vec{i}$$

$\implies \quad (4\vec{i} - 3\vec{j}) + t(5\vec{i} + 5\vec{j}) = k\vec{i} + 0\vec{j} \quad$ (put in $0\vec{j}$)

$\implies \qquad 4\vec{i} - 3\vec{j} + 5t\vec{i} + 5t\vec{j} = k\vec{i} + 0\vec{j}$

$\qquad\qquad (\vec{i} \text{ parts} = \vec{i} \text{ parts}) \qquad\qquad\qquad (\vec{j} \text{ parts} = \vec{j} \text{ parts})$

$\implies \qquad\quad 4 + 5t = k \quad ① \qquad\qquad \text{and} \qquad -3 + 5t = 0 \quad ②$

$-3 + 5t = 0 \quad ②$	$4 + 5t = k \quad ①$
$5t = 3$	$4 + 5(\tfrac{3}{5}) = k$
$t = \tfrac{3}{5}$	$4 + 3 = k$
Put this into ①.	$k = 7$

(ii) $\vec{r} = 7\vec{i} - 4\vec{j}$. Thus, $r^{\perp} = 4\vec{i} + 7\vec{j}$.

(Swop coefficients and **then** change the sign of the coefficient of $\vec{i}$.)

Given: $\qquad\qquad m\vec{r} + n\vec{r}^{\perp} = 5\vec{i} - 40\vec{j}$

$\implies \quad m(7\vec{i} - 4\vec{j}) + n(4\vec{i} + 7\vec{j}) = 5\vec{i} - 40\vec{j}$

$\implies \quad 7m\vec{i} - 4m\vec{j} + 4n\vec{i} + 7n\vec{j} = 5\vec{i} - 40\vec{j}$

$\qquad\qquad (\vec{i} \text{ parts} = \vec{i} \text{ parts}) \qquad\qquad (\vec{j} \text{ parts} = \vec{j} \text{ parts})$

$\implies \qquad 7m + 4n = 5 \quad ① \quad \text{and} \quad -4m + 7n = -40 \quad ②$

Solving ① and ② simultaneously gives $m = 3$ and $n = -4$.

(iii) $\vec{a} = 2\vec{i} - 3\vec{j}, \qquad \vec{ab} = -3\vec{i} + 7\vec{j}$. We need to find $\vec{b}$.

$\vec{ab} = \vec{b} - \vec{a}$

$\implies \quad \vec{b} = \vec{ab} + \vec{a} = -3\vec{i} + 7\vec{j} + 2\vec{i} - 3\vec{j} = -\vec{i} + 4\vec{j}$

Given: $\qquad\qquad p\vec{a} + q\vec{b} = 7\vec{i} - 18\vec{j}$

$\implies \quad p(2\vec{i} - 3\vec{j}) + q(-\vec{i} + 4\vec{j}) = 7\vec{i} - 18\vec{j}$

$\implies \quad 2p\vec{i} - 3p\vec{j} - q\vec{i} + 4q\vec{j} = 7\vec{i} - 18\vec{j}$

$\qquad\qquad (\vec{i} \text{ parts} = \vec{i} \text{ parts}) \qquad\qquad (\vec{j} \text{ parts} = \vec{j} \text{ parts})$

$\implies \qquad 2p - q = 7 \quad ① \quad \text{and} \quad -3p + 4q = -18 \quad ②$

Solving ① and ② simultaneously gives $p = 2$ and $q = -3$.

(iv) $x(x\vec{i} - 6\vec{j}) + x(4\vec{i} + x\vec{j}) - 5\vec{j} = 5(\vec{i} - 2x\vec{j})$

$\implies \quad x^2\vec{i} - 6x\vec{j} + 4x\vec{i} + x^2\vec{j} - 5\vec{j} = 5\vec{i} - 10x\vec{j}$

$\qquad\qquad (\vec{i} \text{ parts} = \vec{i} \text{ parts}) \qquad\qquad (\vec{j} \text{ parts} = \vec{j} \text{ parts})$

$\implies \qquad x^2 + 4x = 5 \qquad\qquad -6x + x^2 - 5 = -10x$

$\implies \quad x^2 + 4x - 5 = ① \qquad\qquad x^2 + 4x - 5 = ②$

$\implies \qquad x^2 + 4x - 5 = 0 \qquad$ (both equations are the same)

$\implies \quad (x + 5)(x - 1) = 0$

$\implies \qquad\qquad x = -5 \text{ or } x = 1$

44

(v) $\vec{p} = \vec{k} + a\overrightarrow{km}$

$\vec{p} = 4\vec{i} - 3\vec{j} + a(-6\vec{i} + 8\vec{j})$
$\vec{p} = 4\vec{i} - 3\vec{j} - 6a\vec{i} + 8a\vec{j}$
$\vec{p} = (4 - 6a)\vec{i} + (-3 + 8a)\vec{j}$

$\overrightarrow{km} = \vec{m} - \vec{k}$
$= (-2\vec{i} + 5\vec{j}) - (4\vec{i} - 3\vec{j})$
$= -2\vec{i} + 5\vec{j} - 4\vec{i} + 3\vec{j}$
$= -6\vec{i} + 8\vec{j}$

If p is a point on the $\vec{j}$ axis, then the $\vec{i}$ parts = 0.

i.e. $4 - 6a = 0$

$\implies \qquad 6a = 4$

$\implies \qquad a = \frac{4}{6} = \frac{2}{3}$

Example

Express the vector $-8\vec{i} + \vec{j}$ as a combination of two vectors, one of which is parallel to $2\vec{i} + 3\vec{j}$ and the other perpendicular to $2\vec{i} + 3\vec{j}$.

Solution:

A vector parallel to $2\vec{i} + 3\vec{j}$ is $k(2\vec{i} + 3\vec{j})$, $k \in \mathbf{R}$.

A vector perpendicular to $2\vec{i} + 3\vec{j}$ is $l(-3\vec{i} + 2\vec{j})$, $l \in \mathbf{R}$.

Thus,

$\qquad k(2\vec{i} + 3\vec{j}) + l(-3\vec{i} + 2\vec{j}) = -8\vec{i} + \vec{j}$

$\implies \qquad 2k\vec{i} + 3k\vec{j} - 3l\vec{i} + 2l\vec{j} = -8\vec{i} + \vec{j}$

$\implies \qquad 2k - 3l = -8$ ① and $3k + 2l = 1$ ②

Solving ① and ② simultaneously gives $k = -1$ and $l = 2$.

Thus, the two vectors are

$\qquad k(2\vec{i} + 3\vec{j}) = -1(2\vec{i} + 3\vec{j}) = -2\vec{i} - 3\vec{j}$

and

$\qquad l(-3\vec{i} + 2\vec{j}) = 2(-3\vec{i} + 2\vec{j}) = -6\vec{i} + 4\vec{j}$

Check:

$\qquad -2\vec{i} - 3\vec{j} - 6\vec{i} + 4\vec{j} = -8\vec{i} + \vec{j}$ (yes!)

Example

If $\vec{p} = 3\vec{i} - 4\vec{j}$ and $\vec{q} = -\vec{i} - 6\vec{j}$, verify $|\vec{p}| + |\vec{q}| > |\vec{pq}|$.

Solution:

$$|\vec{p}| = |3\vec{i} - 4\vec{j}|$$
$$= \sqrt{3^2 + 4^2}$$
$$= \sqrt{9 + 16}$$
$$= \sqrt{25}$$
$$= 5$$

$$|\vec{q}| = |-\vec{i} - 6\vec{j}|$$
$$= \sqrt{1^2 + 6^2}$$
$$= \sqrt{1 + 36}$$
$$= \sqrt{37}$$
$$= 6.08 \quad \text{(2 decimal places)}$$

$$\therefore \quad |\vec{p}| + |\vec{q}| = 5 + 6.08 = 11.08$$

$\vec{pq}$ must be written in the form $a\vec{i} + b\vec{j}$

$$\vec{pq} = \vec{q} - \vec{p}$$
$$= (-\vec{i} - 6\vec{j}) - (3\vec{i} - 4\vec{j})$$
$$= -\vec{i} - 6\vec{j} - 3\vec{i} + 4\vec{j}$$
$$= -4\vec{i} - 2\vec{j}$$

$$|\vec{pq}| = |-4\vec{i} - 2\vec{j}|$$
$$= \sqrt{4^2 + 2^2}$$
$$= \sqrt{16 + 4}$$
$$= \sqrt{20}$$
$$= 4.47 \quad \text{(2 decimal places)}$$

$$\text{As } 11.08 > 4.47, \; |\vec{p}| + |\vec{q}| > |\vec{pq}|$$

Example

If $\vec{a} = \vec{i} + 6\vec{j}, \qquad \vec{b} = 3\vec{i} - \vec{j}$ and $\vec{c} = -2\vec{i} + 4\vec{j}$,

calculate $|\angle abc|$ correct to the nearest minute.

Solution:

Let $|\angle abc| = \theta$.

$$\vec{ba} \cdot \vec{bc} = |\vec{ba}||\vec{bc}| \cos\theta$$
$$\vec{ba} = \vec{a} - \vec{b} = \vec{i} + 6\vec{j} - 3\vec{i} + \vec{j} = -2\vec{i} + 7\vec{j}$$
$$\therefore \quad |\vec{ba}| = \sqrt{2^2 + 7^2} = \sqrt{4 + 49} = \sqrt{53}$$

$$\vec{bc} = \vec{c} - \vec{b} = -2\vec{i} + 4\vec{j} - 3\vec{i} + \vec{j} = -5\vec{i} + 5\vec{j}$$
$$\therefore \quad |\vec{bc}| = \sqrt{5^2 + 5^2} = \sqrt{25 + 25} = \sqrt{50}$$

$$\vec{ba} \cdot \vec{bc} = |\vec{ba}||\vec{bc}| \cos \theta$$
$$(-2\vec{i} + 7\vec{j}) \cdot (-5\vec{i} + 5\vec{j}) = \sqrt{53} \sqrt{50} \cos \theta$$
$$10 + 35 = \sqrt{53} \sqrt{50} \cos \theta$$
$$45 = \sqrt{53} \sqrt{50} \cos \theta$$
$$\cos \theta = \frac{45}{\sqrt{53} \sqrt{50}}$$
$$\theta = \cos^{-1} \frac{45}{\sqrt{53} \sqrt{50}}$$
$$\theta = 29° \, 3'$$

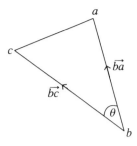

When writing down the dot product

$$\vec{ba} \cdot \vec{bc} = |\vec{ba}||\vec{bc}| \cos \theta$$

it is crucial to have the origin of both vectors, in this case b, at the vertex of the required angle.

Example

(i) If $\vec{a} = \vec{i} - 2\vec{j}$ and $\vec{b} = 6\vec{i} + 3\vec{j}$, verify $\vec{a} \perp \vec{b}$.

(ii) If $\vec{p} = 3\vec{i} - 4\vec{j}$ and $\vec{q} = -8\vec{i} + k\vec{j}$, find k if $\vec{p} \perp \vec{q}$.

Solution:

(i) $\vec{a} \cdot \vec{b} = (\vec{i} - 2\vec{j}) \cdot (6\vec{i} + 3\vec{j})$
$$= (1)(6) + (-2)(3)$$
$$= 6 - 6$$
$$= 0$$
$$\therefore \quad \vec{a} \perp \vec{b}$$

(ii) $\vec{p} = 3\vec{i} - 4\vec{j}, \qquad \vec{q} = -8\vec{i} + k\vec{j}$

Given: $\vec{p} \perp \vec{q}$

$$\Rightarrow \qquad \vec{p} \cdot \vec{q} = 0$$
$$(3\vec{i} - 4\vec{j}) \cdot (-8\vec{i} + k\vec{j}) = 0$$
$$(3)(-8) + (-4)(k) = 0$$
$$-24 - 4k = 0$$
$$-4k = 24$$
$$4k = -24$$
$$k = -6$$

Example

$$\vec{a} = 3\vec{i} - 4\vec{j}, \qquad \vec{b} = h\vec{i} + k\vec{j}.$$

If $\vec{b} - \dfrac{\vec{b}}{|\vec{a}|} = \vec{a}^{\perp}$, find the value of h and the value of k, where $h, k \in \mathbf{R}$.

Solution:

Given:
$$\vec{b} - \frac{\vec{b}}{|\vec{a}|} = \vec{a}^{\perp}$$

$\quad\vec{a} = 3\vec{i} - 4\vec{j}$

$\quad|\vec{a}| = \sqrt{3^2 + 4^2}$

$\qquad = \sqrt{9 + 16} = \sqrt{25} = 5$

$\quad\vec{a}^{\perp} = 4\vec{i} + 3\vec{j}$

$\Rightarrow\quad (h\vec{i} + k\vec{j}) - \dfrac{(h\vec{i} + k\vec{j})}{5} = 4\vec{i} + 3\vec{j}$

$\Rightarrow\quad 5(h\vec{i} + k\vec{j}) - (h\vec{i} + k\vec{j}) = 5(4\vec{i} + 3\vec{j})$

$\Rightarrow\qquad 5h\vec{i} + 5k\vec{j} - h\vec{i} - k\vec{j} = 20\vec{i} + 15\vec{j}$

$\Rightarrow\qquad\qquad 4h\vec{i} + 4k\vec{j} = 20\vec{i} + 15\vec{j}$

$\Rightarrow\qquad\qquad 4h = 20 \text{ and } 4k = 15$

$\Rightarrow\qquad\qquad h = 5 \text{ and } k = \frac{15}{4}$

Example

(i) $\vec{u} = 2\vec{i} - \vec{j}$, $\vec{v} = -2\vec{i} + 2\vec{j}$ and $\vec{w} = 4\vec{i} + s\vec{j}$. Express $\overrightarrow{uv}$ and $\overrightarrow{uw}$ in terms of $\vec{i}$ and $\vec{j}$, and hence, find s if u, v and w are collinear.

(ii) o, a and b are collinear. If $\vec{a} = \vec{i} + 3\vec{j}$ and $\vec{a} \cdot \vec{b} = -20$, find $\vec{b}$.

Solution:

(i) Because of the word 'hence' we cannot use coordinate geometry methods.

$$\vec{u} = 2\vec{i} - \vec{j}, \qquad \vec{v} = -2\vec{i} + 2\vec{j}, \qquad \vec{w} = 4\vec{i} + s\vec{j}$$

$\overrightarrow{uv} = \vec{v} - \vec{u}$

$\quad = -2\vec{i} + 2\vec{j} - 2\vec{i} + \vec{j}$

$\quad = -4\vec{i} + 3\vec{j}$

$\overrightarrow{uw} = \vec{w} - \vec{u}$

$\quad = 4\vec{i} + s\vec{j} - 2\vec{i} + \vec{j}$

$\quad = 2\vec{i} + (s + 1)\vec{j}$

u, v and w are collinear.

Thus, $\qquad \overrightarrow{uv} \parallel \overrightarrow{uw}$,

$\Rightarrow\quad -4\vec{i} + 3\vec{j} \parallel 2\vec{i} + (s + 1)\vec{j}$

$\Rightarrow\qquad \dfrac{-4}{2} = \dfrac{3}{s + 1}\qquad$ (equal ratios)

$\Rightarrow\qquad -4s - 4 = 6$

$\qquad\qquad -4s = 10$

$\qquad\qquad s = -\frac{10}{4} = -\frac{5}{2}$

(ii) $\vec{a} = \vec{i} + 3\vec{j}$

$\qquad o$, a, b collinear $\Rightarrow \vec{b} = k\vec{a}$, $k \in \textbf{R}$.

$\Rightarrow\quad b = k(\vec{i} + 3\vec{j})$

$\qquad\quad = k\vec{i} + 3k\vec{j}$

Given:
$$\vec{a} \cdot \vec{b} = -20$$
$$\Rightarrow \quad (\vec{i} + 3\vec{j}) \cdot (k\vec{i} + 3k\vec{j}) = -20$$
$$\Rightarrow \quad (1)(k) + (3)(3k) = -20$$
$$\Rightarrow \quad 10k = -20$$
$$\Rightarrow \quad k = -2$$

Thus,
$$\vec{b} = k\vec{i} + 3k\vec{j} = -2\vec{i} - 6\vec{j}$$

Example

Verify that h is the circumcentre of $\triangle abc$, where

$$\vec{a} = 5\vec{i} + \vec{j}, \qquad \vec{b} = -2\vec{i}, \qquad \vec{c} = -3\vec{i} - 3\vec{j}, \qquad \vec{h} = 2\vec{i} - 3\vec{j}$$

and find the equation of the circumcircle.

Solution:

$$|\vec{ah}| = |\vec{h} - \vec{a}| = |2\vec{i} - 3\vec{j} - 5\vec{i} - \vec{j}| = |-3\vec{i} - 4\vec{j}| = \sqrt{3^2 + 4^2} = \sqrt{25} = 5$$
$$|\vec{bh}| = |\vec{h} - \vec{b}| = |2\vec{i} - 3\vec{j} + 2\vec{i}| = |4\vec{i} - 3\vec{j}| = \sqrt{4^2 + 3^2} = \sqrt{25} = 5$$
$$|\vec{ch}| = |\vec{h} - \vec{c}| = |2\vec{i} - 3\vec{j} + 3\vec{i} + 3\vec{j}| = |5\vec{i}| = \sqrt{5^2} = \sqrt{25} = 5$$
$$|\vec{ah}| = |\vec{bh}| = |\vec{ch}| = 5$$

i.e. a, b, c are equidistant from h,

$\therefore$ h is the circumcentre of $\triangle abc$.

Equation: centre = $(2, -3)$, radius = 5

$$(x - 2)^2 + (y + 3)^2 = 5^2$$
$$x^2 - 4x + 4 + y^2 + 6y + 9 = 25$$
$$x^2 + y^2 - 4x + 6y - 12 = 0$$

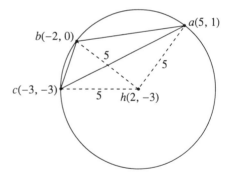

Example

$\vec{p} = 4\vec{i} + \vec{j}$ and $\vec{q} = \vec{i} - \vec{j}$.

If α is a scalar such that $(\vec{p} + \alpha\vec{q}) \perp \vec{pq}$, find the value of α.

Solution:

$$\vec{p} + \alpha\vec{q} = 4\vec{i} + \vec{j} + \alpha(\vec{i} - \vec{j}) = 4\vec{i} + \vec{j} + \alpha\vec{i} - \alpha\vec{j} = (4 + \alpha)\vec{i} + (1 - \alpha)\vec{j}$$
$$\vec{pq} = \vec{q} - \vec{p} = \vec{i} - \vec{j} - 4\vec{i} - \vec{j} = -3\vec{i} - 2\vec{j}$$

Given:
$$(\vec{p} + a\vec{q}) \perp \vec{pq}$$
$$\Rightarrow \qquad (\vec{p} + a\vec{q}) . \vec{pq} = 0$$
$$\Rightarrow \quad [(4 + a)\vec{i} + (1 - a)\vec{j}].[-3\vec{i} - 2\vec{j}] = 0$$
$$\Rightarrow \qquad (4 + a)(-3) + (1 - a)(-2) = 0$$
$$\Rightarrow \qquad -12 - 3a - 2 + 2a = 0$$
$$\Rightarrow \qquad -a = 14$$
$$\Rightarrow \qquad a = -14$$

Example

(i) If $|(p + 1)\vec{i} + (2p - 3)\vec{j}| = 5\sqrt{2}$, find two possible values for p.

(ii) $\vec{r} = \dfrac{1}{\sqrt{17}} (a\vec{i} + \vec{j})$. If $|\vec{r}| = 1$, find two possible values for a.

Solution:

(i) $$|(p + 1)\vec{i} + (2p - 3)\vec{j}| = 5\sqrt{2}$$
$$\Rightarrow \qquad \sqrt{(p + 1)^2 + (2p - 3)^2} = 5\sqrt{2}$$
$$\Rightarrow \quad p^2 + 2p + 1 + 4p^2 - 12p + 9 = 50$$
$$\Rightarrow \qquad 5p^2 - 10p - 40 = 0$$
$$\Rightarrow \qquad p^2 - 2p - 8 = 0$$
$$\Rightarrow \qquad (p - 4)(p + 2) = 0$$
$$\Rightarrow \qquad p = 4 \text{ or } p = -2$$

(ii) $$\vec{r} = \dfrac{1}{\sqrt{17}} (a\vec{i} + \vec{j}) = \dfrac{a}{\sqrt{17}} \vec{i} + \dfrac{1}{\sqrt{17}} \vec{j}$$

Given: $\qquad |\vec{r}| = 1$

$$\Rightarrow \quad \sqrt{\left(\dfrac{a}{\sqrt{17}}\right)^2 + \left(\dfrac{1}{\sqrt{17}}\right)^2} = 1$$
$$\Rightarrow \qquad \dfrac{a^2}{17} + \dfrac{1}{17} = 1$$
$$\Rightarrow \qquad a^2 + 1 = 17$$
$$\Rightarrow \qquad a^2 = 16$$
$$\Rightarrow \qquad a = \pm 4$$

Example

(i) $\vec{p} = 3\vec{i} + 2\vec{j}$,   verify $\left| \dfrac{\vec{p}}{|\vec{p}|} \right| = 1$.

(ii) $\vec{x} = 4\vec{i} - 2\vec{j}$, $\vec{y} = 7\vec{i} - 6\vec{j}$. Find the unit vector in the direction $\overrightarrow{xy}$.

Solution:

(i) $\vec{p} = 3\vec{i} + 2\vec{j}$

$|\vec{p}| = \sqrt{3^2 + 2^2} = \sqrt{9 + 4} = \sqrt{13}$

$\dfrac{\vec{p}}{|\vec{p}|} = \dfrac{3\vec{i} + 2\vec{j}}{\sqrt{13}} = \dfrac{3}{\sqrt{13}}\vec{i} + \dfrac{2}{\sqrt{13}}\vec{j}$

$\left| \dfrac{\vec{p}}{|\vec{p}|} \right| = \sqrt{\left(\dfrac{3}{\sqrt{13}}\right)^2 + \left(\dfrac{2}{\sqrt{13}}\right)^2}$

$= \sqrt{\dfrac{9}{13} + \dfrac{4}{13}} = \sqrt{\dfrac{13}{13}} = \sqrt{1} = 1$

(ii) $\vec{x} = 4\vec{i} - 2\vec{j}$, $\vec{y} = 7\vec{i} - 6\vec{j}$

$\overrightarrow{xy} = \vec{y} - \vec{x}$

$\overrightarrow{xy} = 7\vec{i} - 6\vec{j} - 4\vec{i} + 2\vec{j}$

$\overrightarrow{xy} = 3\vec{i} - 4\vec{j}$

$|\overrightarrow{xy}| = \sqrt{3^2 + 4^2} = \sqrt{9 + 16} = \sqrt{25} = 5$

The unit vector in the direction of $\overrightarrow{xy}$ is

$\dfrac{\overrightarrow{xy}}{|\overrightarrow{xy}|} = \dfrac{3\vec{i} - 4\vec{j}}{5} = \dfrac{3}{5}\vec{i} - \dfrac{4}{5}\vec{j}$

Example

(i) $\vec{p} = 5\vec{i} + 4\vec{j}$, $\vec{q} = 2\vec{i} + 6\vec{j}$. If $\overrightarrow{pr} = 2\overrightarrow{pq}$, express $\vec{r}$ in the form $a\vec{i} + b\vec{j}$.

(ii) $\vec{a} = 5\vec{i}$, $\vec{b} = i + \sqrt{3}\vec{j}$. Calculate $|\angle boa|$.

Solution:

(i) $\vec{p} = 5\vec{i} + 4\vec{j}$, $\vec{q} = 2\vec{i} + 6\vec{j}$

Let

$\vec{r} = a\vec{i} + b\vec{j}$

$\overrightarrow{pr} = \vec{r} - \vec{p}$

$= a\vec{i} + b\vec{j} - 5\vec{i} - 4\vec{j}$

$= (a - 5)\vec{i} + (b - 4)\vec{j}$

$\overrightarrow{pq} = \vec{q} - \vec{p}$

$= 2\vec{i} + 6\vec{j} - 5\vec{i} - 4\vec{j}$

$= -3\vec{i} + 2\vec{j}$

$\therefore \ 2\overrightarrow{pq} = -6\vec{i} + 4\vec{j}$

Given: $\qquad\qquad \overrightarrow{pr} = 2\overrightarrow{pq}$

$\Rightarrow\quad (a-5)\vec{i} + (b-4)\vec{j} = -6\vec{i} + 4\vec{j}$

$\Rightarrow\qquad a-5 = -6$ and $b-4 = 4$

$\Rightarrow\qquad a = -1$ and $b = 8$

Thus, $\qquad \vec{r} = a\vec{i} + b\vec{j} = -\vec{i} + 8\vec{j}$

(ii) $\quad \vec{a} = 5\vec{i}, \quad \vec{b} = \vec{i} + \sqrt{3}\vec{j}$

$$\vec{a}.\vec{b} = |\vec{a}||\vec{b}| \cos\theta \quad \text{(where } \theta = \angle aob)$$

$$(5i + 0j).(i + \sqrt{3}j) = |5i||i + \sqrt{3}| \cos\theta$$

$$5(1) + 0(\sqrt{3}) = 5.2 \cos\theta$$

$$5 = 10 \cos\theta$$

$$\cos\theta = \tfrac{1}{2}$$

$$\theta = \cos^{-1}\tfrac{1}{2}$$

$$\theta = \tfrac{\pi}{3}$$

Example

Vertices p and r of the parallelogram $opqr$ are
$\vec{p} = 4\vec{i} - \vec{j}$ and $\vec{r} = 2\vec{i} + 3\vec{j}$, where o is the origin.

Find

(i) $\quad \vec{p} + \vec{r}$ and $\vec{p} - \vec{r}$

(ii) $\quad |\vec{p} + \vec{r}|$ and $|\vec{p} - \vec{r}|$.

Show that θ, the acute angle between $\overrightarrow{oq}$ and $\overrightarrow{rp}$, is given by

$$\cos^{-1} \frac{1}{5\sqrt{2}}$$

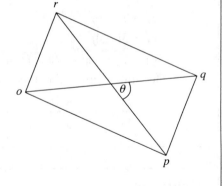

A point d in the plane is such that $\vec{d} = \vec{r} - k\vec{p}$, $k \in R$ and $\vec{d} \perp \vec{p}$. Find the value of k.

Solution:

(i) $\quad \vec{p} + \vec{r} = 4\vec{i} - \vec{j} + 2\vec{i} + 3\vec{j}$
$\qquad\qquad = 6\vec{i} + 2\vec{j}$

$\vec{p} - \vec{r} = (4\vec{i} - \vec{j}) - (2\vec{i} + 3\vec{j})$
$\qquad\quad = 2\vec{i} - 4\vec{j}$

(ii) $\quad |\vec{p} + \vec{r}| = |6\vec{i} + 2\vec{j}|$
$\qquad\qquad = \sqrt{36 + 4} = \sqrt{40} = 2\sqrt{10}$

$|\vec{p} - \vec{r}| = |2\vec{i} - 4\vec{j}|$
$\qquad\qquad = \sqrt{4 + 16} = \sqrt{20} = 2\sqrt{5}$

$$\vec{oq} = \vec{q} = \vec{p} + \vec{r} = 6\vec{i} + 2\vec{j}$$

$$\vec{rp} = \vec{p} - \vec{r} = 2\vec{i} - 4\vec{j}$$

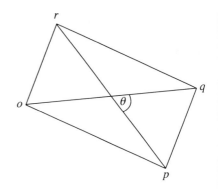

$$\vec{oq}.\vec{rp} = |\vec{oq}||\vec{rp}| \cos \theta$$

Thus, $\cos \theta = \dfrac{\vec{oq}.\vec{rp}}{|\vec{oq}||\vec{rp}|}$

$$\Rightarrow \quad \cos \theta = \dfrac{(6\vec{i} + 2\vec{j}).(2\vec{i} - 4\vec{j})}{|6\vec{i} + 2\vec{j}||2\vec{i} - 4\vec{j}|} = \dfrac{6(2) + 2(-4)}{\sqrt{40}\sqrt{20}} = \dfrac{12 - 8}{\sqrt{800}} = \dfrac{4}{20\sqrt{2}} = \dfrac{1}{5\sqrt{2}}$$

$$\Rightarrow \quad \theta = \cos^{-1}\dfrac{1}{5\sqrt{2}}$$

$$\vec{d} = \vec{r} - k\vec{p} = 2\vec{i} + 3\vec{j} - k(4\vec{i} - \vec{j})$$
$$= 2\vec{i} + 3\vec{j} - 4k\vec{i} + k\vec{j} = (2 - 4k)\vec{i} + (3 + k)\vec{j}$$

Given: $\quad \vec{d} \perp \vec{p} \Rightarrow \vec{d}.\vec{p} = 0$

$$\Rightarrow \quad [(2 - 4k)\vec{i} + (k + 3)\vec{j}].[4\vec{i} - \vec{j}] = 0$$
$$\Rightarrow \quad (2 - 4k)(4) + (k + 3)(-1) = 0$$
$$\Rightarrow \quad 8 - 16k - k - 3 = 0$$
$$\Rightarrow \quad -17k = -5$$
$$\Rightarrow \quad k = \tfrac{5}{17}$$

Example

If $\vec{r} = a\vec{i} + b\vec{j}$ and $\vec{s} = c\vec{i} + d\vec{j}$,

which of the following are always true?

(i) $(\vec{r} + \vec{s})^{\perp} = \vec{r}^{\perp} + \vec{s}^{\perp}$ 　　(ii) $(\vec{r}^{\perp})^{\perp} = \vec{r}$

(iii) $(k\vec{r})^{\perp} = k(\vec{r}^{\perp})$ 　　　　(iv) $\vec{r}^{\perp}.\vec{s} = \vec{r}.\vec{s}^{\perp}$

Solution:

If $\quad \vec{r} = a\vec{i} + b\vec{j} \quad$ and $\quad \vec{s} = c\vec{i} + d\vec{j} \quad \left(\begin{array}{l}\text{swop coefficients and then change}\\ \text{the sign of the } \vec{i} \text{ coefficient}\end{array}\right.$

then $\quad \vec{r}^{\perp} = -b\vec{i} + a\vec{j} \quad$ and $\quad \vec{s}^{\perp} = -d\vec{i} + c\vec{j} \quad$

(i) $\vec{r} + \vec{s} = a\vec{i} + b\vec{j} + c\vec{i} + d\vec{j} = (a + c)\vec{i} + (b + d)\vec{j}$

Thus, $(\vec{r} + \vec{s})^{\perp} = (-b - d)\vec{i} + (a + c)\vec{j}$

$\vec{r}^{\perp} + \vec{s}^{\perp} = -b\vec{i} + a\vec{j} - d\vec{i} + c\vec{j} = (-b - d)\vec{i} + (a + c)\vec{j}$

$\therefore$ $(\vec{r} + \vec{s})^{\perp} = \vec{r}^{\perp} + \vec{s}^{\perp}$ is true

(ii) $\vec{r} = a\vec{i} + b\vec{j}$

$(\vec{r}^{\perp})^{\perp} = (-b\vec{i} + a\vec{j})^{\perp} = -a\vec{i} - b\vec{j}$

$\therefore$ $(\vec{r}^{\perp})^{\perp} = \vec{r}$ is false

(iii) $k\vec{r} = k(a\vec{i} + b\vec{j}) = ka\vec{i} + kb\vec{j}$

Thus, $(k\vec{r})^{\perp} = -kb\vec{i} + ka\vec{j}$

$k(\vec{r}^{\perp}) = k(-b\vec{i} + a\vec{j}) = -kb\vec{i} + ka\vec{j}$

$\therefore$ $(k\vec{r})^{\perp} = k(\vec{r}^{\perp})$ is true

(iv) $\vec{r}^{\perp}.\vec{s} = (-b\vec{i} + a\vec{j}).(c\vec{i} + d\vec{j}) = -bc + ad$

$\vec{r}.\vec{s}^{\perp} = (a\vec{i} + b\vec{j}).(-d\vec{i} + c\vec{j}) = -ad + bc$

$\therefore$ $\vec{r}^{\perp}.\vec{s} = \vec{r}.\vec{s}^{\perp}$ is false

---

Example

$\vec{p} = -\vec{i} - \vec{j}, \qquad \vec{q} = \vec{i} + 5\vec{j}, \qquad \vec{r} = 4\vec{i} + 4\vec{j}, \qquad \vec{s} = a\vec{i} + b\vec{j}.$

If $|\vec{pr}| = |\vec{qs}|$ and $\vec{pr} \perp \vec{qs}$, find the possible values of a and b.

Solution:

$|\vec{pr}| = |\vec{r} - \vec{p}| = |4\vec{i} + 4\vec{j} + \vec{i} + \vec{j}| = |5\vec{i} + 5\vec{j}| = \sqrt{5^2 + 5^2} = \sqrt{50}$

$|\vec{qs}| = |\vec{s} - \vec{q}| = |a\vec{i} + b\vec{j} - \vec{i} - 5\vec{j}| = |(a - 1)\vec{i} + (b - 5)\vec{j}| = \sqrt{(a - 1)^2 + (b - 5)^2}$

Given: $|\vec{pr}| = |\vec{qs}| \implies \qquad \sqrt{(a - 1)^2 + (b - 5)^2} \qquad = \sqrt{50}$

$\implies a^2 - 2a + 1 + b^2 - 10b + 25 = 50$

$\implies a^2 + b^2 - 2a - 10b - 24 \quad = 0 \qquad ①$

Given: $\qquad \vec{pr} \perp \vec{qs} \implies \vec{pr}.\vec{qs} = 0$

$\implies (5\vec{i} + 5\vec{j}).[(a - 1)\vec{i} + (b - 5)\vec{j}] = 0$

$\implies 5(a - 1) + 5(b - 5) = 0$

$\implies a - 1 + b - 5 = 0$

$\implies a + b - 6 = 0 \quad ②$

We now solve the simultaneous equations ① and ②.

$$a + b - 6 = 0 \qquad ②$$
$$\Rightarrow \qquad b = (6 - a)$$

put this into ①.

$$a^2 + b^2 - 2a - 10b - 24 = 0 \qquad ①$$

$$a^2 + (6 - a)^2 - 2a - 10(6 - a) - 24 = 0$$
$$a^2 + 36 - 12a + a^2 - 2a - 60 + 10a - 24 = 0$$
$$2a^2 - 4a - 48 = 0$$
$$a^2 - 2a - 24 = 0$$
$$(a - 6)(a + 4) = 0$$
$$a = 6 \text{ or } a = -4$$

$a = 6 : \quad b = 6 - a = 6 - 6 = 0$

$a = -4: \quad b = 6 - a = 6 + 4 = 10$

Thus, $a = 6$, $b = 0$ or $a = -4$, $b = 10$.

Example

(i) $\vec{a} = k\vec{i} + 2\vec{j}$ and $\vec{b} = 3\vec{i} + \vec{j}$. If $|\angle aob| = \dfrac{\pi}{4}$, find two possible values of k.

(ii) $\vec{a} = 4\vec{i} + \vec{j}$, $\vec{b} = 8\vec{i} + 5\vec{j}$ and $\vec{c} = -3\vec{i} + 2\vec{j}$.

Find **(a)** $|\angle bac|$ **(b)** area of $\triangle abc$

Solution:

(i) $|\vec{a}| = |k\vec{i} + 2\vec{j}| = \sqrt{k^2 + 4}$, $|\vec{b}| = |3\vec{i} + \vec{j}| = \sqrt{9 + 1} = \sqrt{10}$

$$\vec{a}.\vec{b} = |\vec{a}||\vec{b}| \cos\theta \qquad \left[\text{where } \theta = \angle aob = \frac{\pi}{4} \right]$$

$$\Rightarrow \quad (k\vec{i} + 2\vec{j}).(3\vec{i} + \vec{j}) = \sqrt{k^2 + 4}\,\sqrt{10}.\frac{1}{\sqrt{2}} \qquad \left[\cos\theta = \cos\frac{\pi}{4} = \frac{1}{\sqrt{2}} \right]$$

$$\Rightarrow \qquad 3k + 2 = \frac{\sqrt{10}\,\sqrt{k^2 + 4}}{\sqrt{2}} \qquad [3(k) + 2(1) = 3k + 2]$$

$$\Rightarrow \qquad 9k^2 + 12k + 4 = \frac{10(k^2 + 4)}{2} \qquad \text{[square both sides]}$$

$$\Rightarrow \qquad 9k^2 + 12k + 4 = 5k^2 + 20$$
$$\Rightarrow \qquad 4k^2 + 12k - 16 = 0$$
$$\Rightarrow \qquad k^2 + 3k - 4 = 0$$
$$\Rightarrow \qquad (k + 4)(k - 1) = 0$$
$$\Rightarrow \qquad k = -4 \text{ or } k = 1$$

(ii) $\vec{a} = 4\vec{i} + \vec{j}$, $\vec{b} = 8\vec{i} + 5\vec{j}$, $\vec{c} = -3\vec{i} + 2\vec{j}$

(a)

$$\vec{ab} \cdot \vec{ac} = |\vec{ab}||\vec{ac}| \cos \theta$$

$$(4\vec{i} + 4\vec{j}) \cdot (-7\vec{i} + \vec{j}) = 4\sqrt{2} \cdot 5\sqrt{2} \cos \theta$$

$$-28 + 4 = 40 \cos \theta$$

$$40 \cos \theta = -24$$

$$\cos \theta = -\frac{24}{40}$$

$$\cos \theta = -\frac{3}{5}$$

$$\theta = \cos^{-1}\left(-\frac{3}{5}\right)$$

$$\theta = 126°52'$$

(b)

$$\cos \theta = -\frac{3}{5}$$

$$\cos^2 \theta + \sin^2 \theta = 1$$

$$\left(-\frac{3}{5}\right)^2 + \sin^2 \theta = 1$$

$$\frac{9}{25} + \sin^2 \theta = 1$$

$$\sin^2 \theta = \frac{16}{25}$$

$$\sin \theta = \frac{4}{5}$$

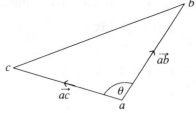

$$\vec{ab} = \vec{b} - \vec{a}$$

$$= 8\vec{i} + 5\vec{j} - 4\vec{i} - \vec{j}$$

$$= 4\vec{i} + 4\vec{j}$$

$$\therefore \quad |\vec{ab}| = \sqrt{16 + 16} = \sqrt{32} = 4\sqrt{2}$$

$$\vec{ac} = \vec{c} - \vec{a}$$

$$= -3\vec{i} + 2\vec{j} - 4\vec{i} - \vec{j}$$

$$= -7\vec{i} + \vec{j}$$

$$\therefore \quad |\vec{ab}| = \sqrt{49 + 1} = \sqrt{50} = 5\sqrt{2}$$

Note: When writing down the dot product it is very important to have the origin of both vectors the same, in this case 'a', the vertex of the required angle.

i.e. $\vec{ab} \cdot \vec{ac} = |\vec{ab}||\vec{ac}| \cos \theta$

Area of $\triangle abc = \frac{1}{2}|\vec{ab}| \cdot |\vec{ac}| \sin \theta = \frac{1}{2} \cdot 4\sqrt{2} \cdot 5\sqrt{2} \cdot \frac{4}{5} = 16$

Example

$\vec{p}$ is a vector parallel to $2\vec{i} + \vec{j}$, $\vec{q}$ is a vector perpendicular to $\vec{i} - \vec{j}$ and
$\vec{p} + \vec{q} = 4m\vec{i} + 3m\vec{j}$, $m > 0$.
If $|\vec{p} + \vec{q}| = 10$, find $|\vec{p}|$ and $|\vec{q}|$.

Solution:

$$\vec{p} + \vec{q} = 4m\vec{i} + 3m\vec{j}$$

Given: $|\vec{p} + \vec{q}| = 10$

$$\Rightarrow \quad \sqrt{(4m)^2 + (3m)^2} = 10$$

$$\Rightarrow \quad 16m^2 + 9m^2 = 100$$

$$\Rightarrow \quad 25m^2 = 100$$

$$\Rightarrow \quad m^2 = 4$$

$$\Rightarrow \quad m = \pm 2$$

Thus, $m = 2$ (as $m > 0$)

$$\therefore \quad \vec{p} + \vec{q} = 4m\vec{i} + 3m\vec{j}$$
$$= 8\vec{i} + 6\vec{j}$$

$$\vec{p} \parallel 2\vec{i} + \vec{j} \implies \vec{p} = k(2\vec{i} + \vec{j})$$

A vector perpendicular to $\vec{i} - \vec{j}$ is $\vec{i} + \vec{j}$

$$\vec{q} \perp \vec{i} - \vec{j} \implies \vec{q} = h(\vec{i} + \vec{j})$$

Given: $\qquad\qquad \vec{p} + \vec{q} = 8\vec{i} + 6\vec{j}$
$$\implies \quad h(2\vec{i} + \vec{j}) + k(\vec{i} + \vec{j}) = 8\vec{i} + 6\vec{j}$$
$$\implies \quad 2h\vec{i} + h\vec{j} + k\vec{i} + k\vec{j} = 8\vec{i} + 6\vec{j}$$
$$\implies \quad 2h + k = 8 \quad ① \text{ and } h + k = 6 \quad ②$$

Solving ① and ② gives $h = 2$, $k = 4$

$$\vec{p} = k(2\vec{i} + \vec{j})$$
$$= 2(2\vec{i} + \vec{j})$$
$$= 4\vec{i} + 2\vec{j}$$
$$\implies |\vec{p}| = \sqrt{4^2 + 2^2}$$
$$= \sqrt{16 + 4} = \sqrt{20} = 2\sqrt{5}$$

$$\vec{q} = h(\vec{i} + \vec{j})$$
$$= 4(\vec{i} + \vec{j})$$
$$= 4\vec{i} + 4\vec{j}$$
$$\implies |\vec{q}| = \sqrt{4^2 + 4^2}$$
$$= \sqrt{16 + 16} = \sqrt{32} = 4\sqrt{2}$$

Example

$$\vec{a} = 2\vec{i} + 8\vec{j}, \qquad \vec{b} = -\vec{i} + 9\vec{j}, \qquad \vec{c} = 4\vec{i} - \vec{j}, \qquad \vec{d} = x\vec{i} + y\vec{j}.$$

The point d lies on the line bc.

Find an equation connecting x and y by finding expressions for $\vec{bc}$ and $\vec{bd}$.

If $\vec{ad} \perp \vec{bc}$, use the dot product $\vec{ad} \cdot \vec{bc}$ to find another equation connecting x and y.

Hence, find the value of x and the value of y.

Solution:

$$\vec{bc} = \vec{c} - \vec{b} = 4\vec{i} - \vec{j} + \vec{i} - 9\vec{j} = 5\vec{i} - 10\vec{j}$$
$$\vec{bd} = \vec{d} - \vec{b} = x\vec{i} + y\vec{j} + \vec{i} - 9\vec{j} = (x + 1)\vec{i} + (y - 9)\vec{j}$$

d lies on the line bc. Thus,

$$\vec{bc} \parallel \vec{bd}$$
$$\implies \quad 5\vec{i} - 10\vec{j} \parallel (x + 1)\vec{i} + (y - 9)\vec{j}$$
$$\implies \quad \frac{5}{x + 1} = \frac{-10}{y - 9} \quad \text{(equal ratios)}$$
$$\implies \quad -10x - 10 = 5y - 45$$
$$\implies \quad -10x - 5y + 35 = 0$$
$$\implies \quad 2x + y - 7 = 0 \quad ①$$

$\vec{ad} = \vec{d} - \vec{a} = x\vec{i} + y\vec{j} - 2\vec{i} - 8\vec{j} = (x - 2)\vec{i} + (y - 8)\vec{j}$

$\vec{bc} = 5\vec{i} - 10\vec{j}$

Given: $\vec{ad} \perp \vec{bc}$

$\Rightarrow \quad \vec{ad} . \vec{bc} = 0$

$[(x - 2)\vec{i} + (y - 8)\vec{j}] . (5\vec{i} - 10\vec{j}) = 0$

$(x - 2)(5) + (y - 8)(-10) = 0$

$5x - 10 - 10y + 80 = 0$

$5x - 10y + 70 = 0$

$x - 2y + 14 = 0 \quad ②$

Solving ① and ② simultaneously gives $x = 0$ and $y = 7$.

Example

r divides the line segment $[ab]$ in the ratio $m:n$.

Verify that $\vec{r} = \dfrac{n}{m+n}\,\vec{a} + \dfrac{m}{m+n}\,\vec{b}$.

Solution:

Draw a diagram, letting o be the origin.

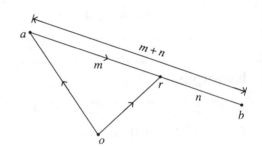

$\vec{or} = \vec{oa} + \vec{ar}$ (Triangle Law)

$\vec{r} = \vec{a} + \dfrac{m}{m+n}\,\vec{ab}$

$\vec{r} = \vec{a} + \dfrac{m}{m+n}\,(\vec{b} - \vec{a})$

$\vec{r} = \vec{a} + \dfrac{m}{m+n}\,\vec{b} - \dfrac{m}{m+n}\,\vec{a}$

$\vec{r} = \vec{a} - \dfrac{m}{m+n}\,\vec{a} + \dfrac{m}{m+n}\,\vec{b}$

$\vec{r} = \left(1 - \dfrac{m}{m+n}\right)\vec{a} + \dfrac{m}{m+n}\,\vec{b}$

$\vec{r} = \dfrac{n}{m+n}\,\vec{a} + \dfrac{m}{m+n}\,\vec{b}$

$1 - \dfrac{m}{m+n}$

$= \dfrac{m+n}{m+n} - \dfrac{m}{m+n}$

$= \dfrac{m+n-m}{m+n}$

$= \dfrac{n}{m+n}$

Example

(a) If $\vec{c} = 3\vec{i} - 2\vec{j}$ and $\vec{d} = 9\vec{i} + 6\vec{j}$, find a unit vector perpendicular to $\vec{cd}$.

(b) **(i)** $opqr$ is a parallelogram where o is the origin,

$\vec{p} = 2\vec{i} - 8\vec{j}$ and $\vec{q} = 11\vec{i} + \vec{j}$.

Express $\vec{r}$ in terms of $\vec{i}$ and $\vec{j}$.

(ii) $s \in [pq]$ and $|ps| : |sq| = 5 : 4$.

Express $\vec{s}$ in terms of $\vec{i}$ and $\vec{j}$.

(iii) If $\vec{w} = x\vec{i} - 4\vec{j}$ and $|\vec{ws}| = \sqrt{37}$, find two values for x.

Show that the larger value gives $\vec{ws} \perp \vec{rs}$.

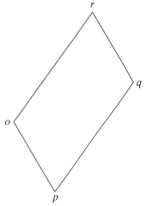

Show that the smaller value gives an angle of $\cos^{-1}\left(\dfrac{-12}{37}\right)$ between $\vec{ws}$ and $\vec{rs}$.

Solution:

(a) $\vec{c} = 3\vec{i} - 2\vec{j}$ and $\vec{d} = 9\vec{i} + 6\vec{j}$

$$\vec{cd} = \vec{d} - \vec{c} = (9\vec{i} + 6\vec{j}) - (3\vec{i} - 2\vec{j})$$
$$= 9\vec{i} + 6\vec{j} - 3\vec{i} + 2\vec{j} = 6\vec{i} + 8\vec{j}$$

A vector perpendicular to $\vec{cd}$ is $8\vec{i} - 6\vec{j}$ or $-8\vec{i} + 6\vec{j}$.

(Swop coefficients and change the sign of one of them.)

Thus, a unit vector perpendicular to $\vec{cd}$ is

$$\frac{8\vec{i} - 6\vec{j}}{|8\vec{i} - 6\vec{j}|} \quad \text{or} \quad \frac{-8\vec{i} + 6\vec{j}}{|-8\vec{i} + 6\vec{j}|}$$

$$= \frac{8\vec{i} - 6\vec{j}}{10} \quad \text{or} \quad \frac{-8\vec{i} + 6\vec{j}}{10}$$

$$= \tfrac{8}{10}\vec{i} - \tfrac{6}{10}\vec{j} \quad \text{or} \quad -\tfrac{8}{10}\vec{i} + \tfrac{6}{10}\vec{j}$$

$$= \tfrac{4}{5}\vec{i} - \tfrac{3}{5}\vec{j} \quad \text{or} \quad -\tfrac{4}{5}\vec{i} + \tfrac{3}{5}\vec{j}$$

(either answer will do)

(b) **(i)** $\vec{or} = \vec{pq}$

$\Rightarrow \qquad \vec{r} = \vec{q} - \vec{r}$

$$= (11\vec{i} + \vec{j}) - (2\vec{i} - 8\vec{j})$$
$$= 11\vec{i} + \vec{j} - 2\vec{i} + 8\vec{j} = 9\vec{i} + 9\vec{j}$$

(ii) $\vec{os} = \vec{op} + \vec{ps}$

$\Rightarrow \qquad \vec{s} = \vec{p} + \frac{5}{9}(\vec{pq})$

$\Rightarrow \qquad \vec{s} = \vec{p} + \frac{5}{9}\vec{r} \qquad\qquad (\vec{pq} = \vec{r})$

$\Rightarrow \qquad \vec{s} = (2\vec{i} - 8\vec{j}) + \frac{5}{9}(9\vec{i} + 9\vec{j}) \qquad$ [from **(i)**]

$\Rightarrow \qquad \vec{s} = 2\vec{i} - 8\vec{j} + 5\vec{i} + 5\vec{j} = 7\vec{i} - 3\vec{j}$

(iii) $\vec{w} = x\vec{i} - 4\vec{j}, \qquad \vec{s} = 7\vec{i} - 3\vec{j}$

$\qquad \vec{ws} = \vec{s} - \vec{w} = (7\vec{i} - 3\vec{j}) - (x\vec{i} - 4\vec{j})$

$\qquad\qquad\quad = 7\vec{i} - 3\vec{j} - x\vec{i} + 4\vec{j}$

$\qquad\qquad\quad = (7 - x)\vec{i} + \vec{j}$

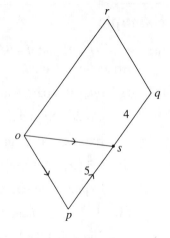

Given: $\qquad\qquad\qquad |\vec{ws}| = \sqrt{37}$

$$|(7 - x)\vec{i} + \vec{j}| = \sqrt{37}$$

$$\sqrt{(7 - x)^2 + 1^2} = \sqrt{37}$$

$$49 - 14x + x^2 + 1 = 37$$

$$x^2 - 14x + 13 = 0$$

$$(x - 13)(x - 1) = 0$$

$$x = 13 \ \text{ or } \ x = 1$$

When $x = 13$, $\qquad \vec{w} = x\vec{i} - 4\vec{j} = 13\vec{i} - 4\vec{j}$.

$\quad \vec{ws} = \vec{s} - \vec{w} = (7\vec{i} - 3\vec{j}) - (13\vec{i} - 4\vec{j}) = 7\vec{i} - 3\vec{j} - 13\vec{i} + 4\vec{j} = -6\vec{i} + \vec{j}$

$\quad \vec{rs} = \vec{s} - \vec{r} = (7\vec{i} - 3\vec{j}) - (9\vec{i} + 9\vec{j}) = 7\vec{i} - 3\vec{j} - 9\vec{i} - 9\vec{j} = -2\vec{i} - 12\vec{j}$

$\quad \vec{ws} \cdot \vec{rs} = (-6\vec{i} + \vec{j}) \cdot (-2\vec{i} - 12\vec{j})$

$\qquad\qquad = (-6)(-2) + (1)(-12)$

$\qquad\qquad = 12 - 12 = 0$

$\qquad\qquad$ Thus $\vec{ws} \perp \vec{rs}$

When $x = 1$, $\qquad \vec{w} = x\vec{i} - 4\vec{j} = \vec{i} - 4\vec{j}$.

$\quad \vec{ws} = \vec{s} - \vec{w} = (7\vec{i} - 3\vec{j}) - (\vec{i} - 4\vec{j}) = 7\vec{i} - 3\vec{j} - \vec{i} + 4\vec{j} = 6\vec{i} + \vec{j}$

$\quad \vec{rs} = -2\vec{i} - 12\vec{j} \qquad$ (from above)

Let θ be the angle between the vectors $\vec{ws}$ and $\vec{rs}$.

$$\vec{ws} \cdot \vec{rs} = |\vec{ws}||\vec{rs}|\cos\theta$$

$\Rightarrow \quad \cos\theta = \dfrac{\vec{ws} \cdot \vec{rs}}{|\vec{ws}||\vec{rs}|}$

$\Rightarrow \quad \cos\theta = \dfrac{(6\vec{i}+\vec{j}) \cdot (-2\vec{i}-12\vec{j})}{|6\vec{i}+\vec{j}||-2\vec{i}-12\vec{j}|}$

$\Rightarrow \quad \cos\theta = \dfrac{-24}{\sqrt{37} \cdot 2\sqrt{37}}$

$\Rightarrow \quad \cos\theta = \dfrac{-12}{37}$

$\Rightarrow \quad \theta = \cos^{-1}\left(\dfrac{-12}{37}\right)$

$(6\vec{i}+\vec{j}) \cdot (-2\vec{i}-12\vec{j})$
$= (6)(-2) + (1)(-12)$
$= -12 - 12 = -24$

$|6\vec{i}+\vec{j}| = \sqrt{36+1} = \sqrt{37}$

$|-2\vec{i}-12\vec{j}| = \sqrt{4+144} = \sqrt{148} = 2\sqrt{37}$

3. THE LINE AND TRANSFORMATION GEOMETRY

In all cases (x_1, y_1) and (x_2, y_2) represent points.

1. Distance between two points

$$\sqrt{(x_2 - x_1)^2 + (y_2 - y_1)^2}$$

2. Midpoint of a line segment

$$\left(\frac{x_1 + x_2}{2}, \frac{y_1 + y_2}{2} \right)$$

3. Area of a triangle

[one point at $(0, 0)$]

$$\tfrac{1}{2} \left| x_1 y_2 - x_2 y_1 \right|$$

Note: To find the area of a quadrilateral (four-sided figure), draw a diagram and divide it into two triangles, find the area of each triangle separately and add the results.

4. Slope of line, given two points

$$m = \frac{y_2 - y_1}{x_2 - x_1}$$

5. Slopes of parallel lines

Parallel lines have equal slopes

$$\text{If } L \parallel K \Longleftrightarrow m_L = m_K$$

6. Slopes of perpendicular lines

If two lines are perpendicular, then the product of their slopes equals -1.

$$\text{If } L \perp K \Longleftrightarrow m_L \cdot m_K = -1$$

(In **5** and **6** above, m_L and m_K are the slopes of the lines L and K, respectively.)

7. Equation of a line

$$(y - y_1) = m(x - x_1)$$

We need the slope m and one point (x_1, y_1) on the line.

8. Point of intersection of two lines

Solve by simultaneous equations.

9. Where lines cut the axes

On the X axis, $y = 0$.

On the Y axis, $x = 0$.

10. General equation of a line

$$ax + by + c = 0$$

$$\text{Slope} = m = -\frac{a}{b} \quad \left(\text{i.e.} - \frac{\text{coefficient of } x}{\text{coefficient of } y}\right)$$

$ax + by + k = 0$ is a line parallel to $ax + by + c = 0$.

$bx - ay + k = 0$ is a line perpendicular to $ax + by + c = 0$.

11. Slope–intercept form of the equation of a line

$$y = mx + c$$

m = slope

c = intercept on the Y axis

Note: $y = mx$, passes through the origin $(0, 0)$.

$y = k$, parallel to the X axis.

$x = h$, parallel to the Y axis.

12. Division of a line segment in a given ratio

The coordinates of the point p which divides the line segment joining (x_1, y_1) and (x_2, y_2) in the ratio $m:n$ is given by

internal divisor	external divisor
$p = \left(\dfrac{mx_2 + nx_1}{m + n}, \dfrac{my_2 + ny_1}{m + n}\right)$	$p = \left(\dfrac{mx_2 - nx_1}{m - n}, \dfrac{my_2 - ny_1}{m - n}\right)$

13. Perpendicular distance from a point to a line

The perpendicular distance d of the point (x_1, y_1) from the line $ax + by + c = 0$ is given by

$$d = \frac{|ax_1 + by_1 + c|}{\sqrt{a^2 + b^2}}$$

14. Concurrent lines

The equation of a line through the point of intersection of the lines $ax + by + c = 0$ and $px + qy + r = 0$ is given by

$$ax + by + c + \lambda(px + qy + r) = 0$$

or

$$\mu(ax + by + c) + \lambda(px + qy + r) = 0$$
$$\mu, \lambda \in \mathbf{R}$$

15. Angle between two lines

If two lines L_1 and L_2 have slopes m_1 and m_2, respectively, and θ is the angle between them, then

$$\tan \theta = \pm \frac{m_1 - m_2}{1 + m_1 m_2}$$

In practice the best approach is to find the acute angle θ, by using $\tan \theta = \left| \dfrac{m_1 - m_2}{1 + m_1 m_2} \right|$.

The obtuse angle is obtained by finding $180° - \theta$.

16. Collinear points

The three points p, q and r are collinear if

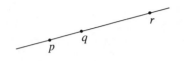

1. slope of pq = slope of qr

    or

2. area of $\Delta pqr = 0$

    or

3. $|pq| + |qr| = |pr|$

17. Points on the same side or opposite sides of a line

1. Substitute the points into the equation of the line, then

2. (a) Same sign $\Rightarrow$ same side of the line.

 (b) Opposite signs $\Rightarrow$ opposite sides of the line.

18. Triangles

(i) Centroid g

$$g = \left(\frac{x_1 + x_2 + x_3}{3}, \ \frac{y_1 + y_2 + y_3}{3} \right)$$

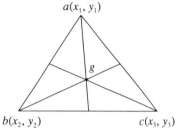

(ii) Circumcentre c

The circumcentre of a triangle is the point of intersection of the perpendicular bisectors of the sides.

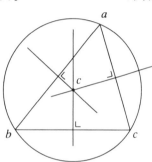

(iii) Orthocentre h

The orthocentre is the point of intersection of the perpendicular lines from the vertices to the opposite sides.

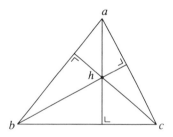

Example

$a(-2, 4)$, $b(2, 2)$ and $c(5, 3)$ are three points.

(i) Find $|ab|$.

(ii) Find the midpoint of $[bc]$.

(iii) Find the area of $\triangle abc$.

(iv) Find the slope of ab.

(v) Find the equation of the line ab.

(vi) Find the equation of the line L through the point c where $L \perp ab$.

(vii) $L \cap ab = \{p\}$. Find the coordinates of p.

(viii) Find the image of c under the axial symmetry in the line ab.

(ix) Find the coordinates of the centroid of Δabc.

Solution:

(i) $a(-2, 4)$, $\quad b(2, 2)$
$\qquad x_1, y_1 \qquad\quad x_2, y_2$

$$|ab| = \sqrt{(x_2 - x_1)^2 + (y_2 - y_1)^2}$$
$$= \sqrt{(2 + 2)^2 + (2 - 4)^2}$$
$$= \sqrt{16 + 4} = \sqrt{20} = 2\sqrt{5}$$

(ii) $b(2, 2)$, $\quad c(5, 3)$
$\qquad x_1, y_1 \qquad\quad x_2, y_2$

$$\text{midpoint} = \left(\frac{x_1 + x_2}{2}, \frac{y_1 + y_2}{2} \right)$$
$$= \left(\frac{2 + 5}{2}, \frac{2 + 3}{2} \right) = \left(\frac{7}{2}, \frac{5}{2} \right)$$

(iii) Area of Δabc

$\quad a(-2, 4) \quad b(2, 2) \quad$ and $\quad c(5, 3)$
$\qquad \downarrow \qquad\quad \downarrow \qquad\qquad\quad \downarrow$
$\quad (0, 0) \qquad (4, -2) \qquad\quad (7, -1) \qquad$ [map the point $a(-2, 4)$ to $(0, 0)$]
$\qquad\qquad\quad x_1, y_1 \qquad\qquad x_2, y_2$

$$\text{area of } \Delta abc = \tfrac{1}{2} |x_1 y_2 - x_2 y_1|$$
$$= \tfrac{1}{2} |(4)(-1) - (7)(-2)| = \tfrac{1}{2} |-4 + 14| = \tfrac{1}{2} |10| = 5$$

(iv) Slope of ab

$\quad a(-2, 4) \quad$ and $\quad b(2, 2)$
$\qquad x_1, y_1 \qquad\qquad x_2, y_2$

$$m = \frac{y_2 - y_1}{x_2 - x_1}$$
$$= \frac{2 - 4}{2 + 2} = \frac{-2}{4} = -\frac{1}{2}$$

(v) Equation of ab

$\qquad$ point $a(-2, 4)$, $\qquad$ slope $= -\frac{1}{2}$
$\qquad\qquad\quad x_1, y_1 \qquad\qquad\qquad\quad m$

$$(y - y_1) = m(x - x_1)$$
$$(y - 4) = -\tfrac{1}{2}(x + 2)$$
$$2y - 8 = -x - 2$$
$$x + 2y - 6 = 0$$

(vi) Through $c(5, 3)$ and $L \perp ab$

Slope of $ab = -\frac{1}{2}$

Thus, slope of $L = 2$
(invert and change sign)

Equation of L

$\qquad$ point $c(5, 3)$, $\qquad$ slope $= 2$
$\qquad\qquad\quad x_1, y_1 \qquad\qquad\qquad m$

$$(y - y_1) = m(x - x_1)$$
$$(y - 3) = 2(x - 5)$$
$$y - 3 = 2x - 10$$
$$2x - y - 7 = 0$$

(vii) $L \cap ab$. Use simultaneous equations.

$$x + 2y = 6 \quad (ab)$$
$$2x - y = 7 \quad (L)$$

$$x + 2y = 6 \quad (ab)$$
$$4x - 2y = 14 \quad (L \times 2)$$

$$5x = 20 \quad \text{(add)}$$
$$x = 4$$

Put $x = 4$ into L or (ab).

$$x + 2y = 6 \quad (ab)$$
$$\downarrow$$
$$\Longrightarrow \quad 4 + 2y = 6$$
$$\Longrightarrow \quad 2y = 6 - 4$$
$$\Longrightarrow \quad y = 2$$
$$\Longrightarrow \quad y = 1$$

$$\therefore \quad L \cap ab = \{p\} = (4, 1)$$

(viii) A diagram is very useful.

c is on L, $L \perp ab$ and $L \cap ab = (4, 1) = \{p\}$.

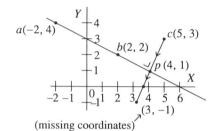
(missing coordinates)

Translation from c to p.

Take 1 from x, take 2 from y.

Apply this to p.

$$p(4, 1) \rightarrow (4 - 1, 1 - 2) \rightarrow (3, -1)$$

$\therefore$ the image of c is $(3, -1)$.

(ix) $\quad a(-2, 4), \quad b(2, 2), \quad c(5, 3)$
$\qquad\;\; x_1, y_1 \qquad x_2, y_2 \qquad x_3, y_3$

$$\text{Centroid} = \left(\frac{x_1 + x_2 + x_3}{3}, \frac{y_1 + y_2 + y_3}{3} \right)$$

$$= \left(\frac{-2 + 2 + 5}{3}, \frac{4 + 2 + 3}{3} \right) = \left(\frac{5}{3}, 3 \right)$$

Example

(i) Investigate if the points $(99, 35)$ and $(56, 19)$ are on the same side of the line $5x - 13y - 37 = 0$.

(ii) Investigate if the points $(30, 16)$ and $(-19, -11)$ are on the same side of the line $10x - 20y - 1 = 0$ as the origin $(0, 0)$.

Solution:

(i) $\quad 5x - 13y - 37 = 0$

$(99, 35): 5(99) - 13(35) - 37 = 495 - 455 - 37 = \; 3 > 0$

$(56, 19): 5(56) - 13(19) - 37 = 280 - 247 - 37 = -4 < 0$

opposite signs, $\quad \therefore \quad$ opposite sides of the line

(ii) $10x - 20y - 1 = 0$

$(30, 16):$ $\quad 10(30) - 20(16) - 1 =$ $\quad 300 - 320 - 1 = -21 < 0$

$(-19, -11):$ $10(-19) - 20(-11) - 1 = -190 + 220 - 1 =$ $\quad 29 > 0$

$(0, 0):$ $\quad\quad 10(0) - 20(0) - 1 =$ $\quad\quad\quad 0 - 0 - 1 = -1 < 0$

Thus, $(30, 16)$ and $(0, 0)$ are on the same side of the line and $(-19, -11)$ and $(0, 0)$ are on opposite sides of the line.

Example

Find the ratio in which the line $3x + 7y - 20 = 0$ divides the line segment joining $a(-5, 1)$ and $b(23, 5)$.

Solution:

Let c be the point of intersection of the line ab and the line $3x + 7y - 20 = 0$.

We require the coordinates of c and then calculate the ratio $|ac|:|cb|$.

$$\text{Slope of } ab = \frac{5 - 1}{23 + 5} = \frac{4}{28} = \frac{1}{7}$$

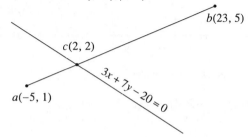

Equation of ab:

$$(y - 1) = \tfrac{1}{7}(x + 5)$$
$$7y - 7 = x + 5$$
$$x - 7y + 12 = 0$$

We now solve simultaneously the equations $x - 7y + 12 = 0$ and $3x + 7y - 20 = 0$.

$$
\begin{array}{rl}
x - 7y = & -12 \\
3x + 7y = & \ \ 20 \\
\hline
4x = & \ \ 8 \\
x = & \ \ 2
\end{array}
\qquad
\begin{array}{rl}
x - 7y = & -12 \\
2 - 7y = & -12 \\
-7y = & -14 \\
y = & \ \ 2
\end{array}
$$

Thus, the coordinates of c are $(2, 2)$.

$a(-5, 1), c(2, 2), b(23, 5)$

$$|ac| = \sqrt{(2 + 5)^2 + (2 - 1)^2} = \sqrt{7^2 + 1^2} = \sqrt{49 + 1} = \sqrt{50} = \sqrt{25.2} = \sqrt{25}\sqrt{2} = 5\sqrt{2}$$

$$|cb| = \sqrt{(23 - 2)^2 + (5 - 2)^2} = \sqrt{21^2 + 3^2} = \sqrt{441 + 9} = \sqrt{450} = \sqrt{225.2} = \sqrt{225}\sqrt{2} = 15\sqrt{2}$$

$$|ac|:|cb| = 5\sqrt{2}:15\sqrt{2} = 5:15 = 1:3$$

Thus, the line $3x + 7y - 20 = 0$ divides $[ab]$ in the ratio $1 : 3$.

Example

Verify that the point $(2, 1)$ is on the line $L: 3x + 2y - 8 = 0$ and find the equation of K, the image of L under the translation $(3, 4) \rightarrow (7, 1)$.

Solution:

$$L: 3x + 2y - 8 = 0$$

Substitute $(2, 1)$: $3(2) + 2(1) - 8 = 6 + 2 - 8 = 0$

$\therefore$ $(2, 1)$ is on the line L.

Translation: $(3, 4) \rightarrow (7, 1)$
(add 4 to x, subtract 3 from y)

$\therefore$ $(2, 1) \rightarrow (6, -2)$

Thus, $(6, -2)$ is on the line K.

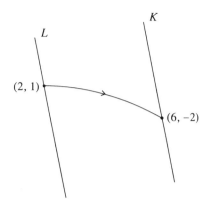

Note: Under a translation a line is mapped onto a parallel line.

We will use two methods to find the equation of K.

Method 1: Equation of K

Slope of L is $-\frac{3}{2}$

$\therefore$ Slope of K is $-\frac{3}{2}$

and the point $(6, -2)$ is on K

$$(y - y_1) = m(x - x_1)$$

$$(y + 2) = -\frac{3}{2}(x - 6)$$

$$2y + 4 = -3x + 18$$

Thus, $3x + 2y - 14 = 0$
is the equation of K.

Method 2: Equation of K

$L \| K$, thus K is of the form:

$$3x + 2y + c = 0$$

We need the value of c.

$(6, -2)$ is on $3x + 2y + c = 0$

$\Rightarrow$ $\qquad 3(6) + 2(-2) + c = 0$

$\Rightarrow$ $\qquad 18 - 4 + c = 0$

$\qquad c = -14$

Thus, $3x + 2y - 14 = 0$
is the equation of K.

Example

(i) $a(-2, -5)$, $b(1, -3)$ and $c(4, -1)$ are three points. Show that a, b and c are collinear.

(ii) If the three points $p(2, 5)$, $q(k, 1)$ and $r(11, -4)$ are collinear, find the value of k, where $k \in \mathbf{R}$.

(iii) The three points $r(2a + 2, 2a)$, $s(a + 1, 1)$ and $t(2a + 1, 3)$ are collinear.

Find the two possible values of a, where $a \in \mathbf{R}$.

Solution:

(i) $a(-2, -5)$, $b(1, -3)$, $c(4, -1)$

$$\text{Slope of } ab = \frac{-3+5}{1+2} = \frac{2}{3}$$

$$\text{Slope of } bc = \frac{-1+3}{4-1} = \frac{2}{3}$$

Thus, a, b and c are collinear

(ii) $p(2, 5)$, $q(k, 1)$, $r(11, -4)$

$$\text{Slope of } pq = \text{Slope of } qr$$

$$\Rightarrow \quad \frac{1-5}{k-2} = \frac{-4-1}{11-k}$$

$$\Rightarrow \quad \frac{-4}{k-2} = \frac{-5}{11-k}$$

$$\Rightarrow \quad -44 + 4k = -5k + 10$$

$$\Rightarrow \quad 9k = 54$$

$$\Rightarrow \quad k = 6$$

(iii) $r(2a+2, 2a)$, $s(a+1, 1)$, $t(2a+1, 3)$

$$\text{Slope of } rs = \text{Slope of } st$$

$$\Rightarrow \quad \frac{1-2a}{(a+1)-(2a+2)} = \frac{3-1}{(2a+1)-(a+1)}$$

$$\Rightarrow \quad \frac{1-2a}{a+1-2a-2} = \frac{2}{2a+1-a-1}$$

$$\Rightarrow \quad \frac{1-2a}{-a-1} = \frac{2}{a}$$

$$\Rightarrow \quad -2a - 2 = a - 2a^2$$

$$\Rightarrow \quad 2a^2 - 3a - 2 = 0$$

$$\Rightarrow \quad (2a+1)(a-2) = 0$$

$$\Rightarrow \quad a = -\tfrac{1}{2} \text{ or } a = 2$$

Example

(i) The slope of the line through the points $a(k, -2)$ and $b(-7, 2k+5)$ is $\tfrac{3}{2}$. Find the value of k.

(ii) $L: 3x + ty - 7 = 0$ and $K: 8x + 12y - 17 = 0$ are two lines.

If $L \perp K$, find the value of $t \in \mathbf{R}$.

Solution:

(i) $a(k, -2)$, $b(-7, 2k + 5)$
          x_1, y_1 x_2, y_2

Given: Slope of $ab = \dfrac{3}{2}$

Thus: $\dfrac{y_2 - y_1}{x_2 - x_1} = \dfrac{3}{2}$

$\Rightarrow$ $\dfrac{2k + 5 + 2}{-7 - k} = \dfrac{3}{2}$

$\Rightarrow$ $4k + 14 = -21 - 3k$

$\Rightarrow$ $7k = -35$

$\Rightarrow$ $k = -5$

(ii) $L : 3x + ty - 7 = 0$ $K : 8x + 12y - 17 = 0$

Given: $L \perp K$

$\therefore$ (Slope of L) . (Slope of K) $= -1$

$\Rightarrow$ $-\dfrac{3}{t} \times -\dfrac{8}{12} = -1$

$\Rightarrow$ $\dfrac{24}{12t} = -1$

$\Rightarrow$ $12t = -24$

$\Rightarrow$ $t = -2$

Example

(i) Find the measure of the obtuse angle between the lines $x - y + 2 = 0$ and $x - 2y - 1 = 0$.

(ii) Find the measure of the acute angle between the lines $\sqrt{3}x - y + 5 = 0$ and $x - \sqrt{3}y - 2 = 0$.

(iii) Find the measure of the acute angle between the lines $ax - by + c = 0$ and $(b - a)x + (a + b)y + d = 0$

(iv) Find the equations of the lines through the point $(4, 3)$ which make an angle of $45°$ with the line $6x + y - 5 = 0$.

Solution:

(i) Let θ be the acute angle between the lines.

Let the slope of $x - y + 2 = 0$ be m_1. Thus, $m_1 = 1$.

Let the slope of $x - 2y - 1 = 0$ be m_2. Thus, $m_2 = \frac{1}{2}$.

$$\tan \theta = \left| \dfrac{m_1 - m_2}{1 + m_1 m_2} \right|$$

$$= \left| \dfrac{1 - \frac{1}{2}}{1 + (1)(\frac{1}{2})} \right| = \left| \dfrac{\frac{1}{2}}{\frac{3}{2}} \right| = \left| \dfrac{1}{3} \right| = \dfrac{1}{3}$$

$\Rightarrow$ $\theta = \tan^{-1} \frac{1}{3}$

$\Rightarrow$ $\theta = 18°26'$

Thus, the obtuse angle $= 180° - \theta = 180° - 18°26' = 161°34'$.

(ii) Let θ be the acute angle between the lines.

Slope of $\sqrt{3}x - y + 5 = 0$ is $\sqrt{3} = m_1$.

Slope of $x - \sqrt{3}y - 2 = 0$ is $\frac{1}{\sqrt{3}} = m_2$.

$$\tan\theta = \left| \frac{m_1 - m_2}{1 + m_1 m_2} \right| \qquad\qquad \text{multiply each part by } \sqrt{3}$$

$$\downarrow$$

$$= \left| \frac{\sqrt{3} - \frac{1}{\sqrt{3}}}{1 + (\sqrt{3})(\frac{1}{\sqrt{3}})} \right| = \left| \frac{\sqrt{3} - \frac{1}{\sqrt{3}}}{1 + 1} \right| = \left| \frac{\sqrt{3} - \frac{1}{\sqrt{3}}}{2} \right| = \left| \frac{3 - 1}{2\sqrt{3}} \right| = \left| \frac{2}{2\sqrt{3}} \right| = \frac{1}{\sqrt{3}}$$

Thus, $\tan\theta = \dfrac{1}{\sqrt{3}}$

$$\Longrightarrow \qquad \theta = \tan^{-1} \frac{1}{\sqrt{3}} = \frac{\pi}{6} \text{ or } 30°$$

(iii) Let θ be the acute angle between the lines.

$$ax - by + c = 0 \qquad\qquad (b - a)x + (a + b)y + d = 0$$

$$\text{Slope} = m_1 = -\frac{a}{-b} = \frac{a}{b} \qquad\qquad \text{Slope} = m_2 = -\frac{b - a}{a + b} = \frac{a - b}{a + b}$$

$$\tan\theta = \frac{m_1 - m_2}{1 + m_1 m_2}$$

$$= \frac{\dfrac{a}{b} - \dfrac{a - b}{a + b}}{1 + \left(\dfrac{a}{b}\right)\left(\dfrac{a - b}{a + b}\right)}$$

$$= \frac{\dfrac{a(a + b) - b(a - b)}{b(a + b)}}{1 + \dfrac{a(a - b)}{b(a + b)}} \qquad \begin{bmatrix} \text{Using the fact that:} \\ \dfrac{a}{b} - \dfrac{c}{d} = \dfrac{ad - bc}{bd} \end{bmatrix}$$

$$= \frac{\dfrac{a^2 + ab - ab + b^2}{ab + b^2}}{1 + \dfrac{a^2 - ab}{ab + b^2}}$$

$$= \frac{a^2 + ab - ab + b^2}{ab + b^2 + a^2 - ab} \qquad \begin{bmatrix} \text{multiply top and bottom} \\ \text{by } (ab + b^2) \end{bmatrix}$$

$$= \frac{a^2 + b^2}{a^2 + b^2} = 1$$

Thus, $\tan\theta = 1$

$$\Longrightarrow \qquad \theta = \tan^{-1} 1 = \frac{\pi}{4} \text{ or } 45°$$

(iv) Draw a diagram.

Let the slope of the line through (4, 3) be m_1.

Let the slope of $6x + y - 5 = 0$ be m_2.
Thus $m_2 = -6$.

$\theta = 45°$ is the angle between the lines.

$$\tan \theta = \pm \frac{m_1 - m_2}{1 + m_1 m_2}$$

$$\tan 45° = \pm \frac{m_1 - (-6)}{1 + m_1(-6)}$$

$$1 = \pm \frac{m_1 + 6}{1 - 6m_1}$$

$\Rightarrow \quad 1 - 6m_1 = \pm(m_1 + 6)$

$\Rightarrow \quad 1 - 6m_1 = m_1 + 6 \quad ① \qquad$ or $\quad 1 - 6m_1 = -m_1 - 6 \quad$ (take + and − separately)

$\Rightarrow \qquad -7m_1 = 5 \qquad\qquad$ or $\qquad -5m_1 = -7$

$\Rightarrow \qquad m_1 = -\frac{5}{7} \qquad\qquad$ or $\qquad m_1 = \frac{7}{5}$

Thus, there are two lines through the point (4, 3) which make an angle of 45° with the line $6x + y - 5 = 0$, one with the slope $-\frac{5}{7}$ and the other slope $\frac{7}{5}$.

Thus, the equations are

$$(y - 3) = -\tfrac{5}{7}(x - 4) \quad \text{and} \qquad (y - 3) = \tfrac{7}{5}(x - 4)$$

$\Rightarrow \qquad 7y - 21 = -5x + 20 \quad$ and $\qquad 5y - 15 = 7x - 28$

$\Rightarrow \quad 5x + 7y - 41 = 0 \qquad$ and $\quad 7x - 5y - 13 = 0$

Example

(i) Find the equation of the line through the point of intersection of the lines
$x - 2y + 6 = 0$ and $3x + 10y - 2 = 0$ and which contains the point $(\frac{1}{4}, 0)$.

(ii) Find the equation of the line through the point of intersection of the lines
$3x - 5y + 6 = 0$ and $5x - 7y + 4 = 0$ and which is parallel to the line $x - 3y - 3 = 0$.

Solution:

(i) Equation of the line is

$$x - 2y + 6 + \lambda(3x + 10y - 2) = 0$$

$(\frac{1}{4}, 0)$ is on this line.

$$\Rightarrow \quad \tfrac{1}{4} - 2(0) + 6 + \lambda[3(\tfrac{1}{4}) + 10(0) - 2] = 0$$

$$\Rightarrow \quad \tfrac{1}{4} + 6 + \lambda(\tfrac{3}{4} - 2) = 0$$

$$\Rightarrow \quad 1 + 24 + \lambda(3 - 8) = 0$$

(multiply across by 4)

$$\Rightarrow \quad 25 - 5\lambda = 0$$

$$\lambda = 5$$

Equation: $x - 2y + 6 + 5(3x + 10y - 2) = 0$

$x - 2y + 6 + 15x + 50y - 10 = 0$

$4x + 12y - 1 = 0$

(ii) Equation of the line is

$3x - 5y + 6 + \lambda(5x - 7y + 4) = 0$

$3x - 5y + 6 + 5\lambda x - 7\lambda y + 4\lambda = 0$

$(3 + 5\lambda)x + (-5 - 7\lambda)y + (6 + 4\lambda) = 0$

$$\text{Slope} = -\frac{3 + 5\lambda}{-5 - 7\lambda} = \frac{3 + 5\lambda}{5 + 7\lambda}$$

Slope of $x - 3y - 3 = 0$ is $\frac{1}{3}$

Parallel, $\therefore \quad \dfrac{3 + 5\lambda}{5 + 7\lambda} = \dfrac{1}{3}$

$$\Rightarrow \quad 9 + 15\lambda = 5 + 7\lambda$$

$$\Rightarrow \quad 8\lambda = -4$$

$$\Rightarrow \quad \lambda = -\tfrac{4}{8} = -\tfrac{1}{2}$$

Equation: $3x - 5y + 6 - \tfrac{1}{2}(5x - 7y + 4) = 0$

$6x - 10y + 12 - 5x + 7y - 4 = 0$

$x - 3y + 8 = 0$

Note: This question could have been done using Junior Certificate methods. However, this can lead to awkward fractions.

Example

(i) Find the value of λ if the line $3x + y - 7 + \lambda(x + 2y - 8) = 0$ is perpendicular to the line $x - y - 2 = 0$.

(ii) Find the value of λ if the line $12x - 5y - 8 + \lambda(3x - 4y + 7) = 0$ has slope $\frac{9}{7}$.

Solution:

(i)
$$3x + y - 7 + \lambda(x + 2y - 8) = 0$$
$$3x + y - 7 + \lambda x + 2\lambda y - 8\lambda = 0$$
$$(3 + \lambda)x + (1 + 2\lambda)y + (-7 - 8\lambda) = 0$$

$$\text{Slope} = -\frac{3 + \lambda}{1 + 2\lambda}$$

Slope of $x - y - 2 = 0$ is 1

As the lines are perpendicular,

$$-\frac{3 + \lambda}{1 + 2\lambda} \cdot 1 = -1$$

$\Longrightarrow \qquad -3 - \lambda = -1 - 2\lambda$

$\Longrightarrow \qquad -\lambda + 2\lambda = -1 + 3$

$\Longrightarrow \qquad \lambda = 2$

(ii)
$$12x - 5y - 8 + \lambda(3x - 4y + 7) = 0$$
$$12x - 5y - 8 + 3\lambda x - 4\lambda y + 7\lambda = 0$$
$$(12 + 3\lambda)x + (-5 - 4\lambda)y + (-8 + 7\lambda) = 0$$

$$\text{Slope} = -\frac{12 + 3\lambda}{-5 - 4\lambda} = \frac{12 + 3\lambda}{5 + 4\lambda}$$

Given: $\qquad \text{Slope} = \frac{9}{7}$

$\Longrightarrow \qquad \dfrac{12 + 3\lambda}{5 + 4\lambda} = \dfrac{9}{7}$

$\Longrightarrow \qquad 45 + 36\lambda = 84 + 21\lambda$

$\Longrightarrow \qquad 15\lambda = 39$

$\Longrightarrow \qquad \lambda = \frac{39}{15}$

Example

Verify that $L: \lambda(3x - 2y + 5) + \mu(5x - 4y - 3) = 0$ is a line.

If $K: 6x + 5y - 1 = 0$ is a line such that $L \perp K$, find a relationship between the real numbers λ and μ.

Solution:

$$\lambda(3x - 2y + 5) + \mu(5x - 4y - 3) = 0$$
$$3\lambda x - 2\lambda y + 5\lambda + 5\mu x - 4\mu y - 3\mu = 0$$
$$(3\lambda + 5\mu)x + (-2\lambda - 4\mu)y + (5\lambda - 3\mu) = 0$$

This is in the form $ax + by + c = 0$.

$\therefore$ L is a line.

$$\text{Slope of } L = -\frac{3\lambda + 5\mu}{-2\lambda - 4\mu} = \frac{3\lambda + 5\mu}{2\lambda + 4\mu}$$

$K: 6x + 5y - 1 = 0.$

Slope of K is $-\frac{6}{5}$.

$\therefore$ slope perpendicular to L is $\frac{5}{6}$.

$\therefore$
$$\frac{3\lambda + 5\mu}{2\lambda + 4\mu} = \frac{5}{6}$$
$$18\lambda + 30\mu = 10\lambda + 20\mu$$
$$8\lambda + 10\mu = 0$$
$$4\lambda + 5\mu = 0$$

Example

Find the relationship between the parameters μ and λ, where $\mu, \lambda \neq 0$, for which the line $\mu(3x - 2y + 3) + \lambda(x - 2y - 5) = 0$

(i) makes an angle measuring $45°$ with the positive sense of the X axis

(ii) contains the origin $(0, 0)$.

Solution:

$$\mu(3x - 2y + 3) + \lambda(x - 2y - 5) = 0$$
$$3\mu x - 2\mu y + 3\mu + \lambda x - 2\lambda y - 5\lambda = 0$$
$$(3\mu + \lambda)x + (-2\mu - 2\lambda)y + (3\mu - 5\lambda) = 0$$

(i) Makes an angle measuring $45°$ with the positive sense of the X axis.

Thus, the slope $= 1$.

$\therefore$
$$-\frac{3\mu + \lambda}{-2\mu - 2\lambda} = 1$$
$$\implies 3\mu + \lambda = 2\mu + 2\lambda$$
$$\implies \mu = \lambda$$

(ii) Contains the origin $(0, 0)$.

Thus, the constant in the equation must equal 0.

$\therefore$ $3\mu - 5\lambda = 0$

$\implies$ $3\mu = 5\lambda$

Example

(i) Write the equation of the line $x = \dfrac{2t-1}{t-1}$, $y = \dfrac{2t}{t-1}$, $t \neq 1$, in the form $ax + by + c = 0$.

(ii) Investigate if the equations $x = 1 - \dfrac{1}{t}$, $y = 1 + \dfrac{1}{t}$, $t \neq 0$, represent a straight line.

(iii) Verify that the parametric equations $x = \dfrac{pt+q}{at+b}$, $y = \dfrac{rt+s}{at+b}$ represent a straight line.

Solution:

(i) $x = \dfrac{2t-1}{t-1}$, $y = \dfrac{2t}{t-1}$

Method 1:

Let $t = 0$ and $t = 2$ and find two points on the line.

$t = 0$, $\quad x = 1$, $\quad y = 0$, thus one point on the line is $(1, 0)$.

$t = 2$, $\quad x = 3$, $\quad y = 4$, thus another point on the line is $(3, 4)$.

Thus, we have two points and we need the slope.

Slope $= \dfrac{4-0}{3-1}$

$\quad = \dfrac{4}{2}$

$\quad = 2$

Equation: $(y - 0) = 2(x - 1)$

$y = 2x - 2$

$2x - y - 2 = 0$

Note: This method is **not acceptable** if the question says 'prove', 'verify', 'show' or 'investigate' if the parametric equations represent a straight line.

Method 2:

Express t in terms of x and t in terms of y and equate both expressions of t.

$x = \dfrac{2t-1}{t-1}$

$\implies tx - x = 2t - 1$

$\implies tx - 2t = x - 1$

$\implies t(x - 2) = x - 1$

$\implies t = \dfrac{x-1}{x-2}$

$y = \dfrac{2t}{t-1}$

$\implies ty - y = 2t$

$\implies ty - 2t = y$

$\implies t(y - 2) = y$

$\implies t = \dfrac{y}{y-2}$

77

$$t = t$$

$$\frac{x-1}{x-2} = \frac{y}{y-2}$$

$$(x-1)(y-2) = (x-2)y$$

$$xy - 2x - y + 2 = xy - 2y$$

$$2x - y - 2 = 0$$

(ii)

$$x = 1 - \frac{1}{t} \qquad\qquad y = 1 + \frac{1}{t}$$

$$tx = t - 1 \qquad\qquad ty = t + 1$$

$$tx - t = -1 \qquad\qquad ty - t = 1$$

$$t(x-1) = -1 \qquad\qquad t(y-1) = 1$$

$$t = \frac{-1}{x-1} \qquad\qquad t = \frac{1}{y-1}$$

$$t = t$$

$$\frac{-1}{x-1} = \frac{1}{y-1}$$

$$x - 1 = -y + 1$$

$$x + y - 2 = 0$$

This is in the form $ax + by + c = 0$, where a, b, $c \in \mathbf{R}$, and so represents a line.

(iii)

$$x = \frac{pt+q}{at+b} \qquad\qquad y = \frac{rt+s}{at+b}$$

$$\Rightarrow \quad atx + bx = pt + q \qquad\qquad \Rightarrow \quad aty + by = rt + s$$

$$\Rightarrow \quad atx - pt = q - bx \qquad\qquad \Rightarrow \quad aty - rt = s - by$$

$$\Rightarrow \quad t(ax - p) = q - bx \qquad\qquad \Rightarrow \quad t(ay - r) = s - by$$

$$\Rightarrow \qquad t = \frac{q-bx}{ax-p} \qquad\qquad \Rightarrow \qquad t = \frac{s-by}{ay-r}$$

$$t = t$$

$$\Rightarrow \qquad \frac{q-bx}{ax-p} = \frac{s-by}{ay-r}$$

$$\Rightarrow \qquad (q-bx)(ay-r) = (ax-p)(s-by)$$

$$\Rightarrow \qquad aqy - qr - abxy + brx = asx - abxy - ps + bpy$$

$$\Rightarrow \qquad brx - asx + aqy - bpy + ps - qr = 0$$

$$\Rightarrow \quad (br - as)x + (aq - bp)y + (ps - qr) = 0$$

This is in the form $ax + by + c = 0$, where a, b, p, q, r, $s \in \mathbf{R}$, and so represents a line.

Example

(i) Show that the point $p(2t - 1, t + 1)$ is on the line $L: x - 2y + 3 = 0, t \in R$.

$a(3, 3)$ and $b(13, 8)$ are two points on L.

Find the values of t for which $p \in [ab]$.

(ii) Find a pair of parametric equations for the lines

    (a) $2x - y - 2 = 0$ and   **(b)** $4x - 3y + 6 = 0$

Solution:

(i) $x - 2y + 3 = 0$

$$p(2t - 1, t + 1): \ (2t - 1) - 2(t + 1) + 3 = 2t - 1 - 2t - 2 + 3 = 0$$

Thus, the point $p(2t - 1, t + 1)$ is on the line $x - 2y + 3 = 0$.

$p(2t - 1, t + 1) = a(3, 3)$	$p(2t - 1, t + 1) = b(13, 8)$
$\Rightarrow \quad 2t - 1 = 3$ and $t + 1 = 3$	$\Rightarrow \quad 2t - 1 = 13$ and $t + 1 = 8$
$\Rightarrow \quad 2t = 4$ and $t = 3 - 1$	$\Rightarrow \quad 2t = 14$ and $t = 8 - 1$
$\Rightarrow \quad t = 2$ and $t = 2$	$\Rightarrow \quad t = 7$ and $t = 7$

Thus, when $2 \leqslant t \leqslant 7$, $p(2t - 1, t + 1) \in [ab]$.

(ii) There are infinite pairs of parametric equations for $2x - y - 2 = 0$ and $4x - 3y + 6 = 0$.

The easiest method to find one of these pairs is

> **1.** Let $x = t$.
>
> **2.** Substitute this value for x into the equation and find y in terms of t.
>
> This gives the two parametric equations required.

(a) $2x - y - 2 = 0$.

Let $x = t$.

$\Rightarrow \ 2t - y - 2 = 0$

$\qquad\qquad -y = -2t + 2$

$\qquad\qquad\ \ y = 2t - 2$

Thus, $x = t, \qquad y = 2t - 2$

(b) $4x - 3y + 6 = 0$.

Let $x = t$.

$\Rightarrow \ 4t - 3y + 6 = 0$

$\qquad\qquad -3y = -4t - 6$

$$y = \frac{4t + 6}{3}$$

Thus, $x = t, \qquad y = \dfrac{4t + 6}{3}$

Example

(i) The parametric equations of the lines L and K are

$$L : x = t + \frac{1}{2}, \qquad y = 2t + 7$$

$$K : x = \frac{1-t}{3}, \qquad y = t - 5$$

Show that their Cartesian equations are

$$L : 2x - y + 6 = 0$$
$$K : 3x + y + 4 = 0$$

and find a, their point of intersection.

(ii) If L and K contain adjacent sides of a parallelogram $abcd$ and the midpoint of $[ac]$ is $(0, 3\tfrac{1}{2})$, find the coordinates of vertices c, b and d.

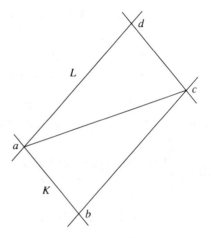

Solution:

(i) $L : x = t + \tfrac{1}{2}, \qquad y = 2t + 7$

$\qquad L : 2x - y + 6 = 0$

$\qquad\quad = 2(t + \tfrac{1}{2}) - (2t + 7) + 6$

$\qquad\quad = 2t + 1 - 2t - 7 + 6 = 0$

$\qquad K : x = \dfrac{1-t}{3}, \qquad y = t - 5$

$\qquad K : 3x + y + 4 = 0$

$\qquad\quad = 3\left(\dfrac{1-t}{3}\right) + (t - 5) + 4$

$\qquad\quad = 1 - t + t - 5 + 4 = 0$

Thus, $L: 2x - y + 6 = 0$ and $K: 3x + y + 4 = 0$ are the Cartesian equations.

To find a, we solve simultaneously the equations $2x - y + 6 = 0$ and $3x + y + 4 = 0$.

$$\begin{array}{l} 2x - y = -6 \\ 3x + y = -4 \\ \hline \quad 5x = -10 \\ \qquad x = -2 \end{array} \qquad\qquad \begin{array}{l} 2x - y = -6 \\ -4 - y = -6 \\ \quad -y = -2 \\ \qquad y = 2 \end{array}$$

Thus, the coordinates of a are $(-2, 2)$.

(ii) $p(0, 3\frac{1}{2})$ is the midpoint of $[ac]$.

Thus, c is the image of a under a central symmetry in p.

$$\overset{\longrightarrow}{a(-2, 2) \qquad p(0, 3\frac{1}{2}) \qquad c(2, 5)}$$

Thus, the coordinates of c are $(2, 5)$.

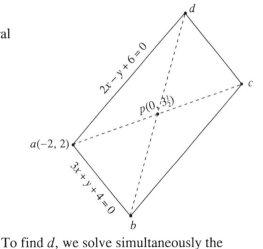

We now need the equation of the line dc, where dc is parallel to $3x + y + 4 = 0$.

Thus, dc is of the form $3x + y + k = 0$.

$c(2, 5)$ is on this line.

Thus, $\quad 3(2) + (5) + k = 0$

$\Rightarrow \qquad\qquad 11 + k = 0$

$\Rightarrow \qquad\qquad\qquad k = -11$

Thus, the equation of dc is $3x + y - 11 = 0$.

To find d, we solve simultaneously the equations $2x - y + 6 = 0$ and $3x + y - 11 = 0$.

$$\begin{array}{l} 2x - y = -6 \\ 3x + y = 11 \\ \hline 5x = 5 \\ x = 1 \end{array} \qquad \begin{array}{l} 2x - y = -6 \\ 2 - y = -6 \\ \hline -y = -8 \\ y = 8 \end{array}$$

Thus, the coordinates of d are $(1, 8)$.

$p(0, 3\frac{1}{2})$ is also the midpoint of $[db]$.

Thus, b is the image of d under a central symmetry in p.

$$\overset{\longrightarrow}{d(1, 8) \qquad p(0, 3\frac{1}{2}) \qquad b(-1, -1)}$$

Thus, the coordinates of b are $(-1, -1)$.

$a(-2, 2)$, $b(-1,-1)$, $c(2, 5)$ and $d(1, 8)$

Example

(i) Find the perpendicular distance from the point $(-2, 3)$ to the line $3x + y - 7 = 0$.

(ii) Find the values of k if the point $(k, -1)$ is equidistant from the lines $3x + 4y - 10 = 0$ and $5x - 12y - 40 = 0$.

(iii) Find the distance between the parallel lines $x - 3y + 6 = 0$ and $2x - 6y + 5 = 0$.

(iv) Find the equation of the locus of the point $p(x, y)$ if the distance from p to the line $2x - y - 3 = 0$ is $\sqrt{20}$.

(v) Find the value of a, if the point $(4, 1)$ is 2 units from the line $ax + 3y - 9 = 0$, $a \neq 0$.

(vi) Find the slopes of the lines containing $(-3, 2)$ if the distance from the point $(-6, 1)$ to the lines is $2\sqrt{2}$.

(vii) Find the equation of the locus of the point $p(x, y)$ such that the distance from p to the line $3x + 4y + 5 = 0$ is twice the distance from p to the line $5x - 12y + 1 = 0$.

Solution:

(i) point $(-2, 3)$; line $3x + y - 7 = 0$.

$$\text{distance} = \frac{|ax_1 + by_1 + c|}{\sqrt{a^2 + b^2}}$$

$$= \frac{|3(-2) + 1(3) - 7|}{\sqrt{3^2 + 1^2}} \qquad \binom{a = 3, \, b = 1, \, c = -7}{x_1 = -2, \, y_1 = 3}$$

$$= \frac{|-6 + 3 - 7|}{\sqrt{9 + 1}} = \frac{|-10|}{\sqrt{10}} \, \frac{10}{\sqrt{10}} = \sqrt{10}$$

$\sqrt{10}$

$(-2, 3)$

$3x + y - 7 = 0$

(ii) Distance from $(k, -1)$ to $3x + 4y - 10 = 0$ = distance from $(k, -1)$ to $5x - 12y - 40 = 0$.

$$\Rightarrow \qquad \frac{|3(k) + 4(-1) - 10|}{\sqrt{3^2 + 4^2}} = \frac{|5(k) - 12(-1) - 40|}{\sqrt{5^2 + (-12)^2}}$$

$$\Rightarrow \qquad \frac{|3k - 14|}{5} = \frac{|5k - 28|}{13}$$

$$\Rightarrow \qquad \frac{(3k - 14)}{5} = \pm \frac{(5k - 28)}{13}$$

$$\Rightarrow \qquad 13(3k - 14) = \pm 5(5k - 28)$$

$$\Rightarrow \qquad 39k - 182 = \pm(25k - 140)$$

$$\Rightarrow \quad 39k - 182 = 25k - 140 \ \text{ or } \ 39k - 182 = -25k + 140$$

$$\Rightarrow \qquad 14k = 42 \qquad \text{ or } \qquad 64k = 322$$

$$\Rightarrow \qquad k = 3 \qquad\qquad\qquad k = \tfrac{322}{64} = \tfrac{161}{32}$$

(iii) Parallel lines $x - 3y + 6 = 0$ and $2x - 6y + 5 = 0$.

Find one point on one of the lines and find the distance from this point to the other line.

One point on $x - 3y + 6 = 0$ is $(0, 2)$.

Thus,

$$\text{distance between lines} = \frac{|2(0) - 6(2) + 5|}{\sqrt{2^2 + 6^2}}$$

$$= \frac{|-12 + 5|}{\sqrt{40}} = \frac{|-7|}{\sqrt{40}} = \frac{7}{\sqrt{40}}$$

$(0, 2)$

$x - 3y + 6 = 0$

$\dfrac{7}{\sqrt{40}}$

$2x - 6y + 5 = 0$

(iv) The distance from $p(x, y)$ to $2x - y - 3 = 0$ is $\sqrt{20}$.

Thus,
$$\frac{|2(x) - (y) - 3|}{\sqrt{2^2 + (-1)^2}} = \sqrt{20}$$

$\Rightarrow \quad \dfrac{|2x - y - 3|}{\sqrt{5}} = \sqrt{20}$

$\Rightarrow \quad \dfrac{2x - y - 3}{\sqrt{5}} = \pm\sqrt{20}$

$\Rightarrow \quad 2x - y - 3 = \pm\sqrt{5}\,\sqrt{20} = \pm\sqrt{5.20} = \pm\sqrt{100} = \pm 10$

$\Rightarrow \quad 2x - y - 3 = \pm 10$

$\Rightarrow \quad 2x - y - 3 = 10 \text{ or } 2x - y - 3 = -10$

$\Rightarrow \quad 2x - y - 13 = 0 \quad \text{or} \quad 2x - y + 7 = 0$

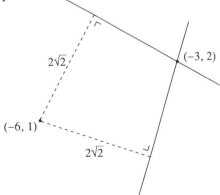

(v) The distance from $(4, 1)$ to $ax + 3y - 9 = 0$, $a \neq 0$, is 2.

$\Rightarrow \quad \dfrac{|a(4) + 3(1) - 9|}{\sqrt{a^2 + 3^2}} = 2$

$\Rightarrow \quad \dfrac{|4a - 6|}{\sqrt{a^2 + 9}} = 2$

$\Rightarrow \quad \dfrac{16a^2 - 48a + 36}{a^2 + 9} = 4 \quad \text{(square both sides)}$

$\Rightarrow \quad 16a^2 - 48a + 36 = 4a^2 + 36$

$\Rightarrow \quad 12a^2 - 48a = 0$

$\Rightarrow \quad a^2 - 4a = 0$

$\Rightarrow \quad a(a - 4) = 0$

$\Rightarrow \quad a = 0 \text{ or } a = 4$

Thus, $a = 4$ (as $a \neq 0$).

(vi) We have a point $(-3, 2)$ and we need the slopes.

Equation: $\qquad\qquad (y - 2) = m(x + 3)$

$\Rightarrow \qquad\qquad\qquad y - 2 = mx + 3m$

$\Rightarrow \qquad\quad mx - y + (3m + 2) = 0$

Given: The distance from $(-6, 1)$ to this line is $2\sqrt{2}$.

Thus, $\dfrac{|m(-6) - 1(1) + (3m + 2)|}{\sqrt{m^2 + (-1)^2}} = 2\sqrt{2}$

$\Rightarrow \qquad \dfrac{|1 - 3m|}{\sqrt{m^2 + 1}} = 2\sqrt{2}$

$\Rightarrow \qquad \dfrac{1 - 6m + 9m^2}{m^2 + 1} = 8$ (square both sides)

$\Rightarrow \qquad 1 - 6m + 9m^2 = 8m^2 + 8$

$\Rightarrow \qquad m^2 - 6m - 7 = 0$

$\Rightarrow \qquad (m - 7)(m + 1) = 0$

$\Rightarrow \qquad m = 7 \text{ or } m = -1$

(vii) Given: distance from $p(x, y)$ to $3x + 4y + 5 = 0 =$ twice distance from $p(x, y)$ to $5x - 12y + 1 = 0$.

Thus, $\dfrac{|3x + 4y + 5|}{\sqrt{3^2 + 4^2}} = \dfrac{2|5x - 12y + 1|}{\sqrt{5^2 + (-12)^2}}$

$\Rightarrow \qquad \dfrac{|3x + 4y + 5|}{5} = \dfrac{2|5x - 12y + 1|}{13}$

$\Rightarrow \qquad 13|3x + 4y + 5| = 10|5x - 12y + 1|$

$\Rightarrow \qquad 39x + 52y + 65 = \pm(50x - 120y + 10)$

$\Rightarrow \quad 39x + 52y + 65 = 50x - 120y + 10 \text{ or } 39x + 52y + 65 = -50x + 120y - 10$

$\Rightarrow \qquad 11x - 172y - 55 = 0 \text{ or } 89x - 68y + 75 = 0$

Example

$a(-2, 3)$ and $b(6, 7)$ are two points. Find the equation of the locus of the point $p(x, y)$ such that $|pa| = |pb|$.

Solution:

$p(x, y),\ a(-2, 3),\ b(6, 7)$

Given: $\qquad\qquad\qquad |pa| = |pb|$

$\Rightarrow \quad \sqrt{(x + 2)^2 + (y - 3)^2} = \sqrt{(x - 6)^2 + (y - 7)^2}$

$\Rightarrow \quad x^2 + 4x + 4 + y^2 - 6y + 9 = x^2 - 12x + 36 + y^2 - 14y + 49$

$\Rightarrow \qquad\qquad 4x - 6y + 13 = -12x - 14y + 85$

$\Rightarrow \qquad\qquad 16x + 8y - 72 = 0$

$\Rightarrow \qquad\qquad 2x + y - 9 = 0$

Note: The locus of $p(x, y)$ is the perpendicular bisector of $[ab]$.

Example

$a(-1, 3)$, $b(1, -1)$ and $c(k - 2, k + 1)$ are the vertices of $\triangle abc$.

If the area of $\triangle abc = 10$, find two possible values of k, where $k \in \mathbf{R}$.

Solution:

$$a(-1, 3) \quad b(1, -1) \quad c(k - 2, k + 1)$$
$$\downarrow \qquad\quad \downarrow \qquad\qquad \downarrow$$
$$(-2, 4) \quad\; (0, 0) \qquad (k - 3, k + 2) \quad [\text{map } (1, -1) \text{ to } (0, 0)]$$
$$x_1, y_1 \qquad\qquad\qquad\quad x_2, y_2$$

Given: area of $\triangle abc = 10$

$\Rightarrow \qquad\qquad\qquad \frac{1}{2}|x_1y_2 - x_2y_1| = 10$

$\Rightarrow \quad \frac{1}{2}|(-2)(k + 2) - (k - 3)(4)| = 10$

$\Rightarrow \qquad\qquad |-2k - 4 - 4k + 12| = 20$

$\Rightarrow \qquad\qquad\qquad\quad |-6k + 8| = 20$

$\Rightarrow \qquad\qquad -6k + 8 = 20 \quad \text{or} \quad -6k + 8 = -20$

$\Rightarrow \qquad\qquad\qquad -6k = 12 \quad \text{or} \qquad -6k = -28$

$\Rightarrow \qquad\qquad\qquad\; 6k = -12 \quad \text{or} \qquad\; 6k = 28$

$\Rightarrow \qquad\qquad\qquad\quad k = -2 \quad \text{or} \qquad\quad k = \frac{28}{6} = \frac{14}{3}$

Example

(i) $a(1, 2)$, $b(-3, 4)$, $c(x, y)$ are three points. Find the equation of the locus of the point $c(x, y)$ such that area of $\triangle abc = 8$.

(ii)   A line through the point $(4, 3)$ forms a triangle in the first quadrant with the axes. If the area of this triangle is 24, find the equation of this line.

Solution:

(i) $a(1, 2) \quad b(-3, 4) \qquad c(x, y)$
           $\downarrow \qquad\;\; \downarrow \qquad\qquad \downarrow$
      $(0, 0) \quad (-4, 2) \quad (x - 1, y - 2)$

                       area of $\triangle abc = 8$

$\Rightarrow \quad \frac{1}{2}|(-4)(y - 2) - (x - 1)(2)| = 8$

$\Rightarrow \qquad\qquad |-4y + 8 - 2x + 2| = 16$

$\Rightarrow \qquad\qquad\quad |-2x - 4y + 10| = 16$

$\Rightarrow \qquad -2x - 4y + 10 = 16 \; \text{or} \; -2x - 4y + 10 = -16$

$\Rightarrow \qquad\quad -2x - 4y - 6 = 0 \;\; \text{or} \; -2x - 4y + 26 = 0$

$\Rightarrow \qquad\quad\;\; x + 2y + 3 = 0 \;\; \text{or} \quad x + 2y - 13 = 0$

85

(ii) We have a point $(4, 3)$ and we need the slope of the line. Let the slope be m.

Equation: $(y - 3) = m(x - 4)$

$\Rightarrow \qquad y - 3 = mx - 4m$

$\Rightarrow \qquad mx - y = 4m - 3$

$\qquad\qquad mx - y = 4m - 3$

$y = 0$	$x = 0$
$mx = 4m - 3$	$-y = 4m - 3$
$x = \dfrac{4m - 3}{m}$	$y = 3 - 4m$

area of triangle $= 24$ (given)

$\dfrac{1}{2}\left(\dfrac{4m - 3}{m}\right)(3 - 4m) = 24$

$\dfrac{(4m - 3)(3 - 4m)}{2m} = 24$

$-16m^2 + 24m - 9 = 48m$

$16m^2 + 24m + 9 = 0$

$(4m + 3)(4m + 3) = 0$

$4m + 3 = 0$

$4m = -3$

$m = -\tfrac{3}{4}$

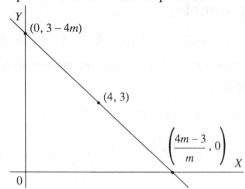
$(0, 3 - 4m)$
$(4, 3)$
$\left(\dfrac{4m - 3}{m}, 0\right)$

$\left[\,|\text{base}| = \left(\dfrac{4m - 3}{m}\right),\ |\text{height}| = (3 - 4m)\right]$

$[\tfrac{1}{2}\ \text{base} \times \text{perpendicular height}]$

Equation: $\qquad (y - y_1) = m(x - x_1)$

$\qquad\qquad (y - 3) = -\tfrac{3}{4}(x - 4)$

$\qquad\qquad 4y - 12 = -3x + 12$

$\qquad\qquad 3x + 4y - 24 = 0$

Example

(i) Find the point that divides the line segment joining $(-2, -3)$ to $(8, -18)$ in the ratio $3:2$

    (a) internally,   **(b)** externally.

(ii) $a(3, 2)$ and $b(18, 12)$ are two points.

    $[ab]$ is produced to c such that $|ac|:|bc| = 7:2$. Find the coordinates of c.

(iii) a is a point on the X axis and b is a point on the Y axis.

    p is $(9, -8)$ and p divides $[ab]$ internally in the ratio $4:3$.

    Find the coordinates of a and b.

Solution:

(i) **Method 1:** Using the formula

(a) internal divisor

$$
\begin{array}{c}
\overset{3}{\rule{3cm}{0.4pt}} \quad \overset{2}{\rule{2cm}{0.4pt}} \\
(-2, -3) \qquad\qquad (x, y) \qquad (8, -18)
\end{array}
$$

$$
(x, y) = \left(\frac{mx_2 + nx_1}{m + n} , \ \frac{my_2 + ny_1}{m + n} \right)
$$

$$
= \left(\frac{3(8) + 2(-2)}{3 + 2} , \ \frac{3(-18) + 2(-3)}{3 + 2} \right)
$$

$$
= \left(\frac{24 - 4}{5} , \ \frac{-54 - 6}{5} \right)
$$

$$
= (4, -12)
$$

(b) external divisor

$$
\begin{array}{c}
(-2, -3) \quad (8, -18) \qquad\qquad (x, y)
\end{array}
$$

$$
(x, y) = \left(\frac{mx_2 - nx_1}{m - n} , \ \frac{my_2 - ny_1}{m - n} \right)
$$

$$
= \left(\frac{3(8) - 2(-2)}{3 - 2} , \ \frac{3(-18) - 2(-3)}{3 - 2} \right)
$$

$$
= \left(\frac{24 + 4}{1} , \ \frac{-54 + 6}{1} \right)
$$

$$
= (28, -48)
$$

(i) **Method 2:** Using similar triangles

(a) internal divisor

$$
\begin{array}{c}
\overset{3}{\rule{3cm}{0.4pt}} \quad \overset{2}{\rule{2cm}{0.4pt}} \\
(-2, -3) \qquad\qquad (x, y) \qquad (8, -18)
\end{array}
$$

$$
\frac{x + 2}{8 - x} = \frac{3}{2} \qquad\qquad \frac{y + 3}{-18 - y} = \frac{3}{2}
$$

$$
2x + 4 = 24 - 3x \qquad\qquad 2y + 6 = -54 - 3y
$$

$$
5x = 20 \qquad\qquad\qquad 5y = -60
$$

$$
x = 4 \qquad\qquad\qquad y = -12
$$

$$
(4, -12)
$$

(b) external divisor

$$\frac{8+2}{x-8} = \frac{1}{2} \qquad \frac{-18+3}{y+18} = \frac{1}{2}$$

$$x-8 = 20 \qquad y+18 = -30$$

$$x = 20+8 \qquad y = -30-18$$

$$x = 28 \qquad y = -48$$

$$(28, -48)$$

(ii)

$$\frac{18-3}{x-18} = \frac{5}{2} \qquad \frac{12-2}{y-12} = \frac{5}{2}$$

$$5x-90 = 30 \qquad 5y-60 = 20$$

$$5x = 120 \qquad 5y = 80$$

$$x = 24 \qquad y = 16$$

Thus, the coordinates of c are $(24, 16)$.

(iii)

$$\frac{x-9}{9-0} = \frac{4}{3} \qquad \frac{0+8}{-8-y} = \frac{4}{3}$$

$$3x-27 = 36 \qquad -32-4y = 24$$

$$3x = 63 \qquad -4y = 56$$

$$x = 21 \qquad y = -14$$

Thus, the coordinates of a are $(21, 0)$ and the coordinates of b are $(0, -14)$.

Linear Transformations

A linear combination of x and y is a combination of the type $ax + by$, $a, b \in R$.

Examples are $3x + 4y$ and $2x - 5y$.

A linear transformation is a transformation of the form

$$f(x, y) = (ax + by, cx + dy), \qquad a, b, c, d \in R \text{ and } ad - bc \neq 0$$

This is often written:

$$f(x, y) = (x', y')$$

where

$$x' = ax + by$$
$$y' = cx + dy$$

Notice that x' and y' are linear combinations of x and y.

Properties of a linear transformation

> **1.** The origin $(0, 0)$ is mapped onto the origin.
>
> **2.** A line is mapped onto a line.
>
> **3.** A line segment is mapped onto a line segment.
>
> **4.** Pairs of parallel lines are mapped onto pairs of parallel lines.
>
> **5.** Parallelograms are mapped onto parallelograms.

Notes:

(a) In general, pairs of perpendicular lines are **not** mapped onto pairs of perpendicular lines.

(b) In general, distances and areas are not invariant (not preserved), i.e. in general, distances and areas are not invariant under a linear transformation.

Example

$a(2, -2)$, $b(4, 1)$, $c(-2, -1)$ and $d(2, 5)$ are four points.

A transformation f is given by

$$f(x, y) \rightarrow (x', y')$$

where

$$x' = x + 2y$$
$$y' = -x + y$$

(a) Find $f(a), f(b), f(c)$ and $f(d)$.

(b) Verify **(i)** $|ab| \neq |f(a)f(b)|$

           (ii) area of $\Delta abc = \frac{1}{3}$ area of $\Delta f(a)f(b)f(c)$

           (iii) $\dfrac{|ab|}{|cd|} = \dfrac{|f(a)f(b)|}{|f(c)f(d)|}$

(c) p is the midpoint of $[bc]$, q is the midpoint of $[f(b)f(c)]$,

     g is the centroid of Δabc, h is the centroid of $\Delta f(a)f(b)f(c)$.

     Investigate if **(i)** $f(p) = q$ **(ii)** $f(g) = h$.

(d) $s(7, 8)$ is the image of $r(x, y)$ under f. Find the coordinates r.

Solution:

(a) $(x, y) \rightarrow (x + 2y, -x + y)$

        $a(2, -2) \rightarrow (2 + 2(-2), -2 - 2) = (2 - 4, -2 - 2) = (-2, -4) = f(a)$

        $b(4, 1) \rightarrow (4 + 2(1), -4 + 1) = (4 + 2, -4 + 1) = (6, -3) = f(b)$

        $c(-2, -1) \rightarrow (-2 + 2(-1), 2 - 1) = (-2 - 2, 2 - 1) = (-4, 1) = f(c)$

        $d(2, 5) \rightarrow (2 + 2(5), -2 + 5) = (2 + 10, -2 + 5) = (12, 3) = f(d)$

89

(b) **(i)** $a(2, -2)$, $b(4, 1)$

$|ab| = \sqrt{(4-2)^2 + (1+2)^2}$

$\quad = \sqrt{2^2 + 3^2}$

$\quad = \sqrt{4 + 9}$

$\quad = \sqrt{13}$

$f(a) = (-2, -4)$, $\quad f(b) = (6, -3)$

$|f(a)f(b)| = \sqrt{(6+2)^2 + (-3+4)^2}$

$\quad = \sqrt{8^2 + 1^2}$

$\quad = \sqrt{64 + 1}$

$\quad = \sqrt{65}$

Thus, $|ab| \neq |f(a)f(b)|$.

(ii) $a(2, -2)$, $b(4, 1)$, $c(-2, -1)$

$(2, -2) \quad (4, 1) \quad (-2, -1)$

$\downarrow \qquad \downarrow \qquad \downarrow$

$(0, 0) \quad (2, 3) \quad (-4, 1)$

area $= \frac{1}{2}|(2)(1) - (-4)(3)|$

$\quad = \frac{1}{2}|2 + 12|$

$\quad = \frac{1}{2}|14| = 7$

$f(a) = (-2, -4), f(b) = (6, -3), f(c) = (-4, 1)$

$(-2, -4) \quad (6, -3) \quad (-4, 1)$

$\downarrow \qquad \downarrow \qquad \downarrow$

$(0, 0) \quad (8, 1) \quad (-2, 5)$

area $= \frac{1}{2}|(8)(5) - (-2)(1)|$

$\quad = \frac{1}{2}|40 + 2|$

$\quad = \frac{1}{2}|42| = 21$

Thus, area of $\Delta abc = \frac{1}{3}$ area of $\Delta f(a)f(b)f(c)$

i.e. $\qquad 7 = \frac{1}{3}(21)$

(iii) $|ab| = \sqrt{13}$ (from **(i)**)

$c(-2, -1)$, $d(2, 5)$

$|cd| = \sqrt{(2+2)^2 + (5+1)^2}$

$\quad = \sqrt{4^2 + 6^2}$

$\quad = \sqrt{16 + 36} = \sqrt{52}$

$\dfrac{|ab|}{|dc|} = \dfrac{\sqrt{13}}{\sqrt{52}}$

$\quad = \sqrt{\dfrac{13}{52}} = \sqrt{\dfrac{1}{4}} = \dfrac{1}{2}$

$|f(a)f(b)| = \sqrt{65}$ (from **(i)**)

$f(c) = (-4, 1)$, $f(d) = (12, 3)$

$|f(c)f(d)| = \sqrt{(12+4)^2 + (3-1)^2}$

$\quad = \sqrt{16^2 + 2^2}$

$\quad = \sqrt{256 + 4} = \sqrt{260}$

$\dfrac{|f(a)f(b)|}{|f(c)f(d)|} = \dfrac{\sqrt{65}}{\sqrt{260}}$

$\quad = \sqrt{\dfrac{65}{260}} = \sqrt{\dfrac{1}{4}} = \dfrac{1}{2}$

Thus,

$$\frac{|ab|}{|cd|} = \frac{|f(a)f(b)|}{|f(c)f(d)|}$$

(c) **(i)** $b(4, 1)$ $\quad c(-2, -1)$

p is the midpoint of $[bc]$

Thus, $p = (1, 0)$

$f(b) = (6, -3)$ $\quad f(c) = (-4, 1)$

q is the midpoint of $[f(b)f(c)]$

Thus, $q = (1, -1)$

$$f(p) = f(1, 0)$$
$$= (1 + 2(0), -1 + 0) = (1, -1)$$

Thus, $f(p) = q$

i.e., the midpoint of $[bc]$ is mapped onto the midpoint of $[f(b)f(c)]$.

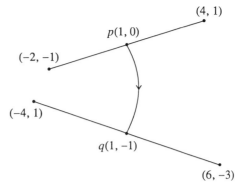

(ii) $a(2, -2)$, $b(4, 1)$, $c(-2, -1)$

g is the centroid of Δabc.

Thus,

$$g = \left(\frac{2 + 4 - 2}{3}, \frac{-2 + 1 - 1}{3} \right)$$

$$g = \left(\frac{4}{3}, -\frac{2}{3} \right)$$

$$f(g) = f\left(\frac{4}{3}, -\frac{2}{3} \right)$$
$$= \left(\frac{4}{3} + 2\left(-\frac{2}{3}\right), -\frac{4}{3} - \frac{2}{3} \right)$$
$$= \left(\frac{4}{3} - \frac{4}{3}, -\frac{6}{3} \right)$$
$$= (0, -2)$$

Thus, $f(g) = h$, i.e., the centroid of Δabc is mapped onto the centroid of $\Delta f(a)f(b)f(c)$.

$f(a) = (-2, -4)$, $f(b) = (6, -3)$, $f(c) = (-4, 1)$

h is the centroid of $\Delta f(a)f(b)f(c)$

Thus,

$$h = \left(\frac{-2 + 6 - 4}{3}, \frac{-4 - 3 + 1}{3} \right)$$

$$h = (0, -2)$$

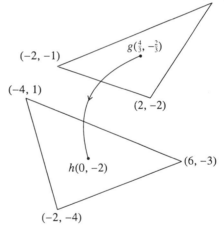

(d) Given: $(x', y') = (7, 8)$

Thus, $(x + 2y, -x + y) = (7, 8)$

$\Rightarrow$ $x + 2y = 7$ ① and $-x + y = 8$ ②

Solving ① and ② simultaneously gives

$$x = -3, \; y = 5$$

Thus, the coordinates of r are $(-3, 5)$.

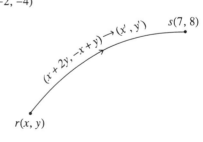

Example

f is a transformation $(x, y) \rightarrow (x', y')$, where

$$x' = 3x + 2y$$
$$y' = 5x + 3y$$

(i) $L: x - 2y - 3 = 0$ and $K: 2x + y = 0$ are two lines. Verify $L \perp K$.

(ii) Express x and y in terms of x' and y'.

(iii) Find the equation of $f(L)$ and $f(K)$ and investigate if $f(L) \perp f(K)$.

Solution:

(i) $L: x - 2y - 3 = 0$. Thus, slope of $L = -\frac{1}{-2} = \frac{1}{2}$.

$K: 2x + y = 0$.   Thus, slope of $K = -\frac{2}{1} = -2$.

(Slope of L) . (Slope of K) $= \frac{1}{2} \times -2 = -1$ $\therefore$ $L \perp K$

(ii)

Remove the y's	Remove the x's
$3x + 2y = x'$ ①	$3x + 2y = x'$ ①
$5x + 3y = y'$ ②	$5x + 3y = y'$ ②
$9x + 6y = 3x'$ ① × 3	$15x + 10y = 5x'$ ① × 5
$10x + 6y = 2y'$ ② × 2	$15x + 9y = 3y'$ ② × 3
$-x \quad = 3x' - 2y'$ (subtract)	$y = 5x' - 3y'$ (subtract)
$x = -3x' + 2y'$	

Thus,

$$x = -3x' + 2y', \qquad y = 5x' - 3y'$$

(iii) To find the equation of $f(L)$ and $f(K)$ we substitute these expressions for x and y into the equations of L and K, simplify and then remove the primes.

$$L : x - 2y - 3 = 0$$

$$f(L): (-3x' + 2y') - 2(5x' - 3y') - 3 = 0$$

$\Rightarrow \qquad -3x' + 2y' - 10x' + 6y' - 3 = 0$

$\Rightarrow \qquad -13x' + 8y' - 3 = 0$

$\Rightarrow \qquad 13x' - 8y' + 3 = 0$

$\Rightarrow \qquad 13x - 8y + 3 = 0$

$$K : 2x + y = 0$$

$$f(K) : 2(-3x' + 2y') + (5x' - 3y') = 0$$
$$\implies \qquad -6x' + 4y' + 5x' - 3y' = 0$$
$$\implies \qquad -x' + y' = 0$$
$$\implies \qquad x' - y' = 0$$
$$\implies \qquad x - y = 0$$

Thus, $13x - 8y + 3 = 0$ is the equation of $f(L)$ and $x - y = 0$ is the equation of $f(K)$.

$$\text{Slope of } f(L) = -\frac{13}{-8} = \frac{13}{8}, \qquad \text{Slope of } f(K) = -\frac{1}{-1} = 1$$

$$(\text{Slope of } f(L)) \,.\, (\text{Slope of } f(K)) = \frac{13}{8} \times 1 = \frac{13}{8} \neq -1$$

Thus, $f(L) \not\perp f(K)$.

Example

Let f be the linear transformation
$$f : (x, y) \rightarrow (x', y')$$
where
$$x' = 3x + 2y$$
$$y' = 5x + 3y$$

(i) Express x and y in terms of x' and y'.

(ii) $P: ax + by + c = 0$ is a line and Q is a line parallel to P.

Find $f(P)$ and $f(Q)$ and investigate if $f(P) \,\|\, f(Q)$

Solution:

(i)

Remove the y's

$$3x + 2y = x' \qquad \text{①}$$
$$5x + 3y = y' \qquad \text{②}$$

$$9x + 6y = 3x' \qquad \text{①} \times 3$$
$$10x + 6y = 2y' \qquad \text{②} \times 2$$

$$-x = 3x' - 2y' \qquad (\text{subtract})$$
$$x = -3x' + 2y'$$

Remove the x's

$$3x + 2y = x' \qquad \text{①}$$
$$5x + 3y = y' \qquad \text{②}$$

$$15x + 10y = 5x' \qquad \text{①} \times 5$$
$$15x + 9y = 3y' \qquad \text{②} \times 3$$

$$y = 5x' - 3y' \qquad (\text{subtract})$$

(ii) $P: ax + by + c = 0$. Thus, $Q: ax + by + d = 0$ is a line such that $P \parallel Q$.

To find $f(P)$ and $f(Q)$ substitute

$$x = -3x' + 2y', \qquad y = 5x' - 3y'$$

$$P: ax + by + c = 0$$

$$f(P): a(-3x' + 2y') + b(5x' - 3y') + c = 0$$

$$\Rightarrow \qquad -3ax' + 2ay' + 5bx' - 3by' + c = 0$$

$$\Rightarrow \qquad (-3a + 5b)x' + (2a - 3b)y' + c = 0$$

$$Q: ax + by + d = 0$$

$$f(Q): a(-3x' + 2y') + b(5x' - 3y') + d = 0$$

$$\Rightarrow \qquad -3ax' + 2ay' + 5bx' - 3by' + d = 0$$

$$\Rightarrow \qquad (-3a + 5b)x' + (2a - 3b)y' + d = 0$$

Thus, $(-3a + 5b)x + (2a - 3b)y + c = 0$ is the equation of $f(P)$,

and $(-3a + 5b)x + (2a - 3b)y + d = 0$ is the equation of $f(Q)$.

$$\text{Slope of } f(P) = -\frac{-3a + 5b}{2a - 3b} \text{ and slope of } f(Q) = -\frac{-3a + 5b}{2a - 3b}$$

Thus, $f(P) \parallel f(Q)$ (as both have the same slope).

Example

For the linear transformation $f: (x, y) \rightarrow (x', y')$, where

$$x' = 3x + y$$
$$y' = x - 3y$$

(i) express x and y in terms of x' and y'.

(ii) $L: ax + by + c = 0$ is a line and K is a line such that $L \perp K$.

Investigate if $f(L) \perp f(K)$.

Solution:

(i)

Remove the y's		Remove the x's	
$3x + y = x'$	①	$3x + y = x'$	①
$x - 3y = y'$	②	$x - 3y = y'$	②
$9x + 3y = 3x'$	① × 3	$3x + y = x'$	①
$x - 3y = y'$	②	$3x - 9y = 3y'$	② × 3
$10x = 3x' + y'$	(add)	$10y = x' - 3y'$	(subtract)
$x = \dfrac{3x' + y'}{10}$		$y = \dfrac{x' - 3y'}{10}$	

94

(ii) $L: ax + by + c = 0$. Thus, $K: bx - ay + d = 0$ is a line such that $L \perp K$.

(Swop coefficients of x and y and then change the sign of one of them.)

To find $f(L)$ and $f(K)$, substitute

$$x = \frac{3x' + y'}{10} \quad \text{and} \quad y = \frac{x' - 3y'}{10}$$

$$L : ax + by + c = 0$$

$$f(L) : a\left(\frac{3x' + y'}{10}\right) + b\left(\frac{x' - 3y'}{10}\right) + c = 0$$

$\implies \quad a(3x' + y') + b(x' - 3y') + 10c = 0$

$\implies \quad 3ax' + ay' + bx' - 3by' + 10c = 0$

$\implies \quad (3a + b)x' + (a - 3b)y' + 10c = 0$

$$K : bx - ay + d = 0$$

$$f(K) : b\left(\frac{3x' + y'}{10}\right) - a\left(\frac{x' - 3y'}{10}\right) + d = 0$$

$\implies \quad b(3x' + y') - a(x' - 3y') + 10d = 0$

$\implies \quad 3bx' + by' - ax' + 3ay' + 10d = 0$

$\implies \quad (-a + 3b)x' + (3a + b)y' + 10d = 0$

Thus, $(3a + b)x + (a - 3b)y + 10c = 0$ is the equation of $f(L)$,
and $(-a + 3b)x + (3a + b)y + 10d = 0$ is the equation of $f(K)$.

$$\text{Slope of } f(L) = -\frac{3a + b}{a - 3b} \quad \text{and slope of } f(K) = -\frac{-a + 3b}{3a + b}$$

$$(\text{Slope of } f(L)) \cdot (\text{Slope of } f(K)) = -\frac{3a + b}{a - 3b} \cdot -\frac{-a + 3b}{3a + b}$$

$$= \frac{-a + 3b}{a - 3b} = \frac{-1(a - 3b)}{(a - 3b)} = -1$$

Thus, $f(L) \perp f(K)$.

Example

f is the transformation $(x, y) \rightarrow (x', y')$, where

$$x' = 3x - y$$
$$y' = x + 2y$$

(i) Express x and y in terms of x' and y'.

(ii) L is a line with equation $ax + by + c = 0$.

Prove that the image $f(L)$ is also a line.

Solution:

(i)

Remove the y's	Remove the x's
$3x - y = x'$ ①	$3x - y = x'$ ①
$x + 2y = y'$ ②	$x + 2y = y'$ ②
$6x - 2y = 2x'$ ① × 2	$3x - y = x'$ ①
$x + 2y = y'$ ②	$3x + 6y = 3y'$ ② × 3
$7x \quad = 2x' + y'$ (add)	$-7y = x' - 3y'$ (subtract)
$x \quad = \dfrac{2x' + y'}{7}$	$y = \dfrac{-x' + 3y'}{7}$

(ii)
$$L : ax + by + c = 0$$
$$f(L) : a\left(\frac{2x' + y'}{7}\right) + b\left(\frac{-x' + 3y'}{7}\right) + c = 0$$

$\Longrightarrow \qquad a(2x' + y') + b(-x' + 3y') + 7c = 0$

$\Longrightarrow \qquad 2ax' + ay' - bx' + 3by' + 7c = 0$

$\Longrightarrow \qquad (2a - b)x' + (a + 3b)y + 7c = 0$

$\Longrightarrow \qquad (2a - b)x + (a + 3b)y + 7c = 0$

This is the equation of a line, as it is in the form $ax + by + c = 0$.

Thus, every point on L is on the same line.

We must now show that every point on $f(L)$ has a corresponding point on L.

So we take the equation for $f(L)$, apply f^{-1}, the inverse transformation, and see if $f(L)$ is mapped back onto L (i.e. $f^{-1}f(L) = L$).

To find $f^{-1}f(L)$, substitute

$x' = 3x - y$ and $y' = x + 2y$

$$f(L) : (2a - b)x' + (a + 3b)y' + 7c = 0$$

$$f^{-1}f(L) : (2a - b)(3x - y) + (a + 3b)(x + 2y) + 7c = 0$$

$\Longrightarrow \quad 6ax - 2ay - 3bx + by + ax + 2ay + 3bx + 6by + 7c = 0$

$\Longrightarrow \qquad\qquad\qquad\qquad\qquad 7ax + 7by + 7c = 0$

$\Longrightarrow \qquad\qquad\qquad\qquad\qquad\qquad ax + by + c = 0$

As this is the equation of L, every point of $f(L)$ is the image of a point on L.

Thus, $f(L)$ is a line.

Example

$a(-5, 0)$ and $b(1, 3)$ are two points. Find the equation of the line ab.

Show that $x = 2t - 1$ and $y = t + 2$, $-2 \leqslant t \leqslant 1$, are parametric equations of the line segment $[ab]$.

Find the image of this line segment under the transformation f:

$$x' = 3x - y$$
$$y' = x - y$$

(i) in parametric form   **(ii)** in Cartesian form.

Solution:

$a(-5, 0)$, $b(1, 3)$

$\text{Slope} = \dfrac{3 - 0}{1 + 5}$

$= \dfrac{3}{6} = \dfrac{1}{2}$

Equation: $(y - 0) = \frac{1}{2}(x + 5)$

$2y = x + 5$

$x - 2y + 5 = 0$

We first verify that $x = 2t - 1$ and $y = t + 2$ are parametric equations of $x - 2y + 5 = 0$.

Method: Replace x with $2t - 1$ and y with $t + 2$.

$$x - 2y + 5 = 0$$

$$(2t - 1) - 2(t + 2) + 5 = 2t - 1 - 2t - 4 + 5 = 0$$

Thus, $x = 2t - 1$ and $y = t + 2$ are parametric equations of $x - 2y + 5 = 0$.

$a(-5, 0), x = 2t - 1, y = t + 2$

$\Rightarrow \quad 2t - 1 = -5 \quad \text{and} \quad t + 2 = 0$

$\Rightarrow \qquad 2t = -4 \quad \text{and} \qquad t = -2$

$\Rightarrow \qquad t = -2 \quad \text{and} \qquad t = -2$

$b(1, 3), x = 2t - 1, y = t + 2$

$\Rightarrow \quad 2t - 1 = 1 \quad \text{and} \quad t + 2 = 3$

$\Rightarrow \qquad 2t = 2 \quad \text{and} \qquad t = 3 - 2$

$\Rightarrow \qquad t = 1 \quad \text{and} \qquad t = 1$

$$\Rightarrow \qquad\qquad -2 \leqslant t \leqslant 1$$

Thus, when $-2 \leqslant t \leqslant 1$, $x = 2t - 1$ and $y = t + 2$ are parametric equations of the line segment $[ab]$.

(i) Parametric form

To find the image, we substitute $x = 2t - 1$, $y = t + 2$ into

$x' = 3x - y$

$\Rightarrow \quad x' = 3(2t - 1) - (t + 2)$

$\Rightarrow \quad x' = 6t - 3 - t - 2$

$\Rightarrow \quad x' = 5t - 5$

and

$y' = x - y$

$\Rightarrow \quad y' = (2t - 1) - (t + 2)$

$\Rightarrow \quad y' = 2t - 1 - t - 2$

$\Rightarrow \quad y' = t - 3$

Thus, $x = 5t - 5$ and $y = t - 3$, $-2 \leqslant t \leqslant 1$, are parametric equations for the image of the line segment $[ab]$.

97

(ii) Cartesian form

$a(-5, 0), \qquad b(1, 3)$

$(x, y) \rightarrow (3x - y, x - y)$

$a(-5, 0) \rightarrow (3(-5) - 0, -5 - 0) = (-15, -5)$

$b(1, 3) \ \rightarrow (3(1) - 3, 1 - 3) \quad = (0, -2)$

We need the equation of the line through $(-15, -5)$ and $(0, -2)$.

$\text{Slope} = \dfrac{-5 + 2}{-15 - 0} = \dfrac{-3}{-15} = \dfrac{1}{5}$

$(-15, -5) \qquad (0, -2)$

Thus, $x - 5y - 10 = 0$

Equation: $\qquad (y + 2) = \frac{1}{5}(x - 0)$

where $-15 \leqslant x \leqslant 0$ or $-5 \leqslant y \leqslant -2$

$\Rightarrow \qquad\qquad 5y + 10 = x$

is the Cartesian equation for the

$\Rightarrow \qquad\quad x - 5y - 10 = 0$

image of the line segment $[ab]$.

4. TRIGONOMETRY

The six trigonometric ratios for a right-angled triangle, $0 < \theta < 90°$, are:

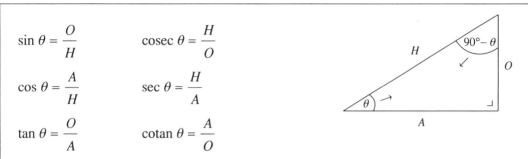

$$\sin \theta = \frac{O}{H} \qquad \qquad \operatorname{cosec} \theta = \frac{H}{O}$$

$$\cos \theta = \frac{A}{H} \qquad \qquad \sec \theta = \frac{H}{A}$$

$$\tan \theta = \frac{O}{A} \qquad \qquad \cot an \theta = \frac{A}{O}$$

From this we can see that:

$$\operatorname{cosec} \theta = \frac{1}{\sin \theta} \qquad \qquad \sec \theta = \frac{1}{\cos \theta}$$

$$\tan \theta = \frac{\sin \theta}{\cos \theta} \qquad \qquad \cot an \theta = \frac{1}{\tan \theta} = \frac{\cos \theta}{\sin \theta}$$

$$\sin (90° - \theta) = \frac{A}{H} = \cos \theta \qquad \cos (90° - \theta) = \frac{O}{H} = \sin \theta$$

Note: These ratios hold for all values of $\theta \in R$, not just for $0 < \theta < 90°$.

Unit Circle

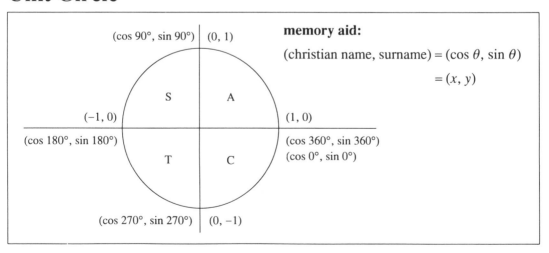

(cos 90°, sin 90°) | (0, 1)

memory aid:

(christian name, surname) $= (\cos \theta, \sin \theta)$

$= (x, y)$

S   A

(−1, 0)

(cos 180°, sin 180°)

T   C

(1, 0)

(cos 360°, sin 360°)
(cos 0°, sin 0°)

(cos 270°, sin 270°) | (0, −1)

Angles between 0° and 360°

The trigonometric ratio of an angle between 0° and 360° can be found with the following steps:

1. Make a rough diagram of the angle on a unit circle.

2. Use 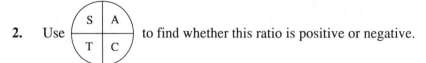 to find whether this ratio is positive or negative.

3. Find its **reference** angle, the acute angle to the X axis.

4. Use the calculator or tables (page 9) to find the value of this reference angle and use the sign in Step 2.

Given the Values of Sin, Cos and Tan

Between 0° and 360° there may be two angles with the same trigonometric ratio.

e.g. $\cos 120° = -\frac{1}{2}$ and $\cos 240° = -\frac{1}{2}$.

To find the two values we do the following:

1. Ignore the sign and evaluate the reference angle using tables (page 9) or calculator.

2. From the sign of the given ratio decide in which quadrants the angles can lie.

3. Using a diagram, state the angles between 0° and 360°.

Sine and Cosine Rule, Area of a Triangle

Sine Rule: $\dfrac{a}{\sin A} = \dfrac{b}{\sin B} = \dfrac{c}{\sin C}$

or $\dfrac{\sin A}{a} = \dfrac{\sin B}{b} = \dfrac{\sin C}{c}$

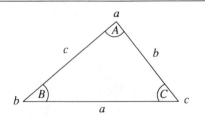

Cosine Rule:

$$a^2 = b^2 + c^2 - 2bc \cos A \qquad b^2 = a^2 + c^2 - 2ac \cos B \qquad c^2 = a^2 + b^2 - 2ab \cos C$$

or

$$\cos A = \frac{b^2 + c^2 - a^2}{2bc} \qquad \cos B = \frac{a^2 + c^2 - b^2}{2ac} \qquad \cos C = \frac{a^2 + b^2 - c^2}{2ab}$$

Area of Δabc $= \frac{1}{2}ab \sin C = \frac{1}{2}ac \sin B = \frac{1}{2}bc \sin A$

Circular Measure

$180° = \pi$

$1° = \dfrac{\pi}{180}$

length of a circular arc: $l = r\theta$

area of a circular sector: $A = \frac{1}{2}r^2\theta$

(where angle θ is in radians)

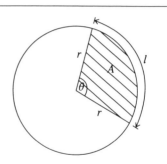

Graphs of Trigonometric Functions

Below is a table of values for $\sin\theta$, $\cos\theta$ and $\tan\theta$, $0 \leqslant \theta \leqslant 2\pi$.

θ	0	$\frac{\pi}{4}$	$\frac{\pi}{2}$	$\frac{3\pi}{4}$	π	$\frac{5\pi}{4}$	$\frac{3\pi}{2}$	$\frac{7\pi}{4}$	2π
$\sin\theta$	0	0.7	1	0.7	0	-0.7	-1	-0.7	0
$\cos\theta$	1	0.7	0	-0.7	-1	-0.7	0	0.7	1
$\tan\theta$	0	1	undefined	-1	0	1	undefined	-1	0

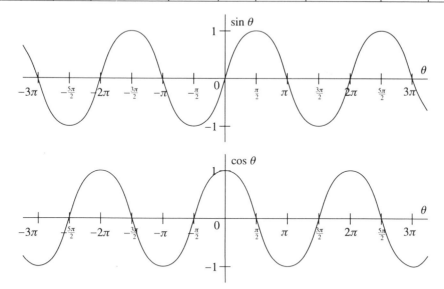

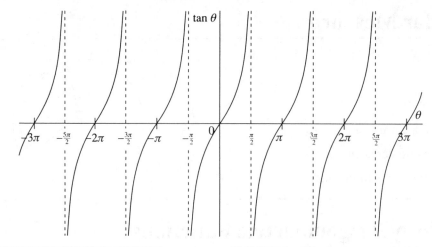

	Period	Range			Period	Range
$\sin \theta$	2π	$[-1, 1]$		$a \sin b\theta$	$\frac{2\pi}{b}$	$[-a, a]$
$\cos \theta$	2π	$[-1, 1]$		$a \cos b\theta$	$\frac{2\pi}{b}$	$[-a, a]$
$\tan \theta$	π	$\boldsymbol{R}$		$a \tan b\theta$	$\frac{\pi}{b}$	$\boldsymbol{R}$

Graphs of Inverse Trigonometric Functions

The graphs of $\sin^{-1} \theta$, $\cos^{-1} \theta$ and $\tan^{-1} \theta$ can be obtained by reflecting the graphs of $\sin \theta$, $\cos \theta$ and $\tan \theta$ in the line $y = x$ or by making out a table of values.

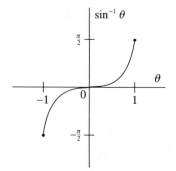

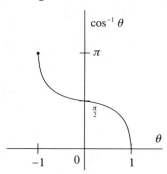

Domain: $-1 \leqslant \theta \leqslant 1$

Range: $[-\frac{\pi}{2}, \frac{\pi}{2}]$

Domain: $-1 \leqslant \theta \leqslant 1$

Range: $[0, \pi]$

By restricting the domain of $\sin^{-1}\theta$ and $\cos^{-1}\theta$ to $-1 \leqslant \theta \leqslant 1$, we ensure that they are functions (i.e. single-value expressions)

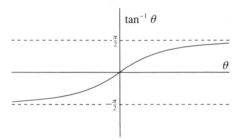

Domain: R

Range: $[-\frac{\pi}{2}, \frac{\pi}{2}]$

Note: $\sin\theta$, $\cos\theta$ and $\tan\theta$ are ratios, whereas

$\sin^{-1}\theta$, $\cos^{-1}\theta$ and $\tan^{-1}\theta$ are angles.

Limits of Trigonometric Functions

$$\lim_{\theta \to 0} \frac{\sin k\theta}{k\theta} = 1 = \lim_{\theta \to 0} \frac{k\theta}{\sin k\theta}, k \in R$$

Note: $\lim_{\theta \to 0} \cos k\theta = 1, k \in R$.

Example

The diagram shows a circle C, centre o and radius r. A sector, of area A, contains the angle θ, θ in radians. The length of the arc is l.

Prove **(i)** $l = r\theta$, **(ii)** $A = \frac{1}{2}r^2\theta$.

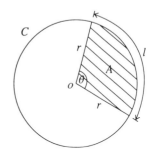

Solution:

(i) $\dfrac{\text{length of arc}}{\text{circumference of circle}} = \dfrac{\theta}{2\pi}$

$\Rightarrow \qquad \dfrac{l}{2\pi r} = \dfrac{\theta}{2\pi}$

$\Rightarrow \qquad l = \dfrac{2\pi r\theta}{2\pi}$

$\Rightarrow \qquad l = r\theta$

(ii) $\dfrac{\text{area of sector}}{\text{area of circle}} = \dfrac{\theta}{2\pi}$

$\Rightarrow \qquad \dfrac{A}{\pi r^2} = \dfrac{\theta}{2\pi}$

$\Rightarrow \qquad A = \dfrac{\pi r^2\theta}{2\pi}$

$\Rightarrow \qquad A = \frac{1}{2}r^2\theta$

Example

(i) The radius of a circle is 10 cm. Find the angle subtended at the centre by an arc of length 4π cm.

(ii) Find the area of a sector of a circle of radius 4 cm if the arc of the sector subtends an angle of $\frac{\pi}{3}$ at the centre.

(iii) The area of a sector of a circle, of radius r, is 12π cm^2. If the angle subtended at the centre of the circle by this sector is $\frac{2\pi}{3}$, calculate r, the radius of the circle.

(iv) Show that the area, A, of the shaded segment of the circle, of radius r, is given by:

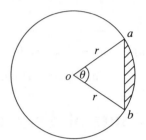

$$A = \tfrac{1}{2}r^2(\theta - \sin\theta) \qquad (\theta \text{ in radians})$$

Hence, evaluate the area of the shaded segment, when $r = 3\sqrt{2}$ and $\theta = \frac{\pi}{3}$, giving your answer in the form $9\left(\frac{\pi}{a} - \frac{\sqrt{a}}{b}\right)$, where a and b are prime numbers.

Solution:

(i) $r = 10, l = 4\pi$, find θ.

$$l = r\theta$$
$$\Rightarrow \quad 4\pi = 10\theta$$
$$\Rightarrow \quad 2\pi = 5\theta$$
$$\Rightarrow \quad \theta = \tfrac{2\pi}{5}$$

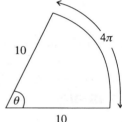

(ii) $r = 4, \theta = \frac{\pi}{3}$, find A.

$$A = \tfrac{1}{2}r^2\theta$$
$$A = \tfrac{1}{2}.4.4.\tfrac{\pi}{3} = \tfrac{8}{3}\pi \text{ cm}^2$$

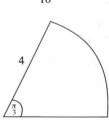

(iii) $A = 12\pi, \theta = \frac{2\pi}{3}$, find r.

$$A = \tfrac{1}{2}r^2\theta$$
$$\Rightarrow \quad 12\pi = \tfrac{1}{2}r^2.\tfrac{2\pi}{3}$$
$$\Rightarrow \quad 36 = r^2$$
$$\Rightarrow \quad r = 6 \text{ cm}$$

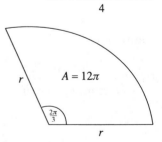

(iv)

Area of shaded segment = area of sector oab − area of $\triangle oab$

$$= \tfrac{1}{2}r^2\theta - \tfrac{1}{2}.r.r\sin\theta$$

$$= \tfrac{1}{2}r^2\theta - \tfrac{1}{2}r^2\sin\theta$$

$$= \tfrac{1}{2}r^2(\theta - \sin\theta)$$

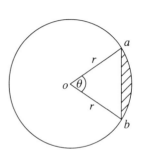

When $r = 3\sqrt{2}$ and $\theta = \tfrac{\pi}{3}$,

Area of shaded segment $= \tfrac{1}{2}(3\sqrt{2})^2(\tfrac{\pi}{3} - \sin\tfrac{\pi}{3})$

$$= \tfrac{1}{2}.18(\tfrac{\pi}{3} - \tfrac{\sqrt{3}}{2})$$

$$= 9(\tfrac{\pi}{3} - \tfrac{\sqrt{3}}{2})$$

Example

A section of roadway $spqr$ has curved edges ps and qr, both of which are arcs of a circle centre o. If the radius of the arc ps is x units and the radius of the arc qr is y units where $|\angle qor| = \tfrac{\pi}{3}$ express in terms of x and/or y:

(i) the area of the section of $pqrs$

(ii) the ratio $|pr|$: length of arc qr.

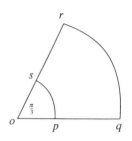

Solution:

(i) Area of $pqrs$.

Note: Area of a sector of a circle $= \tfrac{1}{2}r^2\theta$ (θ in radians).

Area of $pqrs$ = area of sector oqr − area of sector ops

$$= \tfrac{1}{2}.y^2.\tfrac{\pi}{3} - \tfrac{1}{2}.x^2.\tfrac{\pi}{3}$$

$$= \tfrac{\pi}{6}y^2 - \tfrac{\pi}{6}x^2 = \tfrac{\pi}{6}(y^2 - x^2)$$

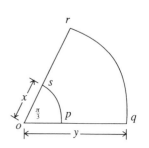

(ii) Using the cosine rule,

$$|pr|^2 = x^2 + y^2 - 2xy\cos 60°$$

$$= x^2 + y^2 - 2xy(\tfrac{1}{2}) = x^2 + y^2 - xy$$

$$\Rightarrow \quad |pr| = \sqrt{x^2 + y^2 - xy}$$

Note: length of an arc $= r\theta$ (θ in radians)

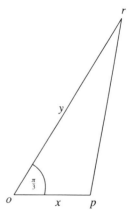

105

length of arc $qr = r\theta$

$$= y \cdot \frac{\pi}{3} = \frac{\pi}{3} y$$

Thus,　　　　$|pr|$: length of arc qr

$$= \sqrt{x^2 + y^2 - xy} : \frac{\pi}{3} y$$

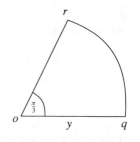

Example

p, q, r are points of a circle, centre k. The length of the radius of the circle is 2 cm. The length of the minor arc pq is $\frac{5\pi}{3}$ cm.

Find the length of the chord $[pq]$, giving your answer in the form $a\sqrt{a + \sqrt{b}}$, where a and b are prime numbers.

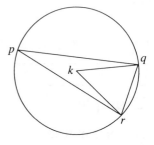

Solution:

We need $\angle pkq$. Let $\theta = \angle pkq$.

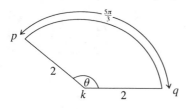

$$r\theta = l$$
$$2\theta = \frac{5\pi}{3}$$
$$\theta = \frac{5\pi}{6}$$

$$\cos \frac{5\pi}{6} = -\cos \frac{\pi}{6}$$
$$= -\frac{\sqrt{3}}{2}$$

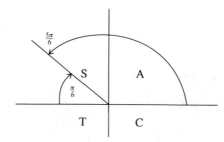

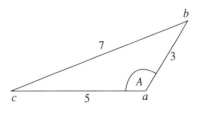

Using the cosine rule:

$$|pq|^2 = |pk|^2 + |qk|^2 - 2|pk|.|qk| \cos \angle pkq$$
$$= 2^2 + 2^2 - 2.2.2 \cos \tfrac{5\pi}{6}$$
$$= 4 + 4 - 8(-\tfrac{\sqrt{3}}{2})$$
$$= 8 + 4\sqrt{3}$$
$$= 4(2 + \sqrt{3})$$
$$\Rightarrow \quad |pk| = \sqrt{4(2 + \sqrt{3})}$$
$$= \sqrt{4}\sqrt{2 + \sqrt{3}} = 2\sqrt{2 + \sqrt{3}}$$

Example

In $\triangle abc$, $|ab| = 3$, $|ac| = 5$ and $|bc| = 7$.

Calculate:

(i) the measure of the greatest angle of the triangle

(ii) area of $\triangle abc$

(iii) the distance from vertex a to the side $[bc]$.

Solution:

(i) The largest angle is opposite the largest side. Using the cosine rule:

$$a^2 = b^2 + c^2 - 2bc \cos A$$
$$\Rightarrow \quad 7^2 = 5^2 + 3^2 - 2(5)(3) \cos A$$
$$\Rightarrow \quad 49 = 25 + 9 - 30 \cos A$$
$$\Rightarrow \quad 30 \cos A = 25 + 9 - 49$$
$$\Rightarrow \quad 30 \cos A = -15$$
$$\Rightarrow \quad \cos A = -\tfrac{1}{2}$$
$$\Rightarrow \quad A = \cos^{-1} -\tfrac{1}{2} = 120°$$

(ii) Area of $\triangle abc = \tfrac{1}{2}bc \sin A = \tfrac{1}{2}(5)(3) \sin 120° = \tfrac{1}{2}(5)(3)(\tfrac{\sqrt{3}}{2}) = \dfrac{15\sqrt{3}}{4}$

(iii) Let d be the distance from a to $[bc]$.

Area of $\Delta abc = \frac{1}{2}$ (base)(perpendicular height)

$$= \frac{1}{2} . 7 . d = \frac{7}{2}d$$

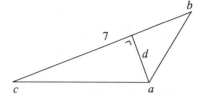

From **(ii)**   Area of $\Delta abc = \dfrac{15\sqrt{3}}{4}$

$\Rightarrow$ $\dfrac{7}{2}d = \dfrac{15\sqrt{3}}{4}$

$\Rightarrow$ $14d = 15\sqrt{3}$ (multiplying both sides by 4)

$\Rightarrow$ $d = \dfrac{15\sqrt{3}}{4}$

Example

In Δpqr, $|pr| = \sqrt{8}$ m, $|\angle rpq| = 30°$ and $|\angle pqr| = 45°$.

Show that the area of $\Delta pqr = 2.7$ m^2, correct to one place of decimals.

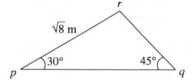

Solution:

Area of $\Delta pqr = \frac{1}{2}|pr| . |qr| \sin R$

$|pr| = \sqrt{8}$, we need $|qr|$ and R.

$R = 180° - 45° - 30° = 105°$

Thus, area $= \frac{1}{2}(2)(\sqrt{8}) \sin 105°$

$\quad = 2.732050808$

$\quad = 2.7$ m^2 (correct to one decimal place)

Using the sine rule to find $|qr|$

$$\frac{|qr|}{\sin P} = \frac{|pr|}{\sin Q}$$

$$\frac{|qr|}{\sin 30°} = \frac{\sqrt{8}}{\sin 45°}$$

$$|qr| = \frac{\sqrt{8} \sin 30°}{\sin 45°}$$

$$= \frac{\sqrt{8}\left(\frac{1}{2}\right)}{\frac{1}{\sqrt{2}}}$$

$$= \frac{2\sqrt{2}\left(\frac{1}{2}\right)}{\frac{1}{\sqrt{2}}} = \frac{\sqrt{2}}{\frac{1}{\sqrt{2}}} = 2$$

Example

If the area of Δpqr is 26 cm^2, where $|pq| = 7$ cm, $|pr| = 8$ cm, find $|\angle qpr|$, correct to the nearest minute.

Solution:

Equation in disguise:

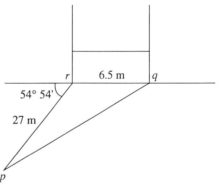

(rough diagram)

$$\text{Area of } \Delta pqr = 26$$
$$\Rightarrow \quad \tfrac{1}{2} qr \sin P = 26$$
$$\Rightarrow \quad \tfrac{1}{2}(8)(7) \sin P = 26$$
$$\Rightarrow \quad 28 \sin P = 26$$
$$\Rightarrow \quad \sin P = \tfrac{26}{28} = \tfrac{13}{14}$$
$$\Rightarrow \quad P = \sin^{-1} \tfrac{13}{14} = 68° \, 12' \, 47.55''$$

Thus, $|\angle qpr| = 68° \, 13'$

Note: 47.55 seconds is greater than half a minute, thus we round up to 13 minutes.

Example

A ball at p is 27 m from the nearer goalpost.

(i) Calculate its distance from the farther goalpost, to the nearest metre.

(ii) Find $|\angle rpq|$.

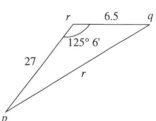

Solution:

Draw a triangle by itself to represent the situation.

(i) Find $|pq|$ [in diagram $|pq| = r$]

We have two sides and included angle
∴ use cosine rule.

$$r^2 = p^2 + q^2 - 2pq \cos R$$
$$= (6.5)^2 + (27)^2 - 2(6.5)(27) \cos 125° \, 6'$$
$$r^2 = 42.25 + 729 - 2(6.5)(27)(-0.5750)$$
$$r^2 = 42.25 + 729 + 201.825$$
$$r^2 = 973.075$$
$$\Rightarrow \quad r = \sqrt{973.075}$$
$$= 31.1942$$

Thus $|pq| = 31$ m (correct to the nearest metre)

(ii) Find $|\angle rpq|$ [From diagram $\angle rpq = P$]

We have two sides and non-included angle $\therefore$ use sine rule

$\dfrac{\sin P}{p} = \dfrac{\sin R}{r}$ (*P* missing, so put that first)

$\Rightarrow \quad \dfrac{\sin P}{6.5} = \dfrac{\sin 125°\,6'}{31}$ (put in known values)

$\Rightarrow \quad \sin P = \dfrac{6.5 \sin 125°\,6'}{31}$ (multiply both sides by 6.5)

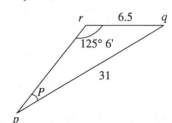

$\Rightarrow \quad \sin P = \dfrac{6.5(0.8181)}{31}$

$\Rightarrow \quad \sin P = 0.1715$

$\qquad P = \sin^{-1} 0.1715 = 9°\,53'$

Thus $|\angle rpq| = 9°\,53'$

Example

In the diagram, $|pq| = 4$ cm, $|pr| = 5$ cm, $|qr| = 6$ cm and $|\angle psr| = 22°$.
Find $|ps|$.

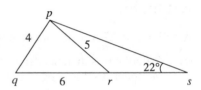

Solution:

Two triangles are linked and we need to work on them separately to find $|ps|$.

1. Consider Δpqr:

We need to use the cosine rule to find $|\angle prq|$, as we are given three sides.

$\cos R = \dfrac{p^2 + q^2 - r^2}{2pq}$ (cosine rule)

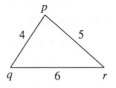

$\qquad = \dfrac{6^2 + 5^2 - 4^2}{2(6)(5)}$

$\qquad = \dfrac{45}{60} = \dfrac{3}{4}$

$\Rightarrow \qquad R = \cos^{-1} \tfrac{3}{4} = 41°\,25'$

$\therefore \quad |\angle prs| = 180° - 41°\,25' = 138°\,35'$

2. Consider Δ*prs*:

We now use the sine rule to find $|ps|$,
[From diagram $|ps| = r$] as we have two angles and one side.

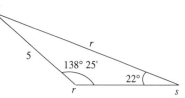

$$\frac{r}{\sin R} = \frac{s}{\sin S}$$ (sine rule, *r* missing so put that first)

$\Rightarrow$ $$\frac{r}{\sin 138°\,25'} = \frac{5}{\sin 22°}$$ (put in known values)

$\Rightarrow$ $$r = \frac{5 \sin 138°\,25'}{\sin 22°}$$ (multiply both sides by sin 138° 25′)

$\Rightarrow$ $$r = \frac{5(0.6637)}{(0.3746)}$$ (sin 138° 25′ = 0.6637 and sin 22° = 0.3746)

$\Rightarrow$ $$r = 8.8588$$

Thus $|ps| = 8.86$ cm (correct to two places of decimals)

Example

pqrs is a quadrilateral. $|pq| = 7$, $|qs| = 8$, $|ps| = 13$.

(i) Show $|\angle pqs| = 120°$.

(ii) Given that the quadrilateral *pqrs* has area $\frac{35\sqrt{3}}{2}$ find the ratio area Δ*pqs* : area Δ*qrs*.

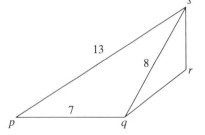

Solution:

(i) Redraw Δ*pqs*.

Using the cosine rule,

$$q^2 = p^2 + s^2 - 2ps \cos Q$$

$\Rightarrow$ $$\cos Q = \frac{p^2 + s^2 - q^2}{2ps}$$

$$= \frac{8^2 + 7^2 - 13^2}{2(8)(7)} = \frac{64 + 49 - 169}{112} = \frac{-56}{112} = -\frac{1}{2}$$

Thus $Q = \cos^{-1} -\tfrac{1}{2} = 120°$

$\Rightarrow$ $|\angle pqs| = 120°$

(ii) Area of $\Delta pqs = \frac{1}{2} ps \sin Q = \frac{1}{2}(8)(7) \sin 120° = \frac{1}{2}.8.7.\frac{\sqrt{3}}{2} = \frac{28\sqrt{3}}{2}$

Given: area of quadrilateral $pqrs = \dfrac{35\sqrt{3}}{2}$

Area of Δqrs = Area of quadrilateral $pqrs$ − Area of Δpqs

$$= \frac{35\sqrt{3}}{2} - \frac{28\sqrt{3}}{2} = \frac{7\sqrt{3}}{2}$$

Thus   Area of Δpqs : Area of Δqrs

$$= \frac{28\sqrt{3}}{2} : \frac{7\sqrt{3}}{2} = 28\sqrt{3} : 7\sqrt{3} = 28 : 7 = 4 : 1$$

Example

A vertical flagpole stands on horizontal ground. The angle of elevation of the top of the pole from a certain point on the ground is θ. From a point on the ground 10 metres closer to the pole the angle of elevation is β. Show that the height of the pole is

$$\frac{10 \sin \theta \sin \beta}{\sin(\beta - \theta)}$$

Solution:

Represent the situation with a diagram, then redraw the two triangles separately.

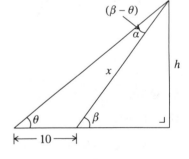

$\alpha + \theta = \beta$ (exterior angle of a triangle)

$\quad \alpha = (\beta - \theta)$

From the right-angled triangle,

$$\sin \beta = \frac{h}{x} \qquad (h = \text{height of flagpole})$$

$$\Rightarrow \qquad x = \frac{h}{\sin \beta} \quad ①$$

Using the sine rule on the other triangle,

$$\frac{x}{\sin \theta} = \frac{10}{\sin(\beta - \theta)}$$

$$x = \frac{10 \sin \theta}{\sin(\beta - \theta)} \quad ②$$

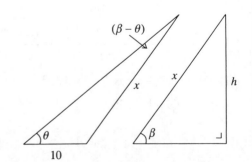

We now equate the two different expressions for x, the common side of both triangles.

$$x = x$$

$$\frac{h}{\sin \beta} = \frac{10 \sin \theta}{\sin(\beta - \theta)}$$

$$h = \frac{10 \sin \theta \sin \beta}{\sin (\beta - \theta)}$$

Example

A triangle is inscribed in a sector of a circle, centre c, radius r, $\theta < 90°$. A right-angled triangle circumscribes the sector (see diagram).

If the area of a sector is $\frac{1}{2}r^2\theta$

[Tables p. 7] prove

$\sin \theta < \theta < \tan \theta.$

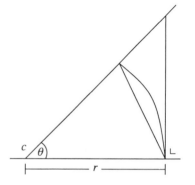

Solution:

Draw the triangles and sector separately and mark points a, b and d.

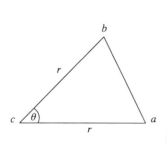 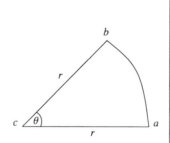 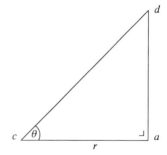

Area of $\triangle abc$

$= \frac{1}{2}.r.r \sin \theta$

$= \frac{1}{2}r^2 \sin \theta$

Area of sector abc

$= \frac{1}{2}r^2\theta$

Area of $\triangle acd$

$= \frac{1}{2}r|ad|$

but $\tan \theta = \dfrac{|ad|}{r}$

$\implies r \tan \theta = |ad|$

Thus, area of $\triangle acd$

$= \frac{1}{2}r(r \tan \theta)$

$= \frac{1}{2}r^2 \tan \theta$

From the diagram:

Area of $\triangle abc <$ Area of sector $abc <$ Area of $\triangle acd$

$\implies \quad \frac{1}{2}r^2 \sin \theta < \frac{1}{2}r^2\theta < \frac{1}{2}r^2 \tan \theta$

$\implies \qquad \sin \theta < \theta < \tan \theta$

Example

Points p, q, r are on the horizontal. $|pq| = 5$, $|qr| = 3$ and $|\angle pqr| = \frac{2\pi}{3}$.

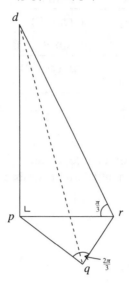

(i) Calculate $|pr|$.

(ii) $[pd]$ represents a vertical mast. The angle of elevation of d from r is $\frac{\pi}{3}$. Find $|dq|$, giving your answer in the form $2\sqrt{a}$ and calculate the measure of $\angle pqd$, correct to the nearest minute.

Solution:

Redraw the triangles separately.

(i) Using the cosine rule:

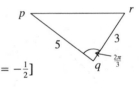

$$|pr|^2 = |pq|^2 + |qr|^2 - 2|pq|.|qr|\cos\frac{2\pi}{3}$$

$$= 5^2 + 3^2 - 2(5)(3)\left(-\tfrac{1}{2}\right) \qquad [\cos\tfrac{2\pi}{3} = -\cos\tfrac{\pi}{3} = -\tfrac{1}{2}]$$

$$= 25 + 9 + 15$$

$$= 49$$

$$\implies \quad |pr| = \sqrt{49} = 7$$

(ii) $\tan\frac{\pi}{3} = \dfrac{|pd|}{|pr|}$

$$\implies \quad \sqrt{3} = \dfrac{|pd|}{7}$$

$$\implies \quad |pd| = 7\sqrt{3}$$

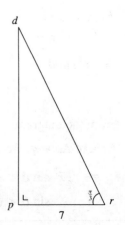

Using Pythagoras' Theorem:

$$|dq|^2 = |dp|^2 + |pq|^2$$
$$= (7\sqrt{3})^2 + 5^2$$
$$= 49.3 + 25$$
$$= 147 + 25$$
$$= 172$$
$$\implies |dq| = \sqrt{172} = \sqrt{4.43} = \sqrt{4}\sqrt{43} = 2\sqrt{43}$$

$$\tan \angle pqd = \frac{7\sqrt{3}}{5}$$

$$\implies |\angle pqd| = \tan^{-1}\frac{7\sqrt{3}}{5} = 67°\,35'$$

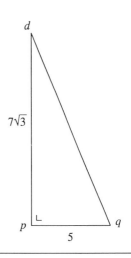

Example

[sp], [tq] are vertical poles each of height 10 m, p, q, r are points on level ground. Two wires of equal length join s and t to r, i.e. $|sr| = |tr|$.

If $|pr| = 8$ m and $|\angle prq| = 120°$, calculate:

(i) $|pq|$ in the form $a\sqrt{b}$, where b is prime.

(ii) $|sr|$ in the form $\sqrt{c}$.

(iii) $|\angle srt|$ to the nearest degree.

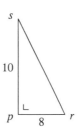

Solution:

$|sr| = |rt| \implies |pr| = |qr| = 8$

Redraw the triangles separately.

(i)

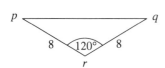

$|pq| = r$

Using the cosine rule:

$$\implies r^2 = p^2 + q^2 - 2pq \cos R$$
$$\implies r^2 = 8^2 + 8^2 - 2(8)(8) \cos 120$$
$$\implies r^2 = 64 + 64 - 2(8)(8)(-\tfrac{1}{2})$$
$$\implies r^2 = 64 + 64 + 64$$
$$\implies r^2 = 64.3$$
$$\implies r = \sqrt{64.3} = \sqrt{64}\sqrt{3} = 8\sqrt{3}$$

(ii)

Using Pythagoras' Theorem:

$$|sr|^2 = |sp|^2 + |pr|^2$$
$$\implies |sr|^2 = 10^2 + 8^2$$
$$\implies |sr|^2 = 100 + 64$$
$$\implies |sr|^2 = 164$$
$$\implies |sr| = \sqrt{164}$$

115

(iii)

$$r^2 = s^2 + t^2 - 2st \cos R$$

$$(8\sqrt{3})^2 = (\sqrt{164})^2 + (\sqrt{164})^2 - 2\sqrt{164}\sqrt{164}\cos R$$

$$192 = 164 + 164 - 328 \cos R$$

$$328 \cos R = 164 + 164 - 192$$

$$328 \cos R = 136$$

$$\cos R = \frac{136}{328} = \frac{17}{41}$$

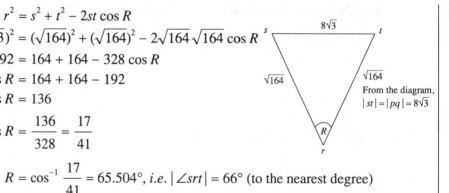

From the diagram,
$|st| = |pq| = 8\sqrt{3}$

$$R = \cos^{-1}\frac{17}{41} = 65.504°, \ i.e. \ |\angle srt| = 66° \text{ (to the nearest degree)}$$

Example

p, q and r are points on level ground. $[sr]$ is a vertical tower of height h. The angles of elevation of the top of the tower from p and q are α and β, respectively.

(i) If $|\alpha| = 60°$ and $|\beta| = 30°$, express $|pr|$ and $|qr|$ in terms of h.

(ii) Find $|qp|$ in terms of h, if $\tan \angle qrp = \sqrt{8}$.

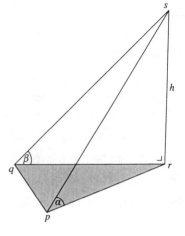

Solution:

Redraw the triangles separately.

(i)

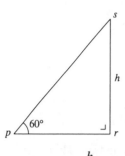

$$\tan 60° = \frac{h}{|pr|}$$

$$\Rightarrow \quad \sqrt{3} = \frac{h}{|pr|}$$

$$\Rightarrow \quad \sqrt{3}|pr| = h$$

$$\Rightarrow \quad |pr| = \frac{h}{\sqrt{3}}$$

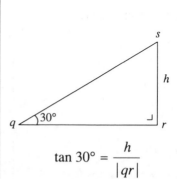

$$\tan 30° = \frac{h}{|qr|}$$

$$\Rightarrow \quad \frac{1}{\sqrt{3}} = \frac{h}{|qr|}$$

$$\Rightarrow \quad |qr| = \sqrt{3}h$$

116

(ii) Using the cosine rule:

$$|qp|^2 = |qr|^2 + |pr|^2 - 2|qr|.|pr|\cos\angle qrp$$

$$= (\sqrt{3}\,h)^2 + \left(\frac{h}{\sqrt{3}}\right)^2 - 2(\sqrt{3}\,h)\left(\frac{h}{\sqrt{3}}\right)\left(\frac{1}{3}\right)$$

$$= 3h^2 + \frac{h^2}{3} - \frac{2}{3}h^2$$

$$= \frac{9h^2 + h^2 - 2h^2}{3}$$

$$= \frac{8h^2}{3}$$

$$\Rightarrow \quad |qp| = \sqrt{\frac{8h^2}{3}} = \sqrt{\frac{8}{3}}\,h$$

$$\tan\angle qrp = \sqrt{8} = \frac{\sqrt{8}}{1}$$

$$\Rightarrow \quad |rq| = 3$$

$$\Rightarrow \quad \cos\angle qrp = \tfrac{1}{3}$$

Example

(i) In a given triangle, with the usual notation, $A = \frac{\pi}{4}$ and $B = \frac{\pi}{3}$. Prove $a^2 : b^2 = 2 : 3$.

(ii) Using the usual notation, prove that in any triangle $a\cos B - b\cos A = \dfrac{a^2 - b^2}{c}$.

Solution:

(i) Sine rule : $\dfrac{a}{\sin A} = \dfrac{b}{\sin B} = \dfrac{c}{\sin C}$

Thus, $\dfrac{a}{\sin A} = \dfrac{b}{\sin B}$

$a\sin B = b\sin A$ (cross-multiply)

$$\Rightarrow \quad \frac{a}{b} = \frac{\sin A}{\sin B} \quad \text{(divide both sides by } b\sin B\text{)}$$

$$\Rightarrow \quad \frac{a^2}{b^2} = \frac{\sin^2 A}{\sin^2 B} \quad \text{(square both sides)}$$

$$\Rightarrow \quad = \frac{\left(\frac{1}{\sqrt{2}}\right)^2}{\left(\frac{\sqrt{3}}{2}\right)^2} \quad \left(\sin\tfrac{\pi}{4} = \tfrac{1}{\sqrt{2}} \text{ and } \sin\tfrac{\pi}{3} = \tfrac{\sqrt{3}}{2}\right)$$

$$\Rightarrow \quad = \frac{\frac{1}{2}}{\frac{3}{4}} = \frac{2}{3} \quad \text{(multiply top and bottom by 4)}$$

Thus, $a^2 : b^2 = 2 : 3$

117

(ii) $a \cos B - b \cos A = \dfrac{a^2 - b^2}{c}$

Cosine rule: $a^2 = b^2 + c^2 - 2bc \cos A$ or $\cos A = \dfrac{b^2 + c^2 - a^2}{2bc}$

Thus, $a \cos B - b \cos A = a\left(\dfrac{a^2 + c^2 - b^2}{2ac}\right) - b\left(\dfrac{b^2 + c^2 - a^2}{2bc}\right)$

$$= \left(\dfrac{a^2 + c^2 - b^2}{2c}\right) - \left(\dfrac{b^2 + c^2 - a^2}{2c}\right)$$

$$= \dfrac{a^2 + c^2 - b^2 - b^2 - c^2 + a^2}{2c}$$

$$= \dfrac{2a^2 - 2b^2}{2c} = \dfrac{a^2 - b^2}{c}$$

Example

Prove $\cos^2 \theta + \sin^2 \theta = 1$.

Hence, prove **(i)** $1 + \tan^2 \theta = \sec^2 \theta$ **(ii)** $\cot^2 \theta + 1 = \operatorname{cosec}^2 \theta$

Solution:

Let θ be any angle as shown in diagram.

The coordinates of p are (x, y) and $|op| = r$.

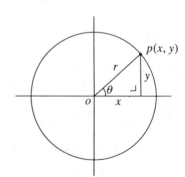

$\cos \theta = \dfrac{x}{r} \Rightarrow \cos^2 \theta = \dfrac{x^2}{r^2}$

$\sin \theta = \dfrac{y}{r} \Rightarrow \sin^2 \theta = \dfrac{y^2}{r^2}$

$x^2 + y^2 = r^2$ (Pytharogas' Theorem)

$\Rightarrow \quad \dfrac{x^2}{r^2} + \dfrac{y^2}{r^2} = 1$ (divide both sides by r^2)

$\Rightarrow \quad \cos^2 \theta + \sin^2 \theta = 1$

(i) $\cos^2 \theta + \sin^2 \theta = 1$

$\Rightarrow \quad \dfrac{\cos^2 \theta}{\cos^2 \theta} + \dfrac{\sin^2 \theta}{\cos^2 \theta} = \dfrac{1}{\cos^2 \theta}$

(dividing both sides by $\cos^2 \theta$)

$\Rightarrow \qquad 1 + \tan^2 \theta = \sec^2 \theta$

(ii) $\cos^2 \theta + \sin^2 \theta = 1$

$\Rightarrow \quad \dfrac{\cos^2 \theta}{\sin^2 \theta} + \dfrac{\sin^2 \theta}{\sin^2 \theta} = \dfrac{1}{\sin^2 \theta}$

(dividing both sides by $\sin^2 \theta$)

$\Rightarrow \qquad \cot^2 \theta + 1 = \operatorname{cosec}^2 \theta$

Example

Given $\cos(A - B) = \cos A \cos B + \sin A \sin B$, prove each of the following:

(i) $\cos(A + B) = \cos A \cos B - \sin A \sin B$

(ii) $\sin(A + B) = \sin A \cos B + \cos A \sin B$

(iii) $\sin(A - B) = \sin A \cos B - \cos A \sin B$

(iv) $\sin 2A = 2 \sin A \cos A$ **(v)** $\cos 2A = \cos^2 A - \sin^2 A$

(vi) $\cos^2 A = \frac{1}{2}(1 + \cos 2A)$ **(vii)** $\sin^2 A = \frac{1}{2}(1 - \cos 2A)$

(viii) $\cos 2A = \dfrac{1 - \tan^2 A}{1 + \tan^2 A}$ **(ix)** $\sin 2A = \dfrac{2 \tan A}{1 + \tan^2 A}$

Solution:

In the following proofs we use the following identities for all $A \in R$:

1. $\cos^2 A + \sin^2 A = 1$ **2.** $\cos(-A) = \cos A$ **3.** $\sin(-A) = -\sin A$

4. $\tan A = \dfrac{\sin A}{\cos A}$ **5.** $\cos(\frac{\pi}{2} - A) = \sin A$ **6.** $\sin(\frac{\pi}{2} - A) = \cos A$

(i)   Prove: $\cos(A + B) = \cos A \cos B - \sin A \sin B$

       Given: $\cos(A - B) = \cos A \cos B + \sin A \sin B$

       Replace B with $(-B)$ on both sides.

       Thus, $\cos[A - (-B)] = \cos A \cos(-B) + \sin A \sin(-B)$

$\Rightarrow$ $\cos(A + B) = \cos A \cos B + \sin A(-\sin B)$

$\Rightarrow$ $\cos(A + B) = \cos A \cos B - \sin A \sin B$

(ii)   Prove: $\sin(A + B) = \sin A \cos B + \cos A \sin B$

       Given: $\cos(A - B) = \cos A \cos B + \sin A \sin B$

       Replace A with $(\frac{\pi}{2} - A)$ on both sides.

       Thus, $\cos[(\frac{\pi}{2} - A) - B] = \cos(\frac{\pi}{2} - A) \cos B + \sin(\frac{\pi}{2} - A) \sin B$

$\Rightarrow$ $\cos[\frac{\pi}{2} - (A + B)] = \sin A \cos B + \cos A \sin B$

$\Rightarrow$ $\sin(A + B) = \sin A \cos B + \cos A \sin B$

(iii) Prove: $\sin(A - B) = \sin A \cos B - \cos A \sin B$

              $\sin(A + B) = \sin A \cos B + \cos A \sin B$

       Replace B with $(-B)$ on both sides.

       Thus, $\sin[A + (-B)] = \sin A \cos(-B) + \cos A \sin(-B)$

$\Rightarrow$ $\sin(A - B) = \sin A \cos B + \cos A(-\sin B)$

$\Rightarrow$ $\sin(A - B) = \sin A \cos B - \cos A \sin B$

(iv) Prove: $\sin 2A = 2 \sin A \cos A$

$$\sin(A + B) = \sin A \cos B + \cos A \sin B$$

Replace B with A on both sides.

$\Rightarrow$ $\sin(A + A) = \sin A \cos A + \cos A \sin A$

$\Rightarrow$ $\sin 2A = 2 \sin A \cos A$

(v) Prove: $\cos 2A = \cos^2 A - \sin^2 A$

$$\cos(A + B) = \cos A \cos B - \sin A \sin B$$

Replace B with A on both sides.

$\Rightarrow$ $\cos(A + A) = \cos A \cos A + \sin A \sin A$

$\Rightarrow$ $\cos 2A = \cos^2 A - \sin^2 A$

(vi) Prove: $\cos^2 A = \frac{1}{2}(1 + \cos 2A)$

$$\cos 2A = \cos^2 A - \sin^2 A$$

$\Rightarrow$ $\cos 2A = \cos^2 A - (1 - \cos^2 A)$

$\Rightarrow$ $\cos 2A = \cos^2 A - 1 + \cos^2 A$

$\Rightarrow$ $\cos 2A = 2 \cos^2 A - 1$

$\Rightarrow$ $2 \cos^2 A = 1 + \cos 2A$

$\Rightarrow$ $\cos^2 A = \frac{1}{2}(1 + \cos 2A)$

(vii) Prove: $\sin^2 A = \frac{1}{2}(1 - \cos 2A)$

$$\cos 2A = \cos^2 A - \sin^2 A$$

$\Rightarrow$ $\cos 2A = (1 - \sin^2 A) - \sin^2 A$

$\Rightarrow$ $\cos 2A = 1 - \sin^2 A - \sin^2 A$

$\Rightarrow$ $\cos 2A = 1 - 2 \sin^2 A$

$\Rightarrow$ $2 \sin^2 A = 1 - \cos 2A$

$\Rightarrow$ $\sin^2 A = \frac{1}{2}(1 - \cos 2A)$

(viii) Prove: $\cos 2A = \dfrac{1 - \tan^2 A}{1 + \tan^2 A}$

$$\text{RHS} = \frac{1 - \dfrac{\sin^2 A}{\cos^2 A}}{1 + \dfrac{\sin^2 A}{\cos^2 A}}$$

$$= \frac{\cos^2 A - \sin^2 A}{\cos^2 A + \sin^2 A}$$

(multiplying top and bottom by $\cos^2 A$)

$$= \frac{\cos 2A}{1} = \cos 2A = \text{LHS}$$

(ix) Prove: $\sin 2A = \dfrac{2\tan A}{1+\tan^2 A}$

$$\text{RHS} = \dfrac{2\,\dfrac{\sin A}{\cos A}}{1+\dfrac{\sin^2 A}{\cos^2 A}}$$

$$= \dfrac{2\sin A\cos A}{\cos^2 A + \sin^2 A}$$

(multiplying top and bottom by $\cos^2 A$)

$$= \dfrac{\sin 2A}{1} = \sin 2A = \text{LHS}$$

Example

Prove $\tan(A+B) = \dfrac{\tan A + \tan B}{1-\tan A\tan B}$

Hence, show that $\tan(A-B) = \dfrac{\tan A - \tan B}{1+\tan A\tan B}$ and $\tan 2A = \dfrac{2\tan A}{1+\tan^2 A}$

Show that $\tan(45° - A) = \dfrac{\cos 2A}{1+\sin 2A}$ and deduce that $\tan 22\tfrac{1}{2}° = \dfrac{1}{\sqrt{2}+1}$

Solution:

$$\tan A = \dfrac{\sin A}{\cos A}$$

Thus, $\tan(A+B) = \dfrac{\sin(A+B)}{\cos(A+B)}$

$$= \dfrac{\sin A\cos B + \cos A\sin B}{\cos A\cos B - \sin A\sin B}$$

$$= \dfrac{\dfrac{\sin A\cos B}{\cos A\cos B} + \dfrac{\cos A\sin B}{\cos A\cos B}}{\dfrac{\cos A\cos B}{\cos A\cos B} - \dfrac{\sin A\sin B}{\cos A\cos B}} \qquad \left(\begin{array}{l}\text{Divide top and bottom}\\ \text{by } \cos A\cos B\end{array}\right)$$

$$= \dfrac{\dfrac{\sin A}{\cos A} + \dfrac{\sin B}{\cos B}}{1 - \dfrac{\sin A}{\cos A}\cdot\dfrac{\sin B}{\cos B}} = \dfrac{\tan A + \tan B}{1-\tan A\tan B}$$

Thus, $\tan(A+B) = \dfrac{\tan A + \tan B}{1-\tan A\tan B}$

121

tan (A − B)

Replace B with (−B) on both sides.

$$\Rightarrow \quad \tan(A + (-B)) = \frac{\tan A + \tan(-B)}{1 - \tan A \tan(-B)}$$

$$\Rightarrow \quad \tan(A - B) = \frac{\tan A - \tan B}{1 + \tan A \tan B}$$

$(\tan(-B) = -\tan B)$

tan 2A

Replace B with A on both sides.

$$\Rightarrow \quad \tan(A + A) = \frac{\tan A + \tan A}{1 - \tan A \tan A}$$

$$\Rightarrow \quad \tan 2A = \frac{2 \tan A}{1 - \tan^2 A}$$

$$\frac{\cos 2A}{1 + \sin 2A} = \frac{\dfrac{1 - \tan^2 A}{1 + \tan^2 A}}{1 + \dfrac{2 \tan A}{1 + \tan^2 A}}$$

$$= \frac{1 - \tan^2 A}{1 + \tan^2 A + 2 \tan A} \qquad \left(\begin{array}{l}\text{multiplying top and bottom} \\ \text{by } 1 + \tan^2 A\end{array}\right)$$

$$= \frac{(1 - \tan A)(1 + \tan A)}{(1 + \tan A)(1 + \tan A)} \qquad \text{(factorising top and bottom)}$$

$$= \frac{1 - \tan A}{1 + \tan A}$$

$$= \frac{\tan 45^\circ - \tan A}{1 + \tan 45^\circ \tan A} \qquad (\tan 45^\circ = 1)$$

$$= \tan(45^\circ - A)$$

Thus, $\tan(45^\circ - A) = \dfrac{\cos 2A}{1 + \sin 2A}$

What we do next is let $A = 22\frac{1}{2}^\circ$ on both sides.

Thus, $\tan(45^\circ - 22\frac{1}{2}^\circ) = \dfrac{\cos 2(22\frac{1}{2}^\circ)}{1 + \sin 2(22\frac{1}{2}^\circ)}$ $\qquad$ (multiply top and bottom by $\sqrt{2}$)

$$\Rightarrow \quad \tan 22\frac{1}{2}^\circ = \frac{\cos 45^\circ}{1 + \sin 45^\circ} = \frac{\frac{1}{\sqrt{2}}}{1 + \frac{1}{\sqrt{2}}} = \frac{1}{\sqrt{2} + 1}$$

Example

Prove: **(i)** $\sin 2\theta = \dfrac{2 \tan \theta}{1 + \tan^2 \theta}$ **(ii)** $\dfrac{\sin x}{1 + \cos x} = \tan \dfrac{x}{2}$

(iii) $\sqrt{\dfrac{1 - \cos 2A}{1 + \cos 2A}} = \tan A$ **(iv)** $\dfrac{\sin \theta}{1 - \cos \theta} + \dfrac{\sin \theta}{1 + \cos \theta} = 2 \operatorname{cosec} \theta$

(v) $(\sin A + \cos A)^2 + (\sin A - \cos A)^2 = 2$

(vi) $\dfrac{\sin \alpha}{\cos \beta} + \dfrac{\cos \alpha}{\sin \beta} = \dfrac{2 \cos (\alpha - \beta)}{\sin 2\beta}$

Solution:

(i) $\sin 2\theta = \dfrac{2 \tan \theta}{1 + \tan^2 \theta}$

$$\text{RHS} = \dfrac{2 \tan \theta}{1 + \tan^2 \theta}$$

$$= \dfrac{2 \dfrac{\sin \theta}{\cos \theta}}{1 + \dfrac{\sin^2 \theta}{\cos^2 \theta}}$$

$$= \dfrac{2 \sin \theta \cos \theta}{\cos^2 \theta + \sin^2 \theta}$$

(multiplying top and bottom by $\cos^2 \theta$)

$$= \dfrac{\sin 2\theta}{1} = \sin 2\theta = \text{LHS}$$

(ii) $\dfrac{\sin x}{1 + \cos x} = \tan \dfrac{x}{2}$

$$\text{LHS} = \dfrac{2 \sin \dfrac{x}{2} \cos \dfrac{x}{2}}{1 + \left(2 \cos^2 \dfrac{x}{2} - 1\right)}$$

$$= \dfrac{2 \sin \dfrac{x}{2} \cos \dfrac{x}{2}}{1 + 2 \cos^2 \dfrac{x}{2} - 1}$$

$$= \dfrac{2 \sin \dfrac{x}{2} \cos \dfrac{x}{2}}{2 \cos^2 \dfrac{x}{2}}$$

$$= \dfrac{\sin \dfrac{x}{2}}{\cos \dfrac{x}{2}}$$

$$= \tan \dfrac{x}{2} = \text{RHS}$$

(iii) $\sqrt{\dfrac{1 - \cos 2A}{1 + \cos 2A}} = \tan A$

$$\text{LHS} = \sqrt{\frac{1 - \cos 2A}{1 + \cos 2A}}$$

$$= \sqrt{\frac{1 - (\cos^2 A - \sin^2 A)}{1 + (\cos^2 A - \sin^2 A)}}$$

$$= \sqrt{\frac{(1 - \cos^2 A) + \sin^2 A}{(1 - \sin^2 A) + \cos^2 A}}$$

$$= \sqrt{\frac{\sin^2 A + \sin^2 A}{\cos^2 A + \cos^2 A}}$$

$$= \sqrt{\frac{2 \sin^2 A}{2 \cos^2 A}}$$

$$= \sqrt{\tan^2 A} = \tan A = \text{RHS}$$

(iv) $\dfrac{\sin \theta}{1 - \cos \theta} + \dfrac{\sin \theta}{1 + \cos \theta} = 2 \operatorname{cosec} \theta$

$$\text{LHS} = \frac{\sin \theta}{1 - \cos \theta} + \frac{\sin \theta}{1 + \cos \theta}$$

$$= \frac{\sin \theta(1 + \cos \theta) + \sin \theta(1 - \cos \theta)}{(1 - \cos \theta)(1 + \cos \theta)}$$

$$= \frac{\sin \theta + \sin \theta \cos \theta + \sin \theta - \sin \theta \cos \theta}{1 + \cos \theta - \cos \theta - \cos^2 \theta}$$

$$= \frac{2 \sin \theta}{1 - \cos^2 \theta}$$

$$= \frac{2 \sin \theta}{\sin^2 \theta}$$

$$= \frac{2}{\sin \theta} = 2 \operatorname{cosec} \theta = \text{RHS}$$

(v) $(\sin A + \cos A)^2 + (\sin A - \cos A)^2 = 2$

$$\text{LHS} = (\sin A + \cos A)^2 + (\sin A - \cos A)^2$$

$$= \sin^2 A + 2 \sin A \cos A + \cos^2 A + \sin^2 A - 2 \sin A \cos A + \cos^2 A$$

$$= 2 \sin^2 A + 2 \cos^2 A$$

$$= 2(\sin^2 A + \cos^2 A) = 2(1) = 2 = \text{RHS}$$

(vi) $\dfrac{\sin \alpha}{\cos \beta} + \dfrac{\cos \alpha}{\sin \beta} = \dfrac{2 \cos (\alpha - \beta)}{\sin 2\beta}$

$\text{LHS} = \dfrac{\sin \alpha}{\cos \beta} + \dfrac{\cos \alpha}{\sin \beta}$

$= \dfrac{\cos \alpha \cos \beta + \sin \alpha \sin \beta}{\sin \beta \cos \beta}$

$= \dfrac{\cos (\alpha - \beta)}{\frac{1}{2} \sin 2\beta}$ $\qquad (\sin 2\beta = 2 \sin \beta \cos \beta \Rightarrow \frac{1}{2} \sin 2\beta = \sin \beta \cos \beta)$

$= \dfrac{2 \cos (\alpha - \beta)}{\sin 2\beta} \longleftarrow = \text{RHS}$ ——(Multiplying top and bottom by 2)

Example

Prove that:

(i) $\dfrac{\cos 3A - \cos 5A}{\sin 3A - \sin A} = 2 \sin 2A$

(ii) $\dfrac{\sin \theta - \sin 2\theta + \sin 3\theta}{\cos \theta - \cos 2\theta + \cos 3\theta} = \tan 2\theta$

(iii) $\dfrac{\cos 2\theta \cos \theta - \sin 4\theta \sin 3\theta}{\sin 8\theta \cos \theta - \sin 6\theta \cos 3\theta} = \cot 2\theta$

Solution:

(i) $\dfrac{\cos 3A - \cos 5A}{\sin 3A - \sin A}$

$= \dfrac{-(\cos 5A - \cos 3A)}{\sin 3A - \sin A}$ [put the larger angle first on top]

$= \dfrac{-\left(-2 \sin\left(\dfrac{5A + 3A}{2}\right) \sin\left(\dfrac{5A - 3A}{2}\right)\right)}{2 \cos\left(\dfrac{3A + A}{2}\right) \sin\left(\dfrac{3A - A}{2}\right)}$

$\left[\begin{array}{l} \text{using} \\[4pt] \cos A - \cos B = -2 \sin\left(\dfrac{A + B}{2}\right) \sin\left(\dfrac{A - B}{2}\right) \\[4pt] \text{on the top and} \\[4pt] \sin A - \sin B = 2 \cos\left(\dfrac{A + B}{2}\right) \sin\left(\dfrac{A - B}{2}\right) \\[4pt] \text{on the bottom} \end{array}\right]$

$= \dfrac{2 \sin 4A \sin A}{2 \cos 2A \sin A}$

$$= \frac{\sin 4A}{\cos 2A} \qquad \text{[dividing top and bottom by 2 sin } A]$$

$$= \frac{2 \sin 2A \cos 2A}{\cos 2A} \qquad [\sin 4A = 2 \sin 2A \cos 2A]$$

$$= 2 \sin 2A \qquad \text{[dividing top and bottom by cos } 2A]$$

(ii) $\dfrac{\sin \theta - \sin 2\theta + \sin 3\theta}{\cos \theta - \cos 2\theta + \cos 3\theta}$

$$= \frac{\sin 3\theta + \sin \theta - \sin 2\theta}{\cos 3\theta + \cos \theta - \cos 2\theta} \qquad \left[\begin{array}{l}\text{linking the odd angles on top and bottom}\\ \text{(or even angles if given) and putting the}\\ \text{larger angle first in both cases}\end{array}\right]$$

$$= \frac{2 \sin\left(\dfrac{3\theta + \theta}{2}\right)\cos\left(\dfrac{3\theta - \theta}{2}\right) - \sin 2\theta}{2 \cos\left(\dfrac{3\theta + \theta}{2}\right)\cos\left(\dfrac{3\theta - \theta}{2}\right) - \cos 2\theta} \qquad \left[\begin{array}{l}\text{using}\\[4pt] \sin A + \sin B = 2 \sin\left(\dfrac{A+B}{2}\right)\cos\left(\dfrac{A-B}{2}\right)\\[4pt] \text{on the top and}\\[4pt] \cos A + \cos B = 2 \cos\left(\dfrac{A+B}{2}\right)\cos\left(\dfrac{A-B}{2}\right)\\[4pt] \text{on the bottom}\end{array}\right]$$

$$= \frac{2 \sin 2\theta \cos \theta - \sin 2\theta}{2 \cos 2\theta \cos \theta - \cos 2\theta}$$

$$= \frac{\sin 2\theta (2 \cos \theta - 1)}{\cos 2\theta (2 \cos \theta - 1)} \qquad \text{[factorising top and bottom]}$$

$$= \frac{\sin 2\theta}{\cos 2\theta} \qquad \text{[dividing top and bottom by } (2 \cos \theta - 1)]$$

$$= \tan 2\theta$$

(iii) $\dfrac{\cos 2\theta \cos \theta - \sin 4\theta \sin 3\theta}{\sin 8\theta \cos \theta - \sin 6\theta \cos 3\theta}$

$$= \frac{\frac{1}{2}(\cos 3\theta + \cos \theta) - \frac{1}{2}(\cos \theta - \cos 7\theta)}{\frac{1}{2}(\sin 9\theta + \sin 7\theta) - \frac{1}{2}(\sin 9\theta + \sin 3\theta)} \qquad \left[\begin{array}{l}\text{using:}\\[4pt] \cos A \cos B = \frac{1}{2}[\cos(A+B) + \cos(A-B)]\\[4pt] \sin A \sin B = \frac{1}{2}[\cos(A-B) - \cos(A+B)]\\[4pt] \sin A \cos B = \frac{1}{2}[\sin(A+B) + \sin(A-B)]\\[4pt] \cos A \sin B = \frac{1}{2}[\sin(A+B) - \sin(A-B)]\end{array}\right]$$

$$= \frac{\cos 3\theta + \cos \theta - \cos \theta + \cos 7\theta}{\sin 9\theta + \sin 7\theta - \sin 9\theta - \sin 3\theta}$$

$$= \frac{\cos 7\theta + \cos 3\theta}{\sin 7\theta - \sin 3\theta}$$

$$= \frac{2 \cos\left(\dfrac{7\theta + 3\theta}{2}\right)\cos\left(\dfrac{7\theta - 3\theta}{2}\right)}{2 \cos\left(\dfrac{7\theta + 3\theta}{2}\right)\sin\left(\dfrac{7\theta - 3\theta}{2}\right)}$$

$$\begin{bmatrix} \text{using:} \\[2pt] \cos A + \cos B = 2 \cos\left(\dfrac{A+B}{2}\right)\cos\left(\dfrac{A-B}{2}\right) \\[2pt] \text{on the top and} \\[2pt] \sin A - \sin B = 2 \cos\left(\dfrac{A+B}{2}\right)\sin\left(\dfrac{A-B}{2}\right) \\[2pt] \text{on the bottom} \end{bmatrix}$$

$$= \frac{2 \cos 5\theta \cos 2\theta}{2 \cos 5\theta \sin 2\theta} = \frac{\cos 2\theta}{\sin 2\theta} = \cot 2\theta$$

Example

(i) Prove $\sin(\theta + \frac{\pi}{4}) - \cos(\theta + \frac{\pi}{4}) = \sqrt{2} \sin \theta$.

(ii) Prove $\cos(\frac{\pi}{3} + \theta) + \sin(\frac{\pi}{6} + \theta) = \cos \theta$.

Solution:

In both questions the compounds angles formulae are used:

$$\sin(A + B) = \sin A \cos B + \cos A \sin B \text{ and } \cos(A + B) = \cos A \cos B - \sin A \sin B$$

(i) $\sin(\theta + \frac{\pi}{4}) - \cos(\theta + \frac{\pi}{4})$

$$= (\sin \theta \cos \tfrac{\pi}{4} + \cos \theta \sin \tfrac{\pi}{4}) - (\cos \theta \cos \tfrac{\pi}{4} - \sin \theta \sin \tfrac{\pi}{4})$$

$$= \sin \theta . \tfrac{1}{\sqrt{2}} + \cos \theta \, \tfrac{1}{\sqrt{2}} - \cos \theta \, \tfrac{1}{\sqrt{2}} + \sin \theta . \tfrac{1}{\sqrt{2}}$$

$$= 2(\sin \theta . \tfrac{1}{\sqrt{2}}) = \tfrac{2}{\sqrt{2}} \sin \theta = \sqrt{2} \sin \theta \qquad (\tfrac{2}{\sqrt{2}} = \tfrac{2}{\sqrt{2}} . \tfrac{\sqrt{2}}{\sqrt{2}} = \tfrac{2\sqrt{2}}{2} = \sqrt{2})$$

(ii) $\cos(\frac{\pi}{3} + \theta) + \sin(\frac{\pi}{6} + \theta)$

$$= \cos \tfrac{\pi}{3} \cos \theta - \sin \tfrac{\pi}{3} \sin \theta + \sin \tfrac{\pi}{6} \cos \theta + \cos \tfrac{\pi}{6} \sin \theta$$

$$= \tfrac{1}{2} \cos \theta - \tfrac{\sqrt{3}}{2} \sin \theta + \tfrac{1}{2} \cos \theta + \tfrac{\sqrt{3}}{2} \sin \theta$$

$$= 2 . \tfrac{1}{2} \cos \theta = \cos \theta$$

Example

Find the value k, if $\qquad k = \dfrac{\cos\left(\dfrac{\pi}{4} + \theta\right) - \cos\left(\dfrac{\pi}{4} - \theta\right)}{\sin\left(\dfrac{\pi}{4} + \theta\right) - \sin\left(\dfrac{\pi}{4} - \theta\right)} \qquad$ where $\sin \theta \neq 0$.

Solution:

$$k = \dfrac{\cos\left(\dfrac{\pi}{4} + \theta\right) - \cos\left(\dfrac{\pi}{4} - \theta\right)}{\sin\left(\dfrac{\pi}{4} + \theta\right) - \sin\left(\dfrac{\pi}{4} - \theta\right)}$$

$$= \dfrac{-2\sin\left(\dfrac{\frac{\pi}{4}+\theta+\frac{\pi}{4}-\theta}{2}\right)\sin\left(\dfrac{\frac{\pi}{4}+\theta-\frac{\pi}{4}+\theta}{2}\right)}{2\cos\left(\dfrac{\frac{\pi}{4}+\theta+\frac{\pi}{4}-\theta}{2}\right)\sin\left(\dfrac{\frac{\pi}{4}+\theta-\frac{\pi}{4}+\theta}{2}\right)} \quad \left[\begin{array}{l} \text{using} \\[4pt] \cos A - \cos B = -2\sin\left(\dfrac{A+B}{2}\right)\sin\left(\dfrac{A-B}{2}\right) \\[8pt] \sin A - \sin B = 2\cos\left(\dfrac{A+B}{2}\right)\sin\left(\dfrac{A-B}{2}\right) \end{array}\right]$$

$$= \dfrac{-2\sin\frac{\pi}{4}\sin\theta}{2\cos\frac{\pi}{4}\sin\theta} = -\dfrac{\sin\frac{\pi}{4}}{\cos\frac{\pi}{4}} = -\tan\frac{\pi}{4} = -1$$

Example

If $\sin \alpha = \dfrac{5}{13}$ and $\cos \beta = \dfrac{4}{5}$, $0 < \alpha < \dfrac{\pi}{2}$, $0 < \beta < \dfrac{\pi}{2}$,

express $\sin(\alpha + \beta)$ in the form $\dfrac{a}{b}$, $a, b \in N$.

Hence, or otherwise, show that $\cos(45° - \alpha - \beta) = \dfrac{89\sqrt{2}}{130}$.

Solution:

We represent each given angle with a right-angled triangle and use Pythagoras'
Theorem to find the third side and the other ratios.

Given: $\sin \alpha = \dfrac{5}{13}$

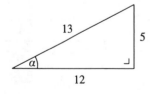

$\Rightarrow \quad \cos \alpha = \dfrac{12}{13}$

Given: $\cos \beta = \dfrac{4}{5}$

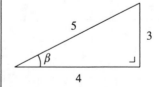

$\Rightarrow \quad \sin \beta = \dfrac{3}{5}$

$$\sin(\alpha + \beta) = \sin \alpha \cos \beta + \cos \alpha \sin \beta$$

$$= \frac{5}{13} \cdot \frac{4}{5} + \frac{12}{13} \cdot \frac{3}{5} = \frac{20}{65} + \frac{36}{65} = \frac{56}{65}$$

$$\cos(45° - \alpha - \beta) = \cos[45° - (\alpha + \beta)]$$

$$= \cos 45° \cos(\alpha + \beta) + \sin 45° \sin(\alpha + \beta)$$

$$= \cos 45°[\cos \alpha \cos \beta - \sin \alpha \sin \beta] + \sin 45° \sin(\alpha + \beta)$$

$$= \frac{1}{\sqrt{2}} \left[\frac{12}{13} \cdot \frac{4}{5} - \frac{5}{13} \cdot \frac{3}{5} \right] + \frac{1}{\sqrt{2}} \cdot \frac{56}{65}$$

$$= \frac{1}{\sqrt{2}} \cdot \frac{33}{65} + \frac{1}{\sqrt{2}} \cdot \frac{56}{65}$$

$$= \frac{33}{65\sqrt{2}} + \frac{56}{65\sqrt{2}}$$

$$= \frac{89}{65\sqrt{2}} = \frac{89}{65\sqrt{2}} \cdot \frac{\sqrt{2}}{\sqrt{2}} = \frac{89\sqrt{2}}{65(2)} = \frac{89\sqrt{2}}{130}$$

Example

(i) If $\cos A = \frac{5}{13}$ and $\sin B = 0.8$, where $0 \leqslant A \leqslant 90°$ and $0 \leqslant B \leqslant 90°$, express
(a) $\cos(A+B)$ and **(b)** $\tan 2A$ in the form $\frac{a}{b}$, a, $b \in N$.

(ii) If $\tan A = \frac{1}{3}$ and $\operatorname{cosec} B = \sqrt{5}$, express $\cos(A + B)$ in the form $\frac{p}{q}$, p, $q \in N$, where
$0 \leqslant A \leqslant 90°$ and $0 \leqslant B \leqslant 90°$, and, hence calculate the value of the angle $(A + B)$.

(iii) If $\sec A = \frac{17}{8}$ and $\operatorname{cosec} B = \frac{5}{4}$, express $\sec(A + B)$ in the form $\frac{m}{n}$, m, $n \in N$, where
$0 \leqslant A \leqslant 90°$ and $0 \leqslant B \leqslant 90°$.

(iv) If $\tan(A - B) = -2$ and $\cot B = 3$, evaluate $\tan A$ and $\tan^{-1} A$, $0 \leqslant A \leqslant \frac{\pi}{2}$,
$0 \leqslant B \leqslant \frac{\pi}{2}$.

Solution:

In each of these questions we represent each given angle with a right-angled triangle
and use Pythagoras' Theorem to find the third side and the other ratios, then apply the
compound or double-angle formulae.

(i)   Given: $\cos A = \frac{5}{13}$ Given: $\sin B = 0.8 = \frac{8}{10} = \frac{4}{5}$

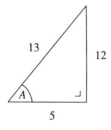 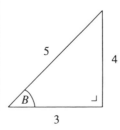

$\Rightarrow$ $\sin A = \frac{12}{13}$ and $\tan A = \frac{12}{5}$ $\Rightarrow$ $\cos B = \frac{3}{5}$

(a) $\cos(A + B) = \cos A \cos B - \sin A \sin B = \frac{5}{13} \cdot \frac{3}{5} - \frac{12}{13} \cdot \frac{4}{5} = \frac{15}{65} - \frac{48}{65} = -\frac{33}{65}$

(b) $\tan 2A = \dfrac{2 \tan A}{1 - \tan^2 A} = \dfrac{2(\frac{12}{5})}{1 - (\frac{12}{5})^2} = \dfrac{\frac{24}{5}}{1 - \frac{144}{25}} = \dfrac{120}{25 - 144} = -\dfrac{120}{119}$

(ii) Given: $\tan A = \frac{1}{3}$

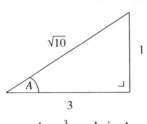

$\implies \cos A = \frac{3}{\sqrt{10}}$ and $\sin A = \frac{1}{\sqrt{10}}$

Given: $\operatorname{cosec} B = \sqrt{5} = \frac{\sqrt{5}}{1}$

$\implies \dfrac{1}{\sin B} = \dfrac{\sqrt{5}}{1} \implies \sin B = \dfrac{1}{\sqrt{5}}$

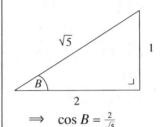

$\implies \cos B = \frac{2}{\sqrt{5}}$

$\cos(A + B) = \cos A \cos B - \sin A \sin B$

$\qquad = \frac{3}{\sqrt{10}} \cdot \frac{2}{\sqrt{5}} - \frac{1}{\sqrt{10}} \cdot \frac{1}{\sqrt{5}} = \frac{6}{\sqrt{50}} - \frac{1}{\sqrt{50}} = \frac{5}{\sqrt{50}} = \frac{5}{5\sqrt{2}} = \frac{1}{\sqrt{2}}$

Thus, $\cos(A + B) = \frac{1}{\sqrt{2}} \implies (A + B) = \cos^{-1} \frac{1}{\sqrt{2}} = 45°$ or $\frac{\pi}{4}$.

(iii) Given: $\sec A = \frac{17}{8}$

$\implies \dfrac{1}{\cos A} = \dfrac{17}{8} \implies \cos A = \dfrac{8}{17}$

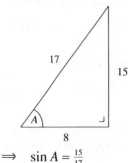

$\implies \sin A = \frac{15}{17}$

Given: $\operatorname{cosec} B = \frac{5}{4}$

$\implies \dfrac{1}{\sin B} = \dfrac{5}{4} \implies \sin B = \dfrac{4}{5}$

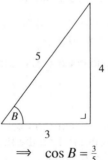

$\implies \cos B = \frac{3}{5}$

$\cos(A + B) = \cos A \cos B - \sin A \sin B = \frac{8}{17} \cdot \frac{3}{5} - \frac{15}{17} \cdot \frac{4}{5} = \frac{24}{85} - \frac{60}{85} = -\frac{36}{85}$

$\sec(A + B) = \dfrac{1}{\cos(A + B)} = -\dfrac{85}{36}$

(iv) Given: $\tan(A - B) = -2$

$\Rightarrow \quad \dfrac{\tan A - \tan B}{1 + \tan A \tan B} = -2$

$\Rightarrow \quad \dfrac{\tan A - \frac{1}{3}}{1 + \frac{1}{3}\tan A} = -2$

$\Rightarrow \quad \dfrac{3\tan A - 1}{3 + \tan A} = -2$

$\Rightarrow \quad 3\tan A - 1 = -6 - 2\tan A$

$\Rightarrow \quad 5\tan A = -5$

$\Rightarrow \quad \tan A = -1$

$\Rightarrow \quad A = \tan^{-1} -1 = 135°$ or $\frac{3\pi}{4}$

Given: $\cot B = 3 = \frac{3}{1}$

$\Rightarrow \quad \dfrac{1}{\tan B} = \dfrac{3}{1}$

$\Rightarrow \quad \tan B = \frac{1}{3}$

Example

(i) Express $\cos 75°$ and, hence, $\cos 255°$ in surd form.

(ii) Express **(a)** $\tan\left(-\dfrac{7\pi}{12}\right)$ and **(b)** $\sin 195°$ in surd form.

Solution:

First express each angle as a combination of $30°$, $45°$ or $60°$ and then use the compound angle formulae on page 9 of the tables.

(i)
$$\cos 75°$$
$$= \cos (45° + 30°)$$
$$= \cos 45° \cos 30° - \sin 45° \sin 30°$$
$$= \frac{1}{\sqrt{2}} \cdot \frac{\sqrt{3}}{2} - \frac{1}{\sqrt{2}} \cdot \frac{1}{2}$$
$$= \frac{\sqrt{3}}{2\sqrt{2}} - \frac{1}{2\sqrt{2}} = \frac{\sqrt{3}-1}{2\sqrt{2}}$$

$$\cos 255°$$
$$= -\cos 75°$$
$$= -\frac{\sqrt{3}-1}{2\sqrt{2}}$$
$$= \frac{1-\sqrt{3}}{2\sqrt{2}}$$

(ii) (a)
$$\tan\left(-\frac{7\pi}{12}\right) = \tan(-105°) = -\tan 105°$$
$$= -\tan(60° + 45°)$$
$$= -\frac{\tan 60° + \tan 45°}{1 - \tan 60° \tan 45°}$$
$$= -\frac{\sqrt{3}+1}{1 - \sqrt{3}(1)} = -\frac{\sqrt{3}+1}{1 - \sqrt{3}} = \frac{\sqrt{3}+1}{\sqrt{3}-1}$$

(b) $\sin 195° = -\sin 15°$

$= -\sin(45° - 30°)$

$= -(\sin 45° \cos 30° - \cos 45° \sin 30°)$

$= -\left(\dfrac{1}{\sqrt{2}} \cdot \dfrac{\sqrt{3}}{2} - \dfrac{1}{\sqrt{2}} \cdot \dfrac{1}{2} \right)$

$= -\left(\dfrac{\sqrt{3} - 1}{2\sqrt{2}} \right) = \dfrac{1 - \sqrt{3}}{2\sqrt{2}}$

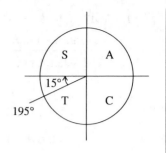

Example

(i) If $\tan A = \frac{2}{3}$, evaluate $\sin 2A$, giving your answer in the form $\frac{a}{b}$, $a, b \in N$.

(ii) If $\cos 2A = \frac{1}{49}$, find the two values of $\cos A$ without using tables or calculator.

(iii) If $\cos 2A = \frac{12}{13}$, find the two possible values of $\tan A$.

(iv) If $\sin 2A = \frac{7}{25}$, $0 \leqslant A \leqslant \frac{\pi}{2}$, find $\tan A$, $\sin A$ and $\cos A$, without using tables or calculator.

(v) If $\tan \frac{\theta}{2} = \frac{1}{5}$, $0 \leqslant \theta \leqslant \frac{\pi}{2}$, evaluate $\sin 2\theta$ without tables or calculator.

Solution:

(i) Method 1

Given: $\tan A = \frac{2}{3}$

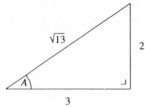

$\Rightarrow \quad \sin A = \dfrac{2}{\sqrt{13}}$ and $\cos A = \dfrac{3}{\sqrt{13}}$

$\sin 2A = 2 \sin A \cos A = 2 \cdot \dfrac{2}{\sqrt{13}} \cdot \dfrac{3}{\sqrt{13}} = \dfrac{12}{13}$

(i) Method 2

Given : $\tan A = \frac{2}{3}$

$\sin 2A = \dfrac{2 \tan A}{1 + \tan^2 A}$

$= \dfrac{2\left(\frac{2}{3}\right)}{1 + \left(\frac{2}{3}\right)^2}$

$= \dfrac{\frac{4}{3}}{1 + \frac{4}{9}} = \dfrac{12}{13}$

132

(ii) Given: $\cos 2A = \dfrac{1}{49}$

$\Rightarrow \quad 2\cos^2 A - 1 = \dfrac{1}{49}$

$\Rightarrow \quad 2\cos^2 A = \dfrac{1}{49} + 1$

$\Rightarrow \quad 2\cos^2 A = \dfrac{50}{49}$

$\Rightarrow \quad \cos^2 A = \dfrac{25}{49}$

$\Rightarrow \quad \cos A = \pm\dfrac{5}{7}$

(iv) Given: $\sin 2A = \dfrac{7}{25}$

$\Rightarrow \quad \dfrac{2\tan A}{1 + \tan^2 A} = \dfrac{7}{25}$

(let $\tan A = t$)

$\Rightarrow \quad \dfrac{2t}{1 + t^2} = \dfrac{7}{25}$

$\Rightarrow \quad 7 + 7t^2 = 50t$

$\Rightarrow \quad 7t^2 - 50t + 7 = 0$

$\Rightarrow \quad (7t - 1)(t - 7) = 0$

$\Rightarrow \quad 7t - 1 = 0 \text{ or } t - 7 = 0$

$\Rightarrow \quad t = \dfrac{1}{7} \text{ or } t = 7$

$\Rightarrow \quad \tan A = \dfrac{1}{7} \text{ or } \tan A = 7$

(iii) Given: $\cos 2A = \dfrac{12}{13}$

$\Rightarrow \quad \dfrac{1 - \tan^2 A}{1 + \tan^2 A} = \dfrac{12}{13}$

$\Rightarrow \quad 12 + 12\tan^2 A = 13 - 13\tan^2 A$

$\Rightarrow \quad 25\tan^2 A = 1$

$\Rightarrow \quad \tan^2 A = \dfrac{1}{25}$

$\Rightarrow \quad \tan A = \pm\dfrac{1}{5}$

1. $\tan A = \dfrac{1}{7}$

$\Rightarrow \quad \sin A = \dfrac{1}{\sqrt{50}}$

and $\cos A = \dfrac{7}{\sqrt{50}}$

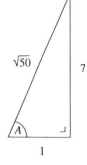

2. $\tan A = \dfrac{7}{1}$

$\Rightarrow \quad \sin A = \dfrac{7}{\sqrt{50}}$

and $\cos A = \dfrac{1}{\sqrt{50}}$

(v) Given: $\tan\dfrac{\theta}{2} = \dfrac{1}{5}, 0 \leqslant \theta \leqslant \dfrac{\pi}{2}$.

$\Rightarrow \quad \sin\dfrac{\theta}{2} = \dfrac{1}{\sqrt{26}}$

and $\cos\dfrac{\theta}{2} = \dfrac{5}{\sqrt{26}}$

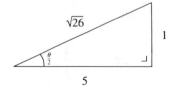

$\sin\theta = 2\sin\dfrac{\theta}{2}\cos\dfrac{\theta}{2}$

$= 2.\dfrac{1}{\sqrt{26}}.\dfrac{5}{\sqrt{26}} = \dfrac{10}{26} = \dfrac{5}{13}$

$\sin\theta = \dfrac{5}{13}$

$\Rightarrow \quad \cos\theta = \dfrac{12}{13}$

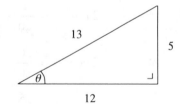

$\sin 2\theta = 2\sin\theta\cos\theta$

$= 2.\dfrac{5}{13}.\dfrac{12}{13} = \dfrac{120}{169}$

Example

If $A + B = \frac{\pi}{4}$, write $\tan A$ in terms of $\tan B$, and hence prove $(1 + \tan A)(1 + \tan B) = 2$.
Show that $\tan 22\frac{1}{2}° = \sqrt{2} - 1$.

Solution:

$A + B = \frac{\pi}{4}$ (given)

$\Rightarrow \qquad A = \frac{\pi}{4} - B$

$\Rightarrow \qquad \tan A = \tan\left(\frac{\pi}{4} - B\right)$

$\qquad = \dfrac{\tan\frac{\pi}{4} - \tan B}{1 + \tan\frac{\pi}{4}\tan B}$

$\Rightarrow \qquad \tan A = \dfrac{1 - \tan B}{1 + \tan B}$

(as $\tan\frac{\pi}{4} = 1$)

$(1 + \tan A)(1 + \tan B)$

$= \left(1 + \dfrac{1 - \tan B}{1 + \tan B}\right)(1 + \tan B)$

$= \left(\dfrac{1 + \tan B + 1 - \tan B}{1 + \tan B}\right)(1 + \tan B)$

$= \left(\dfrac{2}{1 + \tan B}\right)(1 + \tan B)$

$= 2$

$\Rightarrow \qquad (1 + \tan A)(1 + \tan B) = 2$

Let $A = B = 22\frac{1}{2}°$ (as $A + B = \frac{\pi}{4} = 45°$)

$(1 + \tan A)(1 + \tan B) = 2$ (from above)

$\Rightarrow \quad (1 + \tan 22\frac{1}{2}°)(1 + \tan 22\frac{1}{2}°) = 2$

$\Rightarrow \qquad\qquad (1 + \tan 22\frac{1}{2}°)^2 = 2$

$\Rightarrow \qquad\qquad 1 + \tan 22\frac{1}{2}° = \sqrt{2}$

$\Rightarrow \qquad\qquad \tan 22\frac{1}{2}° = \sqrt{2} - 1$

Example

(a) Evaluate **(i)** $\tan\left(\sin^{-1}\dfrac{3}{5}\right)$ **(ii)** $\sin\left(2\cos^{-1}\dfrac{8}{17}\right)$ **(iii)** $\tan\left(\sin^{-1}\dfrac{\sqrt{3}}{2}\right)$

   (iv) $\sin^{-1}\left(\dfrac{1}{2}\tan\dfrac{\pi}{4}\right)$ **(v)** $\sin^2\left(\tan^{-1}\dfrac{3}{5}\right)$ **(vi)** $\tan^2\left(\sin^{-1}\dfrac{15}{17}\right)$

(b) Use the formula for $\sin(A-B)$ to evaluate $\sin\left(\cos^{-1}\dfrac{8}{17}-\sin^{-1}\dfrac{12}{13}\right)$

(c) Prove that $\sin(\tan^{-1}x)=\dfrac{x}{\sqrt{1+x^2}}$

Solution:

(a) **(i)** $\tan\left(\sin^{-1}\dfrac{3}{5}\right)$

   let $\theta = \sin^{-1}\dfrac{3}{5}$

   $\Rightarrow \quad \sin\theta = \dfrac{3}{5}$

   Thus, $\tan\left(\sin^{-1}\dfrac{3}{5}\right)$

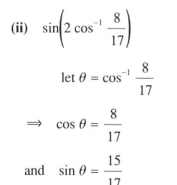

   $= \tan\theta = \dfrac{3}{4}$

(ii) $\sin\left(2\cos^{-1}\dfrac{8}{17}\right)$

   let $\theta = \cos^{-1}\dfrac{8}{17}$

   $\Rightarrow \quad \cos\theta = \dfrac{8}{17}$

   and $\quad \sin\theta = \dfrac{15}{17}$

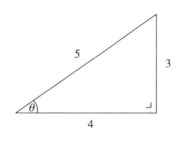

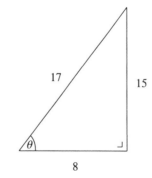

   Thus, $\sin\left(2\cos^{-1}\dfrac{8}{17}\right)$

   $= \sin 2\theta = 2\sin\theta\cos\theta = 2\cdot\dfrac{15}{17}\cdot\dfrac{8}{17} = \dfrac{240}{289}$

135

(iii) $\tan\left(\sin^{-1}\dfrac{\sqrt{3}}{2}\right)$ let $\theta = \sin^{-1}\dfrac{\sqrt{3}}{2}$

$= \tan\theta$ $\Rightarrow$ $\theta = \dfrac{\pi}{3}$

$= \tan\dfrac{\pi}{3}$

$= \sqrt{3}$

(iv) $\sin^{-1}\left(\dfrac{1}{2}\tan\dfrac{\pi}{4}\right)$

$= \sin^{-1}\left(\dfrac{1}{2}(1)\right)$ $\left(\tan\dfrac{\pi}{4} = 1\right)$

$= \sin^{-1}\dfrac{1}{2}$

$= \dfrac{\pi}{6}$

(v) $\sin^2\left(\tan^{-1}\dfrac{3}{4}\right)$

let $\theta = \tan^{-1}\dfrac{3}{4}$

$\Rightarrow$ $\tan\theta = \dfrac{3}{4}$

Thus, $\sin^2\left(\tan^{-1}\dfrac{3}{4}\right)$

$= \sin^2\theta$

$= \left(\dfrac{3}{5}\right)^2 = \dfrac{9}{25}$

(vi) $\tan^2\left(\sin^{-1}\dfrac{15}{17}\right)$

let $\theta = \sin^{-1}\dfrac{15}{17}$

$\Rightarrow$ $\sin\theta = \dfrac{15}{17}$

Thus, $\tan^2\left(\sin^{-1}\dfrac{15}{17}\right)$

$= \tan^2\theta$

$= \left(\dfrac{15}{8}\right)^2 = \dfrac{225}{64}$

(b) $\sin\left(\cos^{-1}\dfrac{8}{17} - \sin^{-1}\dfrac{12}{13}\right)$

let $A = \cos^{-1}\dfrac{8}{17}$

$\Rightarrow \quad \cos A = \dfrac{8}{17}$

$\Rightarrow \quad \sin A = \dfrac{15}{17}$

let $B = \sin^{-1}\dfrac{12}{13}$

$\Rightarrow \quad \sin B = \dfrac{12}{13}$

$\Rightarrow \quad \cos B = \dfrac{5}{13}$

Thus, $\sin\left(\cos^{-1}\dfrac{8}{17} - \sin^{-1}\dfrac{12}{13}\right)$

$= \sin(A - B) = \sin A \cos B - \cos A \sin B$

$= \dfrac{15}{17}\cdot\dfrac{5}{13} - \dfrac{8}{17}\cdot\dfrac{12}{13}$

$= \dfrac{75}{221} - \dfrac{96}{221} = -\dfrac{21}{221}$

(c) $\sin(\tan^{-1} x)$

$= \sin\theta$

$= \dfrac{x}{\sqrt{1+x^2}}$

let $\theta = \tan^{-1} x$

$\Rightarrow \quad \tan\theta = x$

$\Rightarrow \quad \tan\theta = \dfrac{x}{1}$

Example

(i) Solve $\cos\theta = -\dfrac{1}{\sqrt{2}}$, $\quad 0 < \theta < 2\pi$.

(ii) Solve $\sin\theta = \dfrac{\sqrt{3}}{2}$, $\quad 0 < \theta < 2\pi$.

Solution:

(i) $\cos\theta = -\dfrac{1}{\sqrt{2}}$

reference angle (ignore sign) = $45°$ or $\dfrac{\pi}{4}$

cos is negative in the 2nd and 3rd quadrants.

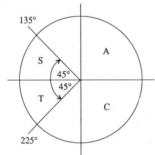

Thus, if $\cos\theta = -\dfrac{1}{\sqrt{2}}$, $\quad 0 < \theta < 2\pi$,

$\theta = 135°, 225°$ or $\theta = \dfrac{3\pi}{4}, \dfrac{5\pi}{4}$

(ii) $\sin\theta = \dfrac{\sqrt{3}}{2}$

reference angle = $60°$ or $\dfrac{\pi}{3}$

sin is positive in the 1st and 2nd quadrants.

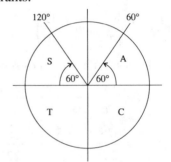

Thus, if $\sin\theta = \dfrac{\sqrt{3}}{2}$, $\quad 0 < \theta < 2\pi$,

$\theta = 60°, 120°$ or $\theta = \dfrac{\pi}{3}, \dfrac{2\pi}{3}$

Example

(i) Solve $\sin^2\theta = \tfrac{1}{2}$, $\quad 0 \leqslant \theta \leqslant 360°$.

(ii) Solve $\sin\left(x + \dfrac{\pi}{6}\right) = -\dfrac{\sqrt{3}}{2}$, $\quad 0 \leqslant x \leqslant 2\pi$.

(iii) Solve $2 = \cos x + 2\sin^2 x$, $\quad 0 \leqslant x \leqslant 360°$.

(iv) Solve $\tan^2 A + 3\sec A + 3 = 0$, $\quad 0 \leqslant A \leqslant 2\pi$.

(v) Solve $2\sin x = 5 - \dfrac{2}{\sin x}$, $\quad 0 \leqslant x \leqslant \pi$.

(vi) Solve $\cos 4x + \cos 2x = \cos x$, $\quad 0 \leqslant x \leqslant 360°$.

(vii) Solve $\dfrac{1}{\sqrt{3}} \sin x - \cos \dfrac{x}{2} = 0$, $\quad 0 \leqslant x \leqslant 2\pi$.

Solution:

(i) $\sin^2 \theta = \frac{1}{2}$, $\quad 0 \leqslant \theta \leqslant 360°$

$\Rightarrow \quad \sin \theta = \pm \dfrac{1}{\sqrt{2}}$, reference angle, $\theta = 45°$

$\Rightarrow \quad \theta = 45°, 135°, 225°, 315°$

or $\quad \theta = \dfrac{\pi}{4}, \dfrac{3\pi}{4}, \dfrac{5\pi}{4}, \dfrac{7\pi}{4}$

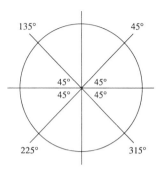

(ii) $\sin\left(x + \dfrac{\pi}{6}\right) = -\dfrac{\sqrt{3}}{2}$, $\quad 0 \leqslant x \leqslant 2\pi$

let $\left(x + \dfrac{\pi}{6}\right) = \theta$

$\Rightarrow \quad \sin \theta = -\dfrac{\sqrt{3}}{2}$

reference angle, $\theta = 60°$

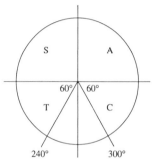

sin is negative in the 3rd and 4th quadrants, thus $\theta = 240°$ or $300°$

Thus, $x + \dfrac{\pi}{6} = 240°$ or $x + \dfrac{\pi}{6} = 300°$

$\Rightarrow \quad x + 30° = 240° \qquad x + 30° = 300°$

$\Rightarrow \qquad x = 210° \qquad\quad x = 270°$

or $\qquad x = \dfrac{7\pi}{6}$ or $\qquad x = \dfrac{3\pi}{2}$

(iii) $2 = \cos x + 2 \sin^2 x$, $\qquad 0 \leqslant x \leqslant 360°$

$\downarrow$

$2 = \cos x + 2(1 - \cos^2 x)$ $\qquad$ (replace $\sin^2 x$ with $1 - \cos^2 x$)

$2 = \cos x + 2 - 2 \cos^2 x$

$2 \cos^2 x - \cos x = 0$

$\cos x(2 \cos x - 1) = 0$

$\cos x = 0$ or $2 \cos x - 1 = 0$

$\cos x = 0$ or $\qquad \cos x = \frac{1}{2}$

$\Rightarrow x = 90°, 270°$ $\qquad$ reference angle, $x = 60°$

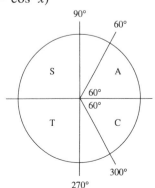

cos is positive in the 1st and 4th quadrants, thus $x = 60°$ or $300°$

$\Rightarrow \quad x = 60°, 90°, 270°, 300° \quad$ or $\quad x = \dfrac{\pi}{3}, \dfrac{\pi}{2}, \dfrac{3\pi}{2}, \dfrac{5\pi}{3}$

(iv) $\qquad \tan^2 A + 3 \sec A + 3 = 0, \qquad 0 \leq A \leq 2\pi.$

$\Rightarrow \quad \sec^2 A - 1 + 3 \sec A + 3 = 0 \qquad$ (replace $\tan^2 A$ with $\sec^2 A - 1$)

$\Rightarrow \qquad \sec^2 A + 3 \sec A + 2 = 0$

$\Rightarrow \qquad (\sec A + 2)(\sec A + 1) = 0$

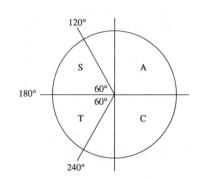

$\Rightarrow \quad \sec A + 2 = 0 \qquad$ or $\quad \sec A - 1 = 0$

$\Rightarrow \qquad \sec A = -2 \qquad$ or $\qquad \sec A = -1$

$\Rightarrow \qquad \dfrac{1}{\cos A} = -\dfrac{2}{1} \qquad$ or $\qquad \dfrac{1}{\cos A} = -1$

$\Rightarrow \qquad \cos A = -\dfrac{1}{2} \qquad$ or $\qquad \cos A = -1$

$\cos A = -\frac{1}{2}$, reference angle is $60°$. $\qquad \cos A = -1 \Rightarrow A = 180°$

cos is negative in the 2nd and 3rd quadrants. Thus, $A = 120°$ or $240°$

$\Rightarrow \quad A = 120°, 180°, 240° \quad$ or $\quad A = \dfrac{2\pi}{3}, \pi, \dfrac{4\pi}{3}$

(v) $\quad 2 \sin x = 5 - \dfrac{2}{\sin x}, \qquad 0 \leq x \leq \pi.$

$\Rightarrow \qquad\qquad 2 \sin^2 x = 5 \sin x - 2 \qquad$ (multiply across by $\sin x$)

$\Rightarrow \quad 2 \sin^2 x - 5 \sin x + 2 = 0$

$\Rightarrow \quad (2 \sin x - 1)(\sin x - 2) = 0$

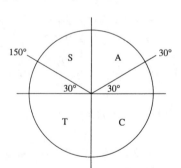

$\Rightarrow \quad 2 \sin x - 1 = 0 \quad$ or $\quad \sin x - 2 = 0$

$\Rightarrow \qquad \sin x = \frac{1}{2} \quad$ or $\qquad \sin x = 2$

$\sin x = \frac{1}{2}$, reference angle, $x = 30°$,

sin is positive in the 1st and 2nd quadrants.

Thus, $\theta = 30°$ or $150° \quad$ or $\quad x = \dfrac{\pi}{6} \quad$ or $\quad \dfrac{5\pi}{6}$

($\sin x = 2$ has no solutions, as $-1 \leq \sin \theta \leq 1$)

(vi) $\qquad\qquad \cos 4x + \cos 2x = \cos x, \qquad 0 \leqslant x \leqslant 360°.$

$\Rightarrow \quad 2 \cos\left(\dfrac{4x + 2x}{2}\right)\cos\left(\dfrac{4x - 2x}{2}\right) = \cos x \qquad \left[\text{use } \cos A + \cos B = \right.$

$$2 \cos\left(\dfrac{A + B}{2}\right)\cos\left(\dfrac{A - B}{2}\right) \text{ on LHS} \Big]$$

$\Rightarrow \qquad\qquad 2 \cos 3x \cos x = \cos x$

$\Rightarrow \qquad\qquad 2 \cos 3x \cos x - \cos x = 0$

$\Rightarrow \qquad\qquad \cos x(2 \cos 3x - 1) = 0 \qquad$ (factorise LHS)

$\Rightarrow \quad \cos x = 0 \quad \text{or} \quad 2 \cos 3x - 1 = 0$

$\Rightarrow \quad \cos x = 0 \quad \text{or} \qquad\qquad \cos 3x = \tfrac{1}{2}$

$\qquad\quad \cos x = 0 \qquad\qquad\qquad \cos 3x = \tfrac{1}{2}$

$\Rightarrow \quad x = 90°, 270° \qquad \text{reference angle } 3x = 60°$

$\qquad\qquad$ cos is positive in the 1st and 4th quadrants

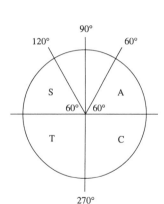

$\Rightarrow \quad 3x = 60°, 60° + 360°, 60° + 720°, 60° + 1080°, ...$

$\text{or} \quad 3x = 300°, 300° + 360°, 300° + 720°, 300° + 1080°, ...$

$\Rightarrow \quad 3x = 60°, 420°, 780°, 1140°, ... \quad \text{or} \quad 3x = 300°, 660°, 1020°, 1380°, ...$

$\Rightarrow \quad x = 20°, 140°, 260°, 380°, ... \quad \text{or} \quad x = 100°, 220°, 340°, 460°, ...$

But we are given $0 \leqslant x \leqslant 360°$

Thus, $x = 20°, 90°, 100°, 140°, 220°, 260°, 270°, 340°.$

(vi) $\qquad\qquad \dfrac{1}{\sqrt{3}} \sin x - \cos \dfrac{x}{2} = 0, \qquad 0 \leqslant x \leqslant 2\pi.$

$\Rightarrow \quad \dfrac{1}{\sqrt{3}} 2 \sin \dfrac{x}{2} \cos \dfrac{x}{2} - \cos \dfrac{x}{2} = 0 \qquad \left(\text{replace } \sin x \text{ with } 2 \sin \dfrac{x}{2} \cos \dfrac{x}{2}\right)$

$\Rightarrow \qquad \cos \dfrac{x}{2}\left[\dfrac{2}{\sqrt{3}} \sin \dfrac{x}{2} - 1\right] = 0 \qquad$ (factorise LHS)

$\Rightarrow \quad \cos \dfrac{x}{2} = 0 \quad \text{or} \quad \dfrac{2}{\sqrt{3}} \sin \dfrac{x}{2} - 1 = 0$

$\Rightarrow \quad \cos \dfrac{x}{2} = 0 \quad \text{or} \qquad \dfrac{2}{\sqrt{3}} \sin \dfrac{x}{2} = 1$

$\Rightarrow \quad \cos \dfrac{x}{2} = 0 \quad \text{or} \qquad \sin \dfrac{x}{2} = \dfrac{\sqrt{3}}{2}$

$\qquad\quad \cos \dfrac{x}{2} = 0 \qquad\qquad \sin \dfrac{x}{2} = \dfrac{\sqrt{3}}{2}$

$$\Rightarrow \quad \frac{x}{2} = 90°, 270°, 450°....$$

reference angle, $\frac{x}{2} = 60°$

$$\Rightarrow \quad x = 180°, 540°, 900°....$$

sin is positive in the 1st and 2nd quadrants

Thus, $\frac{x}{2} = 60°, 120°, 420°, 480°, ...$

$$\Rightarrow \quad x = 120°, 240°, 840°, 960°, ...$$

But we are given $\quad 0 \leqslant x \leqslant 2\pi$

Thus, $x = 120°, 180°, 240°$ or $x = \dfrac{2\pi}{3}, \pi, \dfrac{4\pi}{3}$

Example

$x = 0°$ and $x = 60°$ are two solutions of the equation $a \sin^2 2x + \cos 2x - b = 0$ where $a, b \, \varepsilon \, N$.

Find the value of a and the value of b.

Using these values of a and b, find all the solutions of the equation where $0° \leqslant x \leqslant 360°$.

Solution:

$$a \sin^2 2x + \cos 2x - b = 0$$

Let $x = 0°$

$$a \sin^2 2(0°) + \cos 2(0°) - b = 0$$
$$\Rightarrow \quad a \sin^2 0° + \cos 0° - b = 0$$
$$\Rightarrow \quad a(0) + 1 - b = 0$$
$$\Rightarrow \quad 1 - b = 0$$
$$\Rightarrow \quad b = 1$$

$$a \sin^2 2x + \cos 2x - b = 0$$

Let $x = 60°$

$$a \sin^2 2(60°) + \cos 2(60°) - b = 0$$
$$\Rightarrow \quad a \sin^2 120° + \cos 120° - b = 0$$
$$\Rightarrow \quad a\left(\frac{\sqrt{3}}{2}\right)^2 + (-\tfrac{1}{2}) - b = 0$$

$$\downarrow$$

$$\Rightarrow \quad \tfrac{3}{4}a - \tfrac{1}{2} - 1 = 0$$
$$\Rightarrow \quad 3a - 2 - 4 = 0$$
$$\Rightarrow \quad 3a = 6$$
$$\Rightarrow \quad a = 2$$

Solve $\qquad 2\sin^2 2x + \cos 2x - 1 = 0 \qquad\qquad$ [putting in $a = 2$, $b = 1$]

$\Rightarrow \quad 2(1 - \cos^2 2x) + \cos 2x - 1 = 0 \qquad$ [$\sin^2 2x = 1 - \cos^2 2x$]

$\Rightarrow \quad 2 - 2\cos^2 2x + \cos 2x - 1 = 0$

$\Rightarrow \quad 2\cos^2 2x - \cos 2x - 1 = 0$

$\Rightarrow \quad (2\cos 2x + 1)(\cos 2x - 1) = 0$

$\Rightarrow \qquad 2\cos 2x + 1 = 0 \ \text{ or } \ \cos 2x - 1 = 0$

$\Rightarrow \qquad\qquad \cos 2x = -\tfrac{1}{2} \ \text{ or } \ \cos 2x = 1$

reference angle, $2x = 60°$ $\qquad\qquad$ reference angle, $2x = 0$

cos is negative in the 2nd and 3rd quadrants

$\Rightarrow \quad 2x = 120°, 240°, 480°, 600°, 840°, \ldots \ \Big| \Rightarrow \quad 2x = 0°, 360°, 720°, 1080°, \ldots$

$\Rightarrow \quad x = 60°, 120°, 240°, 300°, 420°, \ldots \ \Big| \Rightarrow \quad x = 0°, 180°, 360°, 540°, \ldots$

But $0° \leqslant x \leqslant 360°$, thus $x = 0°, 60°, 120°, 180°, 240°, 300°, 360°$.

Example

Prove $\cos 3x = 4\cos^3 x - 3\cos x$, and hence solve $\cos 3x + 2\cos x = 0$, $0 \leqslant x \leqslant 180°$.

Solution:

$\cos(A + B) = \cos A \cos B - \sin A \sin B$

$\quad \cos 3x = \cos(2x + x)$

$\qquad\qquad = \cos 2x \cos x - \sin 2x \sin x \qquad$ (let $A = 2x$ and $B = x$)

$\qquad\qquad = (\cos^2 x - \sin^2 x)\cos x - 2\sin x \cos x \sin x$

$\qquad\qquad = \cos^3 x - \cos x \sin^2 x - 2\cos x \sin^2 x$

$\qquad\qquad = \cos^3 x - \cos x(1 - \cos^2 x) - 2\cos x(1 - \cos^2 x)$

$\qquad\qquad = \cos^3 x - \cos x + \cos^3 x - 2\cos x + 2\cos^3 x$

$\qquad\qquad = 4\cos^3 x - 3\cos x$

Solve: $\cos 3x + 2\cos x = 0 \qquad 0 \leqslant x \leqslant 180°$

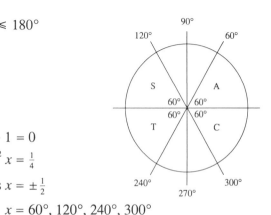

$\Rightarrow \quad (4\cos^3 x - 3\cos x) + 2\cos x = 0$

$\Rightarrow \qquad\qquad 4\cos^3 x - \cos x = 0$

$\Rightarrow \qquad\qquad \cos x(4\cos^2 x - 1) = 0$

$\Rightarrow \quad \cos x = 0 \qquad\quad \text{or} \quad 4\cos^2 x - 1 = 0$

$\Rightarrow \quad \cos x = 0 \qquad\quad \text{or} \qquad \cos^2 x = \tfrac{1}{4}$

$\Rightarrow \quad \cos x = 0 \qquad\quad \text{or} \qquad \cos x = \pm\tfrac{1}{2}$

$\Rightarrow \quad x = 90°, 270° \ \text{ or } \qquad\qquad x = 60°, 120°, 240°, 300°$

But $0 \leqslant x \leqslant 180°$, thus, $x = 60°, 90°$ and $120°$.

Example

Find   **(i)** $\displaystyle\lim_{x\to 0}\frac{\sin 3x + \sin 2x}{x}$ **(ii)** $\displaystyle\lim_{\theta\to 0}\frac{\sin 3\theta}{2\theta}$

     (iii) $\displaystyle\lim_{\theta\to 0}\frac{\sin 5\theta}{\sin 4\theta}$ **(iv)** $\displaystyle\lim_{\theta\to 0}\frac{3\theta}{\tan 2\theta}$

     (v) $\displaystyle\lim_{x\to 0}\frac{x\tan x}{\sin x^2}$ **(vi)** $\displaystyle\lim_{x\to 0}\frac{\cos 7x - \cos x}{x^2}$

Solution:

(i) $\displaystyle\lim_{x\to 0}\frac{\sin 3x + \sin 2x}{x}$

$\displaystyle = \lim_{x\to 0}\frac{\sin 3x}{x} + \lim_{x\to 0}\frac{\sin 2x}{x}$

$\displaystyle = \lim_{x\to 0}\frac{\sin 3x}{3x}\cdot 3 + \lim_{x\to 0}\frac{\sin 2x}{2x}\cdot 2$

$= (1)(3) + (1)(2) = 5$

(ii) $\displaystyle\lim_{\theta\to 0}\frac{\sin 3\theta}{2\theta}$

$\displaystyle = \lim_{\theta\to 0}\frac{\sin 3\theta}{\theta}\cdot\frac{1}{2}$

$\displaystyle = \lim_{\theta\to 0}\frac{\sin 3\theta}{3\theta}\cdot\frac{3}{2}$

$= (1)(\tfrac{3}{2}) = \tfrac{3}{2}$

(iii) $\displaystyle\lim_{\theta\to 0}\frac{\sin 5\theta}{\sin 4\theta}$

$\displaystyle = \lim_{\theta\to 0}\frac{\sin 5\theta}{1}\cdot\frac{1}{\sin 4\theta}$

$\displaystyle = \lim_{\theta\to 0}\frac{\sin 5\theta}{5\theta}\cdot\frac{4\theta}{\sin 4\theta}\cdot\frac{5}{4}$

$= (1)(1)(\tfrac{5}{4}) = \tfrac{5}{4}$

(iv) $\displaystyle\lim_{\theta\to 0}\frac{3\theta}{\tan 2\theta}$

$\displaystyle = \lim_{\theta\to 0}\frac{3\theta}{1}\cdot\frac{\cos 2\theta}{1}\cdot\frac{1}{\sin 2\theta}$

$\displaystyle = \lim_{\theta\to 0}\frac{3}{2}\cdot\frac{\cos 2\theta}{1}\cdot\frac{2\theta}{\sin 2\theta}$

$= (\tfrac{3}{2})(1)(1) = \tfrac{3}{2}$

(v) $\displaystyle\lim_{x\to 0}\frac{x\tan x}{\sin x^2}$

$\displaystyle = \lim_{x\to 0}\frac{x}{\sin x^2}\cdot\frac{\sin x}{1}\cdot\frac{1}{\cos x}$

$\displaystyle = \lim_{x\to 0}\frac{x^2}{\sin x^2}\cdot\frac{\sin x}{x}\cdot\frac{1}{\cos x}$

$= (1)(1)(1) = 1$

(vi) $\displaystyle\lim_{x\to 0}\frac{\cos 7x - \cos x}{x^2}$

$\displaystyle = \lim_{x\to 0}\frac{-2\sin 4x\sin 3x}{x^2}$

$\displaystyle = \lim_{x\to 0}-\frac{2}{1}\cdot\frac{\sin 4x}{x}\cdot\frac{\sin 3x}{x}$

$\displaystyle = \lim_{x\to 0}-\frac{2}{1}\cdot\frac{\sin 4x}{4x}\cdot\frac{\sin 3x}{3x}\cdot 4\cdot 3$

$= (-2)(1)(1)(4)(3) = -24$

Example

If $f(x) = \sin^{-1} x$, copy and complete the table below giving $\sin^{-1} x$ in terms of π.

x	-1	$-\dfrac{\sqrt{3}}{2}$	$-\dfrac{1}{2}$	0	$\dfrac{1}{2}$	$\dfrac{\sqrt{3}}{2}$	1
$\sin^{-1} x$		$-\dfrac{\pi}{3}$		0			

Draw the graph of this function in the domain $[-1, 1]$.

Solution:

Completed table (using page 9 of the tables):

x	-1	$-\dfrac{\sqrt{3}}{2}$	$-\dfrac{1}{2}$	0	$\dfrac{1}{2}$	$\dfrac{\sqrt{3}}{2}$	1
$\sin^{-1} x$	$-\dfrac{\pi}{2}$	$-\dfrac{\pi}{3}$	$-\dfrac{\pi}{6}$	0	$\dfrac{\pi}{6}$	$\dfrac{\pi}{3}$	$\dfrac{\pi}{2}$

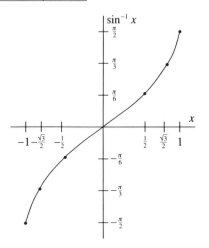

5. DISCRETE MATHEMATICS

Statistics

Weighted mean

$$\text{Weighted mean} = \bar{x}_w = \frac{\sum wx}{\sum w}$$

w is the weight attached to each value of x.

Mean and standard deviation

For an array of values:

$$\text{Mean} = \bar{x} = \frac{\sum x}{n}$$

$$\text{Standard deviation, } \sigma = \sqrt{\frac{\sum (x - \bar{x})^2}{n}} \text{ or } \sqrt{\frac{\sum d^2}{n}}$$

where n is the number of values of x and $d = |x - \bar{x}|$

For a frequency distribution:

$$\text{Mean} = \bar{x} = \frac{\sum fx}{\sum f}$$

$$\text{Standard deviation, } \sigma = \sqrt{\frac{\sum f(x - \bar{x})^2}{\sum f}} \text{ or } \sqrt{\frac{\sum fd^2}{\sum f}}$$

where f is the frequency of each value of x and $d = |x - \bar{x}|$

Notes:

Consider the set of values: $x_1, x_2, x_3, x_4, \ldots, x_n$.

The mean is $\bar{x}$ and the standard deviation is σ.

1. If to each value of x there is added a constant, say k, i.e.

   $$x_1 + k, x_2 + k, x_3 + k, x_4 + k, \ldots, x_n + k,$$

   then the mean is increased by k but the standard deviation remains the same.

   new mean $= \bar{x} + k$,   new standard deviation $= \sigma$ (unchanged).

2. If each value of x is multiplied by a constant, say k, i.e.

   $$kx_1, kx_2, kx_3, kx_4, \ldots, kx_n$$

   then both the mean and standard deviation are multiplied by k.

   new mean $= k\bar{x}$,   new standard deviation $= k\sigma$

Example

(i) In their Leaving Certificate, two students, A and B, obtained the following points:

Subject		Maths	Irish	English	Biology	French	Accounting
Points	A	100	40	20	60	80	40
	B	80	20	60	100	40	40

How many points had each student?

A university attached weights, 4, 3, 4, 2, 1, 1, respectively, to the six subjects as written above. If there was only one place left in the university, which student obtained the place?

(ii) A composite index number is constructed by taking the weighted mean.

The following table gives the index and weighting for each of four commodities:

Commodity	Food	Fuel	Mortgage	Clothing
Index	120	110	90	80
Weight	w	5	4	3

What weight, w, is attached to food if the composite index number is 105.5?

Solution:

(i) Number of points for $A = 100 + 40 + 20 + 60 + 80 + 40 = 340$
Number of points for $B = 80 + 20 + 60 + 100 + 40 + 40 = 340$

Thus both have the same number of points.

We now obtain the weighted mean marks for A and B and then compare them.

Weighted mean for A:

$$\bar{x}_w = \frac{\sum wx}{\sum w}$$

$$= \frac{4(100) + 3(40) + 4(20) + 2(60) + 1(80) + 1(40)}{4 + 3 + 4 + 2 + 1 + 1}$$

$$= \frac{400 + 120 + 80 + 120 + 80 + 40}{15} = \frac{840}{15} = 56$$

$\therefore$ A had a weighted mean mark of 56 points
(or a total of 840)

Weighted mean for B:

$$\bar{x}_w = \frac{\sum wx}{\sum w}$$

$$= \frac{4(80) + 3(20) + 4(60) + 2(100) + 1(40) + 1(40)}{4 + 3 + 4 + 2 + 1 + 1}$$

$$= \frac{320 + 60 + 240 + 200 + 40 + 40}{15} = \frac{900}{15} = 60$$

$\therefore$ B had a weighted mean make of 60 points
(or a total of 900)

Thus, B would get the university place.

(ii) Equation given in disguise: Weighted mean = 105.5

$$\therefore \qquad \frac{\sum wx}{\sum w} = \frac{211}{2}$$

$$\Rightarrow \qquad \frac{w(120) + 5(110) + 4(90) + 3(80)}{w + 5 + 4 + 3} = \frac{211}{2}$$

$$\Rightarrow \qquad \frac{120w + 550 + 360 + 240}{w + 12} = \frac{211}{2}$$

$$\Rightarrow \qquad \frac{120w + 1\,150}{w + 12} = \frac{211}{2}$$

$$\Rightarrow \qquad 240w + 2\,300 = 211w + 2\,532$$

$$\Rightarrow \qquad 240w - 211w = 2\,532 - 2\,300$$

$$\Rightarrow \qquad 29w = 232$$

$$\Rightarrow \qquad w = 8$$

Example

The weighted mean of the data below is € 0.90.

Item	A	B	C	D	E
Price in €	1.40	0.80	0.30	3.50	0.5
Weight	3	5	x	1	3

Find the value of x.

Solution:

Equation given in disguise: Weighted mean $= 0.9$

$$\therefore \quad \frac{3(1.40) + 5(0.80) + x(0.30) + 1(3.50) + 3(0.50)}{3 + 5 + x + 1 + 3} = \frac{9}{10}$$

$$\Rightarrow \quad \frac{4.2 + 4 + 0.3x + 3.5 + 1.5}{x + 12} = \frac{9}{10}$$

$$\Rightarrow \quad \frac{13.2 + 0.3x}{x + 12} = \frac{9}{10}$$

$$\Rightarrow \quad 132 + 3x = 9x + 108$$

$$\Rightarrow \quad -6x = -24$$

$$\Rightarrow \quad x = 4$$

Example

In an examination used to rank candidates in order of suitability to enter a certain course, each candidate sat a test in Irish, English, Maths, French and Science.

The marks awarded for a particular candidate with the assigned weights are given in the following table:

	Irish	English	Maths	French	Science
Mark	73	62	81	41	73
Weight	7	6	p	q	11

If the weighted mean mark for the candidate was 66.24 and $p:q = 1.4:1.2$, find the weights for Maths and French.

Solution:

$1.4 : 1.2 = 14 : 12 = 7 : 6$, thus let the weights p and q be $7x$ and $6x$ respectively.

Equation given in disguise: Weighted mean $= 66.24$

$$\therefore \quad \frac{\sum wx}{\sum w} = \frac{6\,624}{100}$$

$$\Rightarrow \quad \frac{7(73) + 6(62) + 7x(81) + 6x(41) + 11(73)}{7 + 6 + 7x + 6x + 11} = \frac{6\,624}{100}$$

$$\Rightarrow \quad \frac{511 + 372 + 567x + 246x + 803}{13x + 24} = \frac{6\,624}{100}$$

$$\Rightarrow \quad \frac{813x + 1\,686}{13x + 24} = \frac{6\,624}{100}$$

$$\Rightarrow \quad 81\,300x + 168\,600 = 86\,112x + 158\,976$$

$$\Rightarrow \quad 4\,812x = 9\,624$$

$$\Rightarrow \quad x = 2$$

$p = 7x = 7(2) = 14$ and $q = 6x = 6(2) = 12$.

Thus, the weighting for Maths is 14 and the weighting for French is 12.

Example

In the following frequency distribution the mean is 2.

Find a relationship between a and b.

x	1	2	3	4
f	a	6	b	2

In the following frequency distribution the mean is 3.5.

Find a relationship between a and b.

x	0	2	4	6	8
f	3	a	7	b	2

Hence, calculate the value of a and the value of b, if the values of a and b in the first frequency distribution are the same as the values of a and b in the second frequency distribution.

Solution:

x	1	2	3	4
f	a	6	b	2

$$\text{Given: Mean} = 2$$

$$\Rightarrow \quad \frac{a(1) + 6(2) + b(3) + 2(4)}{a + 6 + b + 2} = 2$$

$$\Rightarrow \quad \frac{a + 12 + 3b + 8}{a + b + 8} = 2$$

$$\Rightarrow \quad \frac{a + 3b + 20}{a + b + 8} = 2$$

$$\Rightarrow \quad a + 3b + 20 = 2a + 2b + 16$$

$$\Rightarrow \quad -a + b = -4$$

$$\Rightarrow \quad a - b = 4 \quad \text{①}$$

x	0	2	4	6	8
f	3	a	7	b	2

Given: Mean = 3·5

$$\Rightarrow \quad \frac{3(0) + a(2) + 7(4) + b(6) + 2(8)}{3 + a + 7 + b + 2} = \frac{7}{2}$$

$$\Rightarrow \quad \frac{0 + 2a + 28 + 6b + 16}{a + b + 12} = \frac{7}{2}$$

$$\Rightarrow \quad \frac{2a + 6b + 44}{a + b + 12} = \frac{7}{2}$$

$$\Rightarrow \quad 4a + 12b + 88 = 7a + 7b + 84$$

$$\Rightarrow \quad -3a + 5b = -4$$

$$\Rightarrow \quad 3a - 5b = 4 \quad ②$$

Solving the simultaneous equations ① and ② gives $a = 8$ and $b = 4$

Example

(a) Calculate **(i)** the mean and **(ii)** the standard deviation, correct to two decimal places, of the following array of numbers: 2, 5, 6, 8, 10, 11.

Hence, write down the standard deviation of the array of numbers 200, 500, 600, 800, 1000, 1100, correct to two decimal places.

(b) 20 pupils were given a problem to solve, The following grouped frequency distribution table gives the number of pupils who solved the problem in the given time interval.

Time (minutes)	0–4	4–12	12–24	24–40
Frequency	3	8	7	2

Assuming the data can be taken at the mid-interval values, calculate:

(i) the mean   **(ii)** the standard deviation, correct to 2 places of decimals.

Solution:

When an array or frequency table is given we usually draw a table to help us find the standard deviation.

(a) **(i)** Mean $= \bar{x} = \dfrac{\Sigma x}{n} = \dfrac{2 + 5 + 6 + 8 + 10 + 11}{6} = \dfrac{42}{6} = 7$

(ii) Make out a table:

x	d	d^2
2	5	25
5	2	4
6	1	1
8	1	1
10	3	9
11	4	16

$d = |x - \bar{x}|$

$n = 6$

$$\Sigma d^2 = 56$$

$$\sigma = \sqrt{\dfrac{\Sigma d^2}{n}} = \sqrt{\dfrac{56}{6}} = \sqrt{9.3333333} = 3.06$$

The numbers 200, 500, 600, 800, 1000 and 1100 are each 100 times the other numbers.

Thus, the standard deviation $= 100\sqrt{9.3333333} = 100(3.055050458) = 305.51$

(b) The table can be rewritten using mid-interval values.

Time (minutes)	2	8	18	32
Frequency	3	8	7	2

(i) Mean $= \bar{x} = \dfrac{\Sigma fx}{\Sigma f} = \dfrac{3(2) + 8(8) + 7(18) + 2(32)}{3 + 8 + 7 + 2}$

$$= \dfrac{6 + 64 + 126 + 64}{20} = \dfrac{260}{20} = 13$$

(ii) Make out a table:

f	x	d	d^2	fd^2
3	2	11	121	363
8	8	5	25	200
7	18	5	25	175
2	32	19	361	722

$d = |x - \bar{x}|$

$$\Sigma f = 20 \qquad\qquad \Sigma fd^2 = 1\,460$$

$$\sigma = \sqrt{\dfrac{\Sigma fd^2}{\Sigma f}} = \sqrt{\dfrac{1\,460}{20}} = \sqrt{73} = 8.54$$

Example

(i) In the following grouped frequency distribution table the estimated value of the mean is 8.

Calculate the value of m.

Number	0–2	2–6	6–12	12–20	20–30
Frequency	$m + 1$	4	2	m	1

(**Note:**   0–2 means 0 is included but 2 is not, etc.)

(ii) Show that the mean of the following distribution is independent of the value of x and find the mean:

Number	1	2	3	4	5	6
Frequency	9	9	x	4	7	3

If the standard deviation is $\sqrt{2.6}$, find the value of x.

Solution:

(i) As we are given a grouped frequency distribution we must use the mid-interval values.

Equation given in disguise: Estimated mean = 8

$$\therefore \qquad \frac{\sum fx}{\sum f} = 8$$

$$\Rightarrow \quad \frac{(m + 1)(1) + 4(4) + 2(9) + m(16) + 1(25)}{(m + 1) + 4 + 2 + m + 1} = 8$$

$$\Rightarrow \quad \frac{m + 1 + 16 + 18 + 16m + 25}{2m + 8} = 8$$

$$\Rightarrow \quad \frac{17m + 60}{2m + 8} = 8$$

$$\Rightarrow \quad 17m + 60 = 16m + 64$$

$$\Rightarrow \quad m = 4$$

(ii) $\displaystyle \bar{x} = \frac{\sum fx}{\sum f} = \frac{9(1) + 9(2) + x(3) + 4(4) + 7(5) + 3(6)}{9 + 9 + x + 4 + 7 + 3}$

$$= \frac{9 + 18 + 3x + 16 + 35 + 18}{x + 32}$$

$$= \frac{3x + 96}{x + 32} = \frac{3(x + 32)}{(x + 32)} = 3$$

Thus, the mean is 3 for any value of x, i.e. the mean is independent of x.

$$d = |x - \bar{x}|$$

f	x	d	d^2	fd^2
9	1	2	4	36
9	2	1	1	9
x	3	0	0	0
4	4	1	1	4
7	5	2	4	28
3	6	3	9	27

$$\Sigma f = (x + 32) \qquad\qquad \Sigma fd^2 = 104$$

Given: Standard deviation $= \sqrt{2.6}$

Thus, $\qquad \sqrt{\dfrac{\Sigma fd^2}{\Sigma f}} = \sqrt{2.6}$

$\Rightarrow \qquad \sqrt{\dfrac{104}{x + 32}} = \sqrt{2.6}$

$\Rightarrow \qquad \dfrac{104}{x + 32} = 2.6$

$\Rightarrow \qquad 2.6x + 83.2 = 104$

$\Rightarrow \qquad 2.6x = 20.8$

$\Rightarrow \qquad x = 8$

Example

Find $\sigma(x)$, the standard deviation of 0, x, 1.

Show that $\sigma(x) = \sigma(1 - x)$ for all $x \in \mathbf{R}$.

Show that in $0 \leqslant x \leqslant 1$, the minimum of $\sigma(x)$ is $\dfrac{1}{\sqrt{6}}$.

Solution:

0, x, 1

$$\bar{x} = \frac{0 + x + 1}{3} = \frac{x + 1}{3}$$

$$\sigma(x) = \sqrt{\frac{\Sigma(x - \bar{x})^2}{n}} = \sqrt{\frac{\left(0 - \dfrac{x+1}{3}\right)^2 + \left(x - \dfrac{x+1}{3}\right)^2 + \left(1 - \dfrac{x+1}{3}\right)^2}{3}}$$

$$= \sqrt{\frac{\left(\dfrac{-x-1}{3}\right)^2 + \left(\dfrac{2x-1}{3}\right)^2 + \left(\dfrac{2-x}{3}\right)^2}{3}}$$

$$= \sqrt{\frac{\frac{1}{9}[x^2 + 2x + 1 + 4x^2 - 4x + 1 + 4 - 4x + x^2]}{3}}$$

$$= \sqrt{\frac{\frac{1}{9}(6x^2 - 6x + 6)}{3}}$$

$$= \sqrt{\tfrac{1}{9}(2x^2 - 2x + 2)} = \sqrt{\tfrac{1}{9}} \sqrt{2x^2 - 2x + 2} = \tfrac{1}{3}\sqrt{2x^2 - 2x + 2}$$

Thus, $\sigma(1-x) = \frac{1}{3}\sqrt{2(1-x)^2 - 2(1-x) + 2}$ [replacing x with $(1-x)$]

$$= \frac{1}{3}\sqrt{2 - 4x + 2x^2 - 2 + 2x + 2}$$

$$= \frac{1}{3}\sqrt{2x^2 - 2x + 2} = \sigma(x)$$

Thus, $\sigma(x) = \sigma(1-x)$, for all $x \in \mathbf{R}$.

Let $y = \sigma(x)$

$\Rightarrow$ $y = \frac{1}{3}(2x^2 - 2x + 2)^{\frac{1}{2}}$ (using the chain rule)

$\Rightarrow$ $\dfrac{dy}{dx} = \frac{1}{2} \cdot \frac{1}{3}(2x^2 - 2x + 2)^{-\frac{1}{2}}(4x - 2) = 0$ (for a max or min)

$\Rightarrow$ $\dfrac{4x - 2}{6(2x^2 - 2x + 2)^{\frac{1}{2}}} = 0$

$\Rightarrow$ $4x - 2 = 0$ [fraction $= 0 \Rightarrow$ top $= 0$]

$\Rightarrow$ $4x = 2$

$\Rightarrow$ $x = \frac{1}{2}$

Thus, $\sigma(x)_{\min} = \sigma(\frac{1}{2}) = \frac{1}{3}\sqrt{2(\frac{1}{2})^2 - 2(\frac{1}{2}) + 2}$

$$= \frac{1}{3}\sqrt{\frac{3}{2}} = \sqrt{\frac{3}{9.2}} = \sqrt{\frac{1}{6}} = \frac{1}{\sqrt{6}}$$

Example

Given that $\bar{x}_1$ and σ_1 are the mean and standard deviation of the set $\{x_1, x_2, x_3, \ldots, x_n\}$, verify that the mean, $\bar{x}_2$ and the standard deviation, σ_2, from the set $\{4x_1 + 3, 4x_2 + 3, 4x_3 + 3, \ldots, 4x_n + 3\}$ are $4\bar{x}_1 + 3$ and $4\sigma_1$, respectively.

Solution:

$$\bar{x}_1 = \frac{x_1 + x_2 + x_3 + \cdots + x_n}{n}$$

$$\bar{x}_2 = \frac{(4x_1 + 3) + (4x_2 + 3) + (4x_3 + 3) + \cdots + (4x_n + 3)}{n}$$

$$= \frac{4(x_1 + x_2 + x_3 + \cdots + x_n) + n(3)}{n}$$

$$= \frac{4(x_1 + x_2 + x_3 + \cdots + x_n)}{n} + \frac{n(3)}{n}$$

$$= 4\bar{x}_1 + 3$$

$$\sigma_1 = \sqrt{\frac{(x_1 - \bar{x}_1)^2 + (x_2 - \bar{x}_1)^2 + (x_3 - \bar{x}_1)^2 + \cdots + (x_n - \bar{x}_1)^2}{n}}$$

$$\sigma_2 = \sqrt{\frac{(4x_1 + 3 - \bar{x}_2)^2 + (4x_2 + 3 - \bar{x}_2)^2 + (4x_3 + 3 - \bar{x}_2)^2 + \cdots + (4x_n + 3 - \bar{x}_2)^2}{n}}$$

$$= \sqrt{\frac{(4x_1 + 3 - 4\bar{x}_1 - 3)^2 + (4x_2 + 3 - 4\bar{x}_1 - 3)^2 + (4x_3 + 3 - 4\bar{x}_1 - 3)^2 + \cdots + (4x_n + 3 - 4\bar{x}_1 - 3)^2}{n}}$$

(replace $\bar{x}_2$ with $4\bar{x}_1 + 3$)

$$= \sqrt{\frac{(4x_1 - 4\bar{x}_1)^2 + (4x_2 - 4\bar{x}_1)^2 + (4x_3 - 4\bar{x}_1)^2 + \cdots + (4x_n - 4\bar{x}_1)^2}{n}}$$

$$= \sqrt{\frac{4^2[(x_1 - \bar{x}_1)^2 + (x_2 - \bar{x}_1)^2 + (x_3 - \bar{x}_1)^2 + \cdots + (x_n - \bar{x}_1)^2]}{n}}$$

$$= \sqrt{4^2}\,\sigma_1 = 4\sigma_1$$

Example

Prove that if $\bar{x}_1$ and σ_1 are the mean and standard deviation of the set $\{x_1, x_2, x_3, \ldots, x_r\}$ and $\bar{x}_2$ and σ_2 are the mean and standard deviation of the set $\{kx_1, kx_2, kx_3, \ldots, kx_r\}$, then:

(i) $\bar{x}_2 = k\bar{x}_1$ (ii) $\sigma_2 = k\sigma_1$

Solution:

(i) $\bar{x}_1 = \dfrac{x_1 + x_2 + x_3 + \cdots + x_r}{r}$

$\bar{x}_2 = \dfrac{kx_1 + kx_2 + kx_3 + \cdots + kx_r}{r}$

$= k\left(\dfrac{x_1 + x_2 + x_3 + \cdots + x_r}{r}\right)$

$= k\bar{x}_1$

(ii) $\sigma_1 = \sqrt{\dfrac{(x_1 - \bar{x}_1)^2 + (x_2 - \bar{x}_1)^2 + (x_3 - \bar{x}_1)^2 + \cdots + (x_n - \bar{x}_1)^2}{r}}$

$\sigma_2 = \sqrt{\dfrac{(kx_1 - \bar{x}_2)^2 + (kx_2 - \bar{x}_2)^2 + (kx_3 - \bar{x}_2)^2 + \cdots + (kx_r - \bar{x}_2)^2}{r}}$

$= \sqrt{\dfrac{(kx_1 - k\bar{x}_1)^2 + (kx_2 - k\bar{x}_1)^2 + (kx_3 - k\bar{x}_1)^2 + \cdots + (kx_r - k\bar{x}_1)^2}{r}}$

(replace $\bar{x}_2$ with $k\bar{x}_1$)

$= \sqrt{\dfrac{k^2[(x_1 - \bar{x}_1)^2 + (x_2 - \bar{x}_1)^2 + (x_3 - \bar{x}_1)^2 + \cdots + (x_r - \bar{x}_1)]^2}{r}}$

$= \sqrt{k^2}\,\sigma_1 = k\sigma_1$

Example

(a) Four numbers have a mean p.
Five numbers have a mean x.
These nine numbers have a mean q.
Express x in terms of p and q.

(b) Real numbers x_1, x_2 and x_3 are each greater than a and less than b as shown on the number line, $a, b > 0$.

$$a \quad x_1 \qquad x_2 \qquad x_3 \quad b$$

Prove that:

(i) $a < \bar{x} < b$ where $\bar{x}$ is the mean of x_1, x_2 and x_3.

(ii) $\sigma < b - a$ where σ is the standard deviation of x_1, x_2 and x_3.

Solution:

(a) The mean of the four numbers is p, $\therefore$ their sum $= 4p$

The mean of the five numbers is x, $\therefore$ their sum $= 5x$

$$\text{Mean of the nine numbers} = \frac{\text{sum of the four numbers} + \text{sum of the five numbers}}{9} = q$$

$$\Rightarrow \quad \frac{4p + 5x}{9} = q$$

$$\Rightarrow \quad 4p + 5x = 9q$$

$$\Rightarrow \quad 5x = 9q - 4p$$

$$\Rightarrow \quad x = \frac{9q - 4p}{5}$$

(b) **(i)** **Method 1**

$$a < x_1 < b \qquad ① \quad \text{given}$$
$$a < x_2 < b \qquad ② \quad \text{given}$$
$$a < x_3 < b \qquad ③ \quad \text{given}$$

$$\Rightarrow \quad 3a < x_1 + x_2 + x_3 < 3b \qquad \text{(add)}$$

$$\Rightarrow \quad a < \frac{x_1 + x_2 + x_3}{3} < b$$

$$\Rightarrow \quad a < \bar{x} < b$$

(i) Method 2

$$\bar{x} = \frac{x_1 + x_2 + x_3}{3} \qquad \bar{x} = \frac{x_1 + x_2 + x_3}{3}$$

$$> \frac{a + a + a}{3} \qquad < \frac{b + b + b}{3}$$

$$> \frac{3a}{3} \qquad < \frac{3b}{3}$$

$$> a \qquad < b$$

Thus, $a < \bar{x} < b$

(ii)

$$\sigma = \sqrt{\frac{(x_1 - \bar{x})^2 + (x_2 - \bar{x})^2 + (x_3 - \bar{x})^2}{3}}$$

$$< \sqrt{\frac{(b - a)^2 + (b - a)^2 + (b - a)^2}{3}}$$

$$< \sqrt{\frac{3(b - a)^2}{3}}$$

$$< \sqrt{(b - a)^2}$$

$$< b - a$$

Thus, $\sigma < b - a$

$$a < x_1 < b$$
$$\Rightarrow \quad a - a < x_1 - a < b - a$$
$$\Rightarrow \quad 0 < x_1 - a < b - a$$
$$\Rightarrow \quad x_1 - a < b - a$$
$$\Rightarrow \quad x_1 - \bar{x} < b - a \text{ (as } \bar{x} > a)$$

Thus, $(x_1 - \bar{x})^2 < (b - a)^2$

Similarly $(x_2 - \bar{x})^2 < (b - a)^2$

and $(x_3 - \bar{x})^2 < (b - a)^2$

Example

$\{x_1, x_2, x_3, x_4, \ldots, x_n\}$ is a set of numbers such that

$$x_1 < x_2 < x_3 < \ldots < x_n$$

Prove that $x_1 < \bar{x} < x_n$

Solution:

Method 1:

$$x_1 = x_1 < x_n$$
$$x_1 < x_2 < x_n$$
$$x_1 < x_3 < x_n$$
$$\vdots \quad \vdots \quad \vdots$$
$$x_1 < x_n = x_n$$

$$\overline{\phantom{x_1 < x_n = x_n}}$$

$$\Rightarrow \quad nx_1 < x_1 + x_2 + x_3 + \cdots + x_n < nx_n \text{ (add)}$$

$$\Rightarrow \quad x_1 < \frac{x_1 + x_2 + x_3 + \cdots + x_n}{n} < x_n$$

Thus, $x_1 < \bar{x} < x_n$

Method 2:

$$\bar{x} = \frac{x_1 + x_2 + x_3 + \cdots + x_n}{n}$$

$$> \frac{x_1 + x_1 + x_1 + \cdots + x_1}{n}$$

$$= \frac{nx_1}{n} = x_1 \quad (\text{i.e. } x_1 < \bar{x})$$

$$\bar{x} = \frac{x_1 + x_2 + x_3 + \cdots + x_n}{n}$$

$$< \frac{x_n + x_n + x_n + \cdots + x_n}{n}$$

$$= \frac{nx_n}{n} = x_n \quad (\text{i.e. } x_n > \bar{x})$$

Thus, $x_1 < \bar{x} < x_n$

Example

$\bar{x}$ and σ are the mean and the standard deviation of the set x_1, x_2, x_3.

Find the mean and the standard deviation of the set

$$\frac{x_1 - \bar{x}}{\sigma}, \qquad \frac{x_2 - \bar{x}}{\sigma}, \qquad \frac{x_3 - \bar{x}}{\sigma}$$

Solution:

Let the mean $= \mu$

$$\mu = \frac{\dfrac{x_1 - \bar{x}}{\sigma} + \dfrac{x_2 - \bar{x}}{\sigma} + \dfrac{x_3 - \bar{x}}{\sigma}}{3}$$

$$= \frac{1}{\sigma}\left(\frac{x_1 - \bar{x} + x_2 - \bar{x} + x_3 - \bar{x}}{3}\right)$$

$$= \frac{1}{\sigma}\left(\frac{x_1 + x_2 + x_3 - 3\bar{x}}{3}\right)$$

$$= \frac{1}{\sigma}\left(\frac{x_1 + x_2 + x_3}{3} - \frac{3\bar{x}}{3}\right)$$

$$= \frac{1}{\sigma}(\bar{x} - \bar{x})$$

$$= \frac{1}{\sigma}(0) = 0$$

$$\sigma = \sqrt{\frac{\sum (x - \bar{x})^2}{n}}$$

$$= \sqrt{\frac{\left(\dfrac{x_1 - \bar{x}}{\sigma} - \mu\right)^2 + \left(\dfrac{x_2 - \bar{x}}{\sigma} - \mu\right)^2 + \left(\dfrac{x_3 - \bar{x}}{\sigma} - \mu\right)^2}{3}}$$

$$= \sqrt{\frac{\left(\dfrac{x_1 - \bar{x}}{\sigma}\right)^2 + \left(\dfrac{x_2 - \bar{x}}{\sigma}\right)^2 + \left(\dfrac{x_3 - \bar{x}}{\sigma}\right)^2}{3}}$$

$(u = 0)$

$$= \sqrt{\frac{1}{\sigma^2} \cdot \frac{(x_1 - \bar{x})^2 + (x_2 - \bar{x})^2 + (x_3 - \bar{x})^2}{3}}$$

$$= \sqrt{\frac{1}{\sigma^2}} \sqrt{\frac{(x_1 - \bar{x})^2 + (x_2 - \bar{x})^2 + (x_3 - \bar{x})^2}{3}}$$

$$= \frac{1}{\sigma} \cdot \sigma$$

$$= 1$$

Permutations and Combinations

Permutations

A permutation is a selection of a number of items in a certain order.

A permutation is also called an **arrangement**.

An aid to solving problems is to represent each choice with an empty box at the beginning of the problem. Always start with the choice, or operation, in the arrangement whose choice from the given set is **most** restricted.

We make use of the fundamental principle of counting:

If a first operation has m different outcomes, and for each of these outcomes a second operation has n different outcomes, then operation 1 followed by operation 2 has $m \times n$ outcomes.

The principle can be extended to three or more operations.

In some quesions we also make use of the following fact:

$$\left(\begin{array}{c}\text{The number of arrangements in} \\ \text{which event } E \text{ does not occur}\end{array}\right) = \left(\begin{array}{c}\text{Total number} \\ \text{of arrangements}\end{array}\right) - \left(\begin{array}{c}\text{The number of arrangements} \\ \text{in which } E \text{ does occur}\end{array}\right)$$

Example

(i) How many different arrangements can be made of the letters of the word *C O M P A N Y*, using all the letters each time?

(ii) How many of these begin with the letter *C*?

(iii) How many begin with *C* and end with *Y*?

Solution:

Represent each choice with a box.

(i) We have 7 letters to fill into 7 spaces.

$$\boxed{7}.\boxed{6}.\boxed{5}.\boxed{4}.\boxed{3}.\boxed{2}.\boxed{1} = 7.6.5.4.3.2.1 = 5\,040$$

(ii) Begin with *C*.

Thus, the first place can only be filled in one way, with *C*.

C
$$\boxed{1}.\boxed{6}.\boxed{5}.\boxed{4}.\boxed{3}.\boxed{2}.\boxed{1} = 1.6.5.4.3.2.1 = 720$$

(iii) Begin with *C* and end with *Y*.

Thus, the first place can only be filled in one way, with *C*, and the last place can only be filled in one way, with *Y*.

C   *Y*
$$\boxed{1}.\boxed{5}.\boxed{4}.\boxed{3}.\boxed{2}.\boxed{1}.\boxed{1} = 1.5.4.3.2.1.1 = 120$$

Example

How many different arrangements can be made from the letters *V*, *W*, *X*, *Y*, *Z*, taking all the letters at a time, if *V* must be second and *Z* can never be last?

Solution:

Represent each choice with a box.

The second place can only be filled in one way, with *V*. The last place can only be filled in 3 ways (cannot use *V* or *Z*). These choices must be filled in first, then fill in the other places.

   V   no *Z*
$$\boxed{3}.\boxed{1}.\boxed{2}.\boxed{1}.\boxed{3} = 3.1.2.1.3 = 18$$

Example

A number-plate is to consist of three letters of the English alphabet followed by two digits. If no letter or digit can be repeated and 0 can never be used as the first digit, how many different plates can be manufactured?

| B | A | T | 4 | 5 |

(an example)

Solution:

Represent each choice with a box.

$$\boxed{26}.\boxed{25}.\boxed{24}.\overset{\text{no }0}{\boxed{9}}.\boxed{9} = 26 . 25 . 24 . 9 . 9 = 1\,263\,600$$

Example

A, B, C, D, E and F represent six students. In how many ways can they be seated in a row if:

(i)   there are no restrictions on the seating

(ii) A and B must sit beside each other

(iii) D, E and F must sit beside each other

(iv) A and F must sit at each end of the row

(v) A and B must not sit beside each other?

Solution:

(i)   No restrictions

$$\boxed{6}.\boxed{5}.\boxed{4}.\boxed{3}.\boxed{2}.\boxed{1} = 6! \qquad = 720 \text{ ways}$$

(ii) A and B beside each other.

Consider A and B as one unit.

$$\boxed{A, B},\boxed{C},\boxed{D},\boxed{E},\boxed{F}$$

The 5 objects can be arranged in 5! ways.

But A and B can sit as AB or BA, i.e. 2! ways, while seated together.

Thus, Answer = 2!5! = (2)(120) = 240 ways.

(iii) D, E and F beside each other.

Consider D, E and F as one unit.

$$\boxed{A},\boxed{B},\boxed{C},\boxed{D, E, F}$$

The 4 objects can be arranged in 4! ways.

But D, E and F can be arranged in 3! ways while seated together.

Thus, answer = 4!3! = (24)(6) = 144 ways.

(iv) *A* and *F* at the ends.

Put *A* and *F* at the ends.

$\boxed{A}$, $\boxed{B, C, D, E}$, $\boxed{F}$

If *A* and *F* sit at the ends, then *B*, *C*, *D* and *E* can be arranged in 4! ways while seated together.

But *A* and *F* can exchange places.

Thus, answer = 4!2! = (24)(2) = 48 ways.

(v) *A* and *B* must not sit beside each other.

$$\begin{pmatrix} \text{Number of arrangements with} \\ A \text{ and } B \text{ not together} \end{pmatrix} = \begin{pmatrix} \text{Total number} \\ \text{of arrangements} \end{pmatrix} - \begin{pmatrix} \text{Number of arrangements} \\ \text{with } A \text{ and } B \text{ together} \end{pmatrix}$$

$$= 720 - 240 = 480$$

Example

In how many ways can all of the letters of the word *M A R K E T I N G* be arranged?

In how many of these arrangements are:

(i) the 3 vowels together   **(ii)** all 3 vowels not together?

Solution:

All 9 letters can be arranged in 9! ways = 362 880 ways.

(i)   the 3 vowels are together.

Consider the 3 vowels, *A*, *E*, *I* as one unit.

$\boxed{A, E, I}$, $\boxed{M}$, $\boxed{R}$, $\boxed{K}$, $\boxed{T}$, $\boxed{N}$, $\boxed{G}$

The 7 objects can be arranged in 7! ways.

But *A*, *E* and *I* can be arranged in 3! ways when together.

Thus, answer = 3!7! = (6)(5 040) = 30 240

(ii)

$$\begin{pmatrix} \text{Number of arrangements with} \\ \text{the 3 vowels not together} \end{pmatrix} = \begin{pmatrix} \text{Total number} \\ \text{of arrangements} \end{pmatrix} - \begin{pmatrix} \text{Number of arrangements with} \\ \text{the 3 vowels together} \end{pmatrix}$$

$$= 362 880 - 30 240$$

$$= 332 640 \text{ ways}$$

Example

On a shelf there are 5 different Maths books, 4 different Irish books and 3 different English books. In how many ways can the books be arranged on the shelf?

In how many of these arrangements are:

(i) the books in each particular subject standing together

(ii) the Maths books together?

Solution:

All 12 books can be arranged in 12! ways = 479 001 600 ways.

(i) Consider each subject as a separate unit.

$$\boxed{\text{Maths}} , \boxed{\text{Irish}} , \boxed{\text{English}}$$

These can be arranged in 3! ways.

But the Maths books can be arranged in 5! ways when standing together, and the Irish books can be arranged in 4! ways when standing together, and the English books can be arranged in 3! ways when standing together.

Thus, answer = 3!5!4!3! = 103 680 ways.

(ii) Only the Maths books together.

Consider the 5 Maths books as one unit.

$$\boxed{\text{5 Maths books}} , \boxed{\text{7 Other books}}$$

The 8 objects can be arranged in 8! ways.

But the five Maths books can be arranged in 5! ways when standing together.

Thus, answer = 5!8! = (120)(40 320) = 4 838 400

Example

How many different four-digit numbers greater than 6 000 can be formed using the digits 1, 2, 4, 5, 6, 7 if (a) no digit can be repeated, (b) repetitions are allowed?

Solution:

Represent each choice with a box. The number must be greater than 6 000, thus, the first place can be filled in only 2 ways (with 6 or 7). Fill this in first, then fill the other places. Only use 4 boxes as our choice is restricted to 4 digits at a time.

(i) No digit can be repeated

$$\boxed{2} . \boxed{5} . \boxed{4} . \boxed{3} = 120$$

(ii) Repetitions are allowed

$$\boxed{2} . \boxed{6} . \boxed{6} . \boxed{6} = 432$$

Example

How many different five-digit numbers can be formed from the digits, 1, 2, 3, 4 and 5 if:

(i) there are no restrictions on digits and repetitions are allowed

(ii) the number is odd and no repetitions are allowed

(iii) the number is even and repetitions are allowed

(iv) the number is greater than 50 000 and no repetitions are allowed?

Solution:

Represent each choice with a box.

(i) no restrictions and repetitions allowed

$$\boxed{5}.\boxed{5}.\boxed{5}.\boxed{5}.\boxed{5} = 3\,125$$

(ii) must be odd and no repetitions

Thus, the last place can be filled in only 3 ways (1, 3 or 5). Fill this in first, then fill in the other places.

$$\boxed{4}.\boxed{3}.\boxed{2}.\boxed{1}.\boxed{3} = 72$$

(iii) must be even and repetitions allowed

Thus, the last place can be filled in only 2 ways (2 or 4). Fill this in first, then fill in the other places.

$$\boxed{5}.\boxed{5}.\boxed{5}.\boxed{5}.\boxed{2} = 1\,250$$

(iv) must be greater than 50 000 and no repetitions

Thus, the first place can be filled in only 1 way (with 5). Fill this in first, then fill in the other places.

$$\boxed{1}.\boxed{4}.\boxed{3}.\boxed{2}.\boxed{1} = 24$$

Example

How many 5-digit numbers can be formed in which the first and last digits are greater than 5, the three centre digits are identical and the last digit is odd?

Solution:

0, 1, 2, 3, 4, 5, 6, 7, 8, 9.

There are 4 digits greater than 5, these are 6, 7, 8, and 9.

Thus, the first place can be filled in 4 ways.

Of these 4 digits, two are odd, these are 7 and 9.

Thus, the last place can be filled in 2 ways.

The three centre digits must be identical, i.e.

$$\boxed{0 \mid 0 \mid 0} \text{ or } \boxed{1 \mid 1 \mid 1} \text{ or } \boxed{2 \mid 2 \mid 2} \text{ or } .... \text{ or } \boxed{9 \mid 9 \mid 9}$$

6 or 7 or 8 or 9	0 1 2 : 9	0 1 2 : 9	0 1 2 : 9	7 or 9
4	←	10	→	2

Thus, the three centre digits can be filled in 10 ways.

Thus, answer $= 4 \times 10 \times 2 = 80$

165

Combinations

A combination is a selection where the order makes no difference.

$\binom{n}{r}$ gives the number of ways of choosing r items from n different items.

Thus, n = the number of items we have to choose from.

$\qquad r$ = the number of items we choose.

In short: $\qquad \binom{n}{r} = \binom{\text{Have}}{\text{Choose}}$

Before attempting a problem on combinations it is good practice to write down the values of n (number we have to choose from) and r (the number we choose).

Key words: | And = Multiply | | Or = Add |

Example

Ten distinct points are taken on the circumference of a circle (as shown).

(a) **(i)** Calculate the number of different chords that can be formed using these points as end points.

(ii) How many different triangles can be formed using these points as vertices?

(b) **(i)** Calculate the number of different quadrilaterals that can be formed using these points as vertices.

(ii) Two of the ten points are labelled x and y respectively. How many of the above quadrilaterals have x and y as vertices?

(iii) How many of the quadrilaterals do not have x and y as vertices?

Solution:

(a) **(i)** Number of chords.

We have 10 points.
Each chord uses 2 points.
Thus, $n = 10, r = 2$

$$\binom{10}{2} = \frac{10.9}{2.1} = \frac{90}{2} = 45$$

∴ number of chords is 45

(ii) Number of triangles.

We have 10 points.
Each triangle uses 3 points.
Thus, $n = 10, r = 3$

$$\binom{10}{3} = \frac{10.9.8}{3.2.1} = \frac{720}{6} = 120$$

∴ number of triangles is 120

166

(b) (i) Number of quadrilaterals.

We have 10 points.
Each quadrilateral uses 4 points.
Thus, $n = 10$, $r = 4$

$$\binom{10}{4} = \frac{10 \cdot 9 \cdot 8 \cdot 7}{4 \cdot 3 \cdot 2 \cdot 1} = 210$$

∴ number of quadrilaterals = 210

(ii) Number of quadrilaterals with x and y as vertices.

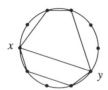

We have 10 points.
Each quadrilateral uses 4 points.
But two of these, x and y, are fixed.
Thus, we have 8 points from which we can choose 2, i.e. $n = 8$, $r = 2$

$$\binom{8}{2} = \frac{8 \cdot 7}{2 \cdot 1} = 28$$

∴ number of quadrilaterals with x and y as vertices = 28

(iii)

$$\begin{pmatrix} \text{Number of quadrilaterals} \\ \text{without } [xy] \text{ as vertices} \end{pmatrix} = \begin{pmatrix} \text{Total number of} \\ \text{quadrilaterals} \end{pmatrix} - \begin{pmatrix} \text{Number of quadrilaterals} \\ \text{with } [xy] \text{ as vertices} \end{pmatrix}$$

$$= 210 - 28 = 182$$

Example

In how many ways can a selection of 5 books be made from 12?

(a) If a certain book must always be chosen, in how many ways can the selection be made?

(ii) If a certain book must never be chosen, in how many ways can the selection be made?

Solution:

We **have** 12 books, of which we want to **choose** 5.

Thus, $n = 12$, $r = 5$.

$$\binom{12}{5} = \frac{12.11.10.9.8}{5.4.3.2.1} = \frac{95\,040}{120} = 792$$

(a) A certain book must always be one of the five.

$\therefore$ we **have** 11 books, of which we want to **choose** 4   (already chosen one).

Thus, $n = 11$, $r = 4$

$$\binom{11}{4} = \frac{11.10.9.8}{4.3.2.1} = \frac{7\,920}{24} = 330$$

(b) A certain book must never be one of the five.

$\therefore$ We **have** 11 books, of which we want to **choose** 5.

Thus $n = 11$, $r = 5$

$$\binom{11}{5} = \frac{11.10.9.8.7}{5.4.3.2.1} = \frac{55\,440}{120} = 462$$

Example

In how many ways can a group of five be selected from ten people?

How many groups can be selected if two particular people from the ten cannot be in the same group?

Solution:

We have ten from which we want to choose 5. Thus, $n = 10$, $r = 5$.

$$\binom{10}{5} = \frac{10.9.8.7.6}{5.4.3.2.1} = 252$$

In order to calculate how many groups of 5 can be selected if two particular people cannot be included, we first need to calculate the number of ways of selecting 5 people with these particular two people always included, i.e. we have 8 from which we choose 3 (because two are already selected). Thus $n = 8$, $r = 3$.

$$\binom{8}{3} = \frac{8.7.6}{3.2.1} = 56$$

$$\begin{pmatrix} \text{The number of ways of selecting} \\ \text{a group of 5 people from 10} \\ \text{when two particular people are} \\ \text{not to be in the same group} \end{pmatrix} = \begin{pmatrix} \text{Total number} \\ \text{of ways of} \\ \text{selecting a group} \\ \text{of 5 from 10} \end{pmatrix} - \begin{pmatrix} \text{The number of ways of} \\ \text{selecting a group of 5} \\ \text{people from 10 with} \\ \text{these two particular people} \end{pmatrix}$$

$$= 252 - 56$$
$$= 196$$

Example

How many bundles of 5 different books can be made from 8 Maths books and 6 Physics books, if the number of Maths books must always be greater than the number of Physics books?

Solution:

The possibilities are:

5 Maths and 0 Physics books $= \binom{8}{5} \times \binom{6}{0} = (56)(1) = 56$

or

4 Maths and 1 Physics books $= \binom{8}{4} \times \binom{6}{1} = (70)(6) = 420$

or

3 Maths and 2 Physics books $= \binom{8}{3} \times \binom{6}{2} = (56)(15) = 840$

Thus, answer $= 56 + 420 + 840 = 1\,316$

Example

(a) Find the number of ways a committee of 5 men and 5 women can be chosen from 8 men and 7 women.

(b) A committee of 6 persons is to be chosen from 5 men and 6 women.

In how many ways can this be done if:

(i) there are 4 men on each committee

(ii) there is a majority of women on each committee?

Solution:

(a) Must have 5 men and 5 women.

The number of ways to choose 5 men from 8 $= \binom{8}{5} = 56$

The number of ways to choose 5 women from 7 $= \binom{7}{5} = 21$

(and, $\therefore$ we multiply, using the fundamental principle of counting)

Thus, answer $= (56)(21) = 1\,176$ ways

(b) (i) Must have 4 men on each committee. We have 5 men and 6 women.

Thus, we must also have 2 women.

4 men and 2 women $= \binom{5}{4} \times \binom{6}{2} = (5)(15) = 75$ ways

(and, $\therefore$ we multiply, using the fundamental principle of counting)

(ii) Majority of women on each committee

The possibilities are:

6 women and 0 men $= \binom{6}{6} \times \binom{5}{0} = (1)(1) = 1$

or

5 women and 1 man $= \binom{6}{5} \times \binom{5}{1} = (6)(5) = 30$

or

4 women and 2 men $= \binom{6}{4} \times \binom{5}{2} = (15)(10) = 150$

Thus, the number of committees with a majority of women $= 1 + 30 + 150 = 181$

Example

An examination has two sections, Section A containing 5 questions and Section B also containing 5 questions. A student must answer exactly 7 questions. Given that the student must answer at least 3 questions from Section A, find the number of ways in which the student may select the 7 questions.

Solution:

Section A, 5 questions. Section B, 5 questions

The student must answer at least 3 questions from Section A, and questions from Section B to make a total of 7.

Possibilities	Number of ways
5 from A and 2 from B	$\binom{5}{5} \times \binom{5}{2} = (1)(10) = 10$
4 from A and 3 from B	$\binom{5}{4} \times \binom{5}{3} = (5)(10) = 50$
3 from A and 4 from B	$\binom{5}{3} \times \binom{5}{4} = (10)(5) = 50$

Thus, the student may select the 7 questions in $10 + 50 + 50 = 110$ ways.

Probability

Laws of Probability

1.	$P(E) = \dfrac{\text{no. of desirable outcomes}}{\text{no. of possible outcomes}}$
2.	$0 \leqslant P(E) \leqslant 1$ i.e. answer must be between 0 and 1.
3.	$P(A \text{ and } B) = P(A) . P(B)$ (Key word: And $\Rightarrow$ Multiply)
4.	$P(A \text{ or } B) = P(A) + P(B) - P(A \text{ and } B)$ (Key word: Or $\Rightarrow$ Add)
5.	$P(E) + P(\text{not } E) = 1$ Very useful in the 'at least one' type of problem $P(\text{at least once}) = 1 - P(\text{does not happen at all})$

Example

A letter is selected at random from the letters of the word $M\,I\,S\,S\,I\,S\,S\,I\,P\,P\,I$.

Find the probability that the letter is:

(i) M **(ii)** S or P **(iii)** a vowel

Solution:

There are 11 letters in the word $M\,I\,S\,S\,I\,S\,S\,I\,P\,P\,I$.

(i) There is just one M

$\therefore P(M) = \frac{1}{11}$

(ii) There are 4 Ss and 2 Ps (6 altogether)

$\therefore P(S \text{ or } P) = \frac{6}{11}$

(iii) There is one vowel, I. However, I occurs 4 times.

$\therefore P(\text{vowel}) = P(I) = \frac{4}{11}$

Example

There are 40 people in a club, 24 male, 16 female.

Four of the males and two of the females wear glasses.

When a person is selected at random what is the probability that the person:

(i) is a male?

(ii) is a female not wearing glasses?

(iii) is a female wearing glasses or a male not wearing glasses?

(iv) is a male, given that the person wears glasses?

(v) does not wear glasses, given that the person is a female?

Solution:

Represent the information in a table:

	Male	Female	Total
Glasses	4	2	6
No Glasses	20	14	34
Total	24	16	40

(i) There are 24 males

$\therefore P(\text{male}) = \frac{24}{40} = \frac{3}{5}$

(ii) There are 14 females not wearing glasses.

$\therefore P(\text{female not wearing glasses}) = \frac{14}{40} = \frac{7}{20}$

(iii) There are 2 females wearing glasses and 20 males not wearing glasses.

∴ P(female wearing glasses or a male not wearing glasses) $= \frac{22}{40} = \frac{11}{20}$

(iv) We are told that the person chosen wears glasses and is male.

6 persons wear glasses, 4 males wear glasses.

∴ P(male, given that the person wear glasses)

$$= \frac{\text{number of males wearing glasses}}{\text{number of persons wearing glasses}} = \frac{4}{6} = \frac{2}{3}$$

(v) We are told that the person chosen is a female and does not wear glasses.

There are 16 females and of these 14 do not wear glasses.

∴ P(does not wear glasses given that the person is female)

$$= \frac{\text{number of females that do not wear glasses}}{\text{total number of females}} = \frac{14}{16} = \frac{7}{8}$$

Example

In a school 64% of the students are girls.

Physics is studied by 75% of the boys and 50% of the girls.

Biology is studied by $33\frac{1}{3}\%$ of the boys and $87\frac{1}{2}\%$ of the girls.

When a student is selected at random what is the probability that the student:

(i) studies Physics? **(ii)** studies Biology?

(iii) is a girl, given that the student studies Biology?

(iv) is a boy, given that the student studies Physics?

Solution:

Suppose that there are 100 students in the school.

Then, there are 64 girls and 36 boys. The information is in the table below.

	Girls	Boys	Total
Physics	32	27	59
Biology	56	12	68

50% of 64 = 32 and 75% of 36 = 27

$87\frac{1}{2}\%$ of 64 = 56 and $33\frac{1}{3}\%$ of 36 = 12

(i) P(student studies Physics) = $\dfrac{\text{number of students studying Physics}}{\text{total number of students}} = \dfrac{59}{100}$

(ii) P(student studies Biology) = $\dfrac{\text{number of students studing Biology}}{\text{total number of students}} = \dfrac{68}{100} = \dfrac{17}{25}$

(iii) P(student is a girl, given that the student studies Biology)

$= \dfrac{\text{number of girls studying Biology}}{\text{total number of students studying Biology}} = \dfrac{56}{68} = \dfrac{14}{17}$

(iv) P(student is a boy, given that the student studies Physics)

$= \dfrac{\text{number of boys studying Physics}}{\text{total number of students studying Physics}} = \dfrac{27}{59}$

Example

Two dice are thrown. What is the probability of getting two equal scores or a total of 10?

Solution:

Two-way table

36 possible outcomes (6×6)

The dots indicate where the two scores are equal and/or they add up to 10.

There are 8 dots.

$\therefore$ P(two equal scores or a total of 10) $= \frac{8}{36} = \frac{2}{9}$

Example

Two dice are thrown. Calculate the probability that the sum of the outcomes is even when the 5 on one die and the 2 on the other die are excluded when forming an even sum.

Solution:

In this type of problem it is a good idea to imagine one die is red and the other is black or similar.

Construct a two-way table:

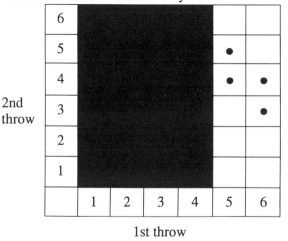

Black die

Red die

The shaded regions indicate where the 5 on the red die and the 2 on the black die are excluded when forming a sum.

There are 36 possibilities which must include the shaded regions as shown.

The dots indicate when the sum of the scores is even.

$$P(\text{even score}) = \frac{12}{36} = \frac{1}{3}$$

Example

An unbiased die is thrown. Whenever a 5 or a 6 is thrown, a second throw is allowed and the scores are added together. What is the probability of a score greater than 8 and less than 11?

Solution:

Method 1: Construct a two-way table:

2nd throw

1st throw

Shaded region indicates non-feasible sums, because a 5 or 6 must be achieved on the first throw.

There are 36 possible outcomes which must include the shaded regions as shown.

The dots indicate a score greater than 8 and less than 11.

$P(\text{score greater 8 and less than 11})$

$$= \frac{4}{36} = \frac{1}{9}$$

Method 2:

Score greater than 8 and less than 11 is only possible with:

(5 and then a 4) or (5 and then a 5) or (6 and then a 3) or (6 and then a 4)

Thus P(score greater than 8 and less than 11)

$= P(5 \text{ and then a } 4) \text{ or } P(5 \text{ and then a } 5) \text{ or } P(6 \text{ and then a } 3) \text{ or } P(6 \text{ and then a } 4)$

$= \frac{1}{6} \cdot \frac{1}{6} + \frac{1}{6} \cdot \frac{1}{6} + \frac{1}{6} \cdot \frac{1}{6} + \frac{1}{6} \cdot \frac{1}{6}$

$= \frac{1}{36} + \frac{1}{36} + \frac{1}{36} + \frac{1}{36} = \frac{4}{36} = \frac{1}{9}$

Example

When a biased die is thrown a score of 1 is twice as likely as a score of 2 and a score of 2 is twice as likely as a score of 3. Scores of 3, 4, 5 and 6 are equally likely.

Find the probability of a score of **(i)** 6   **(ii)** 1.

If then a fair die is thrown simultaneously with the biased die, calculate the probability of a total score of 8.

Solution:

Let the biased die have 10 sides, four 1s, two 2s, and one 3, one 4, one 5 and one 6.

1, 1, 1, 1, 2, 2, 3, 4, 5 and 6.

(i) $P(6) = \frac{1}{10}$ **(ii)** $P(1) = \frac{4}{10} = \frac{2}{5}$

Represent the two dice with a two-way table:

6				●	●					
5						●				
4							●			
3								●		
2									●	
1										
	1	1	1	1	2	2	3	4	5	6

Fair die (vertical axis)

Biased die (horizontal axis)

There are $10 \times 6 = 60$ possible outcomes.

The dots indicate where the outcome $= 8$.

$P(8) = \frac{6}{60} = \frac{1}{10}$

Example

Two dice, one coloured red and one coloured black, are thrown. Let

      A be the event that the two numbers are the same

      B the event that the combined score is ≥ 9

      C the event that at least one six is thrown.

(i)   List the possible outcomes for *A*, *B* and *C*.

(ii) Find $P(A)$, $P(B)$, $P(C)$, $P(A \cap C)$.

(iii) Verify that $P(A) + P(C) - P(A \cap C) = P(A \cup C)$.

Solution:

Represent the situation with a two-way table and mark in the events *A*, *B* and *C*.

(i)

Red die						
6	C	C	B,C	B,C	B,C	A,B,C
5				B	A,B	B,C
4				A	B	B,C
3			A			B,C
2		A				C
1	A					C
	1	2	3	4	5	6

Black die

(ii) From the table:

$$P(A) = \tfrac{6}{36} = \tfrac{1}{6}$$

$$P(B) = \tfrac{10}{36} = \tfrac{5}{18}$$

$$P(C) = \tfrac{11}{36}$$

$$P(A \cap C) = \tfrac{1}{36}$$

    (**Note:** $\cap$ = and, $\cup$ = or)

(iii) $P(A) + P(C) - P(A \cap C) = \tfrac{6}{36} + \tfrac{11}{36} - \tfrac{1}{36} = \tfrac{16}{36} = \tfrac{4}{9}$

       $P(A \cup C) = \tfrac{16}{36} = \tfrac{4}{9}$ (from the table)

Example

A bag contains 5 red and 3 yellow discs only. When a disc is drawn from the bag, it is returned before the next draw. What is the probability that two draws will yield

(i) both discs yellow?

(ii) both discs the same colour?

Solution:

Method 1:

Use the laws of probability. There are 8 discs altogether.

$$P(\text{red}) = \tfrac{5}{8} \qquad P(\text{yellow}) = \tfrac{3}{8}$$

(i) $P(\text{both discs yellow}) = P(\text{yellow and then a yellow})$
$$= P(\text{yellow}) \cdot P(\text{yellow})$$
$$= \tfrac{3}{8} \cdot \tfrac{3}{8} = \tfrac{9}{64}$$

(ii) If the two discs are the same colour we could get a yellow and then a yellow **or** a red and then a red

$P(\text{both discs the same colour})$
$= P(\text{both discs yellow}) + P(\text{both discs red})$
$= P(\text{yellow}) \cdot P(\text{yellow}) + P(\text{red}) \cdot P(\text{red})$
$= \tfrac{3}{8} \cdot \tfrac{3}{8} + \tfrac{5}{8} \cdot \tfrac{5}{8}$
$= \tfrac{9}{64} + \tfrac{25}{64} = \tfrac{34}{64} = \tfrac{17}{32}$

Method 2: Using two-way tables:

There are 64 possible outcomes ($8 \times 8 = 64$).

(i)

second selection

	R	R	R	R	R	Y	Y	Y
Y						•	•	•
Y						•	•	•
Y						•	•	•
R								
R								
R								
R								
R								

first selection

$P(\text{both yellow discs}) = \tfrac{9}{64}$

(ii)

second selection

	R	R	R	R	R	Y	Y	Y
Y						•	•	•
Y						•	•	•
Y						•	•	•
R	•	•	•	•	•			
R	•	•	•	•	•			
R	•	•	•	•	•			
R	•	•	•	•	•			
R	•	•	•	•	•			

first selection

$P(\text{both discs the same colour})$
$= \tfrac{34}{64} = \tfrac{17}{32}$

Example

A game consists of spinning an unbiased arrow on a square board and throwing an unbiased die.

The board contains the letters A, B, C and D. The board is so designed that when the arrow stops spinning it can only point at one letter and it is equally likely to point at A or B or C or D.

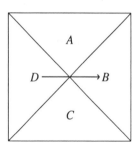

List all possible outcomes of the game, that is, of spinning the arrow and throwing the die. Find the probability that in any one game the outcome will be:

(i)   an A and a 6

(ii) a B and an even number

(iii) an A and an even number or a B and an odd number

(iv) a C and a number ≥ 4 or a D and a number ≤ 2

Solution:

Method 1: Make out a two-way table for each question.

There are 24 possible outcomes (6 numbers, 4 letters, $6 \times 4 = 24$)

(i)

D						
C						
B						
A						●
	1	2	3	4	5	6

$P(\text{an } A \text{ and a } 6) = \frac{1}{24}$

(ii)

D						
C						
B		●		●		●
A						
	1	2	3	4	5	6

$P(\text{a } B \text{ and an even number}) = \frac{3}{24} = \frac{1}{8}$

(iii)

D						
C						
B	●		●		●	
A		●		●		●
	1	2	3	4	5	6

$P\left(\begin{array}{l}\text{an } A \text{ and an even number} \\ \text{or a } B \text{ and an odd number}\end{array}\right) = \frac{6}{24} = \frac{1}{4}$

(iv)

D	●	●				
C				●	●	●
B						
A						
	1	2	3	4	5	6

$P\left(\begin{array}{l}\text{a } C \text{ and a number } \geq 4 \text{ or} \\ \text{a } B \text{ and a number } \leq 2\end{array}\right) = \frac{5}{24}$

Method 2: Write out all the possible couples (number, letter).

$(1,A)$ $(1,B)$ $(1,C)$ $(1,D)$

$(2,A)$ $(2,B)$ $(2,C)$ $(2,D)$

$(3,A)$ $(3,B)$ $(3,C)$ $(3,D)$

$(4,A)$ $(4,B)$ $(4,C)$ $(4,D)$

$(5,A)$ $(5,B)$ $(5,C)$ $(5,D)$

$(6,A)$ $(6,B)$ $(6,C)$ $(6,D)$

There are 24 couples.

(i) $P(\text{an } A \text{ and a } 6) = \frac{1}{24}$

(ii) $P(\text{a } B \text{ and an even number}) = \frac{3}{24} = \frac{1}{8}$

(iii) $P\left(\begin{array}{c}\text{an } A \text{ and an even number or} \\ \text{a } B \text{ and an odd number}\end{array}\right) = \frac{6}{24} = \frac{1}{4}$

(iv) $P\left(\begin{array}{c}\text{a } C \text{ and a number } \geqslant 4 \text{ or} \\ \text{a } B \text{ and a number } \leqslant 2\end{array}\right) = \frac{5}{24}$

Note: Be careful if after the first selection there is no replacement, as in the next example.

Example

A girl selects two different numbers at random, one after another without replacement, from the whole numbers 1, 2, 3, 4 and 5 and uses these to form a two-digit number in the order in which she selects them.

(i) How many outcomes are possible?

(ii) Calculate the probability that the sum of the numbers is less than 7.

Solution:

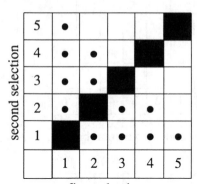

first selection

The shaded regions indicate that you can't pick the same number twice. There are 20 blank spaces, hence there are 20 possible outcomes.

The dots indicate where the two numbers added together are less than 7.

There are 12 dots.

(i) There are 20 possible outcomes.

(ii) $P(\text{total is less than } 7) = \frac{12}{20} = \frac{3}{5}$

Example

Of five balls in a bag, one bears the number 1, another the number 3, two others the number 4 and one the number 6. Two balls are drawn together. If an outcome is the product of the numbers on the two balls, write out all the possible outcomes. Calculate the probability of an outcome of:

(i) 4 **(ii)** 6 **(iii)** 3 or 24

Solution:

Note: 'Product' means 'multiply'.

Picking two numbers at a time is the same as picking one after another without replacement.

	⑥	6	18	24	24	
	④	4	12	16		24
	④	4	12		16	24
	③	3		12	12	18
	①		3	4	4	6
		①	③	④	④	⑥

second selection (vertical label, left)

first selection

The shaded regions indicate you can't pick the same ball twice.

(i) $P(4) = \frac{4}{20} = \frac{1}{5}$

(ii) $P(6) = \frac{2}{20} = \frac{1}{10}$

(iii) $P(3 \text{ or } 24) = P(3) + P(24) = \frac{2}{20} + \frac{4}{20} = \frac{6}{20} = \frac{3}{10}$

Example

A bag contains 20 marbles, 8 of which are white and the remainder black.

Three marbles are removed at random, one at a time, without replacement.

Find the probability that:

(i) all are black **(ii)** at least one is white

Solution:

(i) There are 20 marbles, 8 white, 12 black.

$P(\text{1st black}) = \frac{12}{20}$

$P(\text{2nd black}) = \frac{11}{19}$ (as one black marble has been removed)

$P(\text{3rd black}) = \frac{10}{18}$ (as two black marbles have been removed)

$P(\text{all black}) = P(\text{1st black}) . P(\text{2nd black}) . P(\text{3rd black})$

$= \frac{12}{20} \times \frac{11}{19} \times \frac{10}{18}$

$= \frac{11}{57}$

(ii) P(at least one white) $= 1 - P$(none are white)

$$\downarrow$$

$$= 1 - P\text{(all black)}$$
$$= 1 - \tfrac{11}{57}$$
$$= \tfrac{46}{57}$$

Example

The probability that a woman will hit the target with a single shot at a rifle range is $\tfrac{2}{5}$.

Find the probability that she first hits the target with her third shot.

Solution:

$$P\text{(hit)} + P\text{(miss)} = 1 \qquad \text{(either she hits the target or she misses it)}$$
$$P\text{(hit)} = \tfrac{2}{5}$$
$$P\text{(miss)} = 1 - P\text{(hit)} = 1 - \tfrac{2}{5} = \tfrac{3}{5}$$

P(she first hits the target on the third shot)

$= P$(misses on 1st shot) . P(misses on 2nd shot) . P(hits target on 3rd shot)

$= \tfrac{3}{5} \times \tfrac{3}{5} \times \tfrac{2}{5} = \tfrac{18}{125}$

Example

Nine discs were each given a natural number from two to ten inclusive, each number different from the others. All nine were placed in a box.

(i) A disc was picked at random and replaced. A disc was then picked. Find the probability that both discs showed prime numbers.

(ii) Three discs were picked at random. What is the probability that three odd-numbered discs or three even-numbered discs were picked?

Solution:

9 discs, numbered 2, 3, 4, 5, 6, 7, 8, 9, 10

The prime numbers are 2, 3, 5 and 7 (i.e. 4 prime numbers)

(i) $P(\text{both primes}) = P(\text{1st prime}) \cdot P(\text{2nd prime})$

$$= \tfrac{4}{9} \cdot \tfrac{4}{9} = \tfrac{16}{81}$$

(ii) $P(\text{3 odd numbers}) = P(\text{1st odd}) \cdot P(\text{2nd odd}) \cdot P(\text{3rd odd})$

$$= \tfrac{4}{9} \cdot \tfrac{3}{8} \cdot \tfrac{2}{7} = \tfrac{1}{21}$$

$P(\text{3 even numbers}) = P(\text{1st even}) \cdot P(\text{2nd even}) \cdot P(\text{3rd even})$

$$= \tfrac{5}{9} \cdot \tfrac{4}{8} \cdot \tfrac{3}{7} = \tfrac{5}{42}$$

$P(\text{3 odd numbers or 3 even numbers}) = P(\text{3 odd numbers}) + P(\text{3 even numbers})$

$$= \tfrac{1}{21} + \tfrac{5}{42} = \tfrac{7}{42} = \tfrac{1}{6}$$

Example

Of the 100 tickets sold in a raffle, 40 were red, 30 were blue and 30 were green. The winning ticket is drawn at random.

(i) Find the probability that:

- it is red

- it is not blue.

(ii) every red ticket is even-numbered, every blue ticket is odd numbered, and of the green tickets, 20 are even-numbered and 10 are odd-numbered. Find the probability that **(a)** the winning ticket is green or even-numbered **(b)** the winning ticket is green given that it is odd.

(iii) A ticket is drawn and then replaced. If three such tickets are drawn what is the probability that at least two are red?

Solution:

40 red, 30 blue and 30 green

(i) $P(\text{red}) = \dfrac{40}{100} = \dfrac{2}{5}$ $\qquad P(\text{not blue}) = \dfrac{40+30}{100} = \dfrac{70}{100} = \dfrac{7}{10}$

(ii) We represent the situation in a table:

	Red	Blue	Green	Total
Even	40	0	20	60
Odd	0	30	10	40
Total	40	30	30	100

(a) $P(\text{green or even}) = P(\text{green}) + P(\text{even}) - P(\text{green and even})$

$$= \frac{30}{100} + \frac{60}{100} - \frac{20}{100} = \frac{70}{100} = \frac{7}{10}$$

Or using the table directly: $P(\text{green or even}) = \dfrac{40 + 20 + 10}{100} = \dfrac{70}{100} = \dfrac{7}{10}$

(b) $P(\text{green given that it is odd}) = \dfrac{\text{number of odd-numbered green tickets}}{\text{total number of odd-numbered tickets}} = \dfrac{10}{40} = \dfrac{1}{4}$

(iii) $R = \text{red}$, $O = \text{other colour (i.e. blue or green)}$

At least two reds can occur in 4 ways:

$R.R.R$ or $R.R.O$ or $R.O.R$ or $O.R.R$

Thus, $P(\text{at least two reds from 3 draws with replacement})$

$= P(R.R.R)$ or $P(R.R.O)$ or $P(R.O.R)$ or $P(O.R.R)$

$= \frac{2}{5} \cdot \frac{2}{5} \cdot \frac{2}{5} + \frac{2}{5} \cdot \frac{2}{5} \cdot \frac{3}{5} + \frac{2}{5} \cdot \frac{3}{5} \cdot \frac{2}{5} + \frac{3}{5} \cdot \frac{2}{5} \cdot \frac{2}{5}$

$= \frac{8}{125} + \frac{12}{125} + \frac{12}{125} + \frac{12}{125} = \frac{44}{125}$

Note: From (i), $P(\text{red}) = \frac{2}{5}$ $\therefore\ P(\text{not red}) = \frac{3}{5}$

Example

There were 100 discs in a bag, each having one of the 100 natural numbers from 1 to 100 printed on it. There was a different number on each disc. Forty numbers were red. The rest were black. Twenty-six of the black numbers were even.

(i)   How many red discs had even numbers?

(ii) If a disc was selected at random what was the probability that its number was odd given that it was red?

(iii) A disc was drawn and replaced. Then a disc was drawn. Find the probability that the first had a red number given that it was odd and that the second had an odd number given that it was black.

Solution:

Represent the data in a table.

	Even	Odd	Total
Red	24	16	40
Black	26	34	60
Total	50	50	100

(i) 24 red discs have even numbers

(ii) $P(\text{number is odd given that it is red}) = \dfrac{\text{number of red odd-numbered discs}}{\text{total number of red discs}} = \dfrac{16}{40} = \dfrac{2}{5}$

(iii) $P(\text{red given that is is odd}) = \dfrac{\text{number of red odd-numbered discs}}{\text{total number of odd-numbered discs}} = \dfrac{16}{50} = \dfrac{8}{25}$

$P(\text{odd given that it is black}) = \dfrac{\text{number of black odd-numbered discs}}{\text{total number of black discs}} = \dfrac{34}{60} = \dfrac{17}{30}$

Thus, $P(\text{red given that it is odd})$ and $P(\text{odd given that it was black}) = \dfrac{8}{25} \cdot \dfrac{17}{30} = \dfrac{136}{750} = \dfrac{68}{375}$

(and means multiply)

Example

There are seven white and four black beads in a bag. A bead is picked at random and not replaced. A second bead is then picked.

(i) Find the probability that both beads are the same colour.

The two beads are returned to the bag and three red beads are added. Three beads are then picked at random without replacement. Find the probability that

(ii) all three beads are different in colour

(iii) at least two beads of the same colour are picked.

Solution:

(i) $7W, 4B$ (where W = white beads and B = black beads, 11 beads in total)

$P(\text{both the same colour}) = P(W \text{ and then a } W) \text{ or } P(B \text{ and then a } B)$
$= P(W).P(W) + P(B).P(B)$
$= \dfrac{7}{11} \cdot \dfrac{6}{10} + \dfrac{4}{11} \cdot \dfrac{3}{10} = \dfrac{42}{110} + \dfrac{12}{110} = \dfrac{54}{110} = \dfrac{27}{55}$

This question could also have been solved using a two-way table (why not try it as an exercise?).

(ii) $7W, 4B, 3R$ (14 beads in total, because 3 reds added to the bag)

185

Method 1:

P(all three beads are different in colour)

$= P(W.B.R)$ or $P(W.R.B)$ or $P(B.W.R)$ or $P(B.R.W)$ or $P(R.W.B)$
or $P(R.B.W)$

$= \frac{7}{14} \cdot \frac{4}{13} \cdot \frac{3}{12} + \frac{7}{14} \cdot \frac{3}{13} \cdot \frac{4}{12} + \frac{4}{14} \cdot \frac{7}{13} \cdot \frac{3}{12} + \frac{4}{14} \cdot \frac{3}{13} \cdot \frac{7}{12} + \frac{3}{14} \cdot \frac{7}{13} \cdot \frac{4}{12} + \frac{3}{14} \cdot \frac{4}{13} \cdot \frac{7}{12}$

$= \frac{1}{26} + \frac{1}{26} + \frac{1}{26} + \frac{1}{26} + \frac{1}{26} + \frac{1}{26} = \frac{6}{26} = \frac{3}{13}$

Method 2:

P(all three beads are different in colour)

$= \dfrac{\binom{7}{1} \cdot \binom{4}{1} \cdot \binom{3}{1}}{\binom{14}{3}} = \dfrac{7.4.3}{364} = \dfrac{84}{364} = \dfrac{3}{13}$

(iii) P(at least two beads of the same colour)

$= 1 - P$(all three beads are different in colour)

$= 1 - \frac{3}{13} = \frac{10}{13}$

Example

The probability that each of three marksmen, Eugene, Paul and Dave, will hit a target at a single attempt is $\frac{1}{3}$, $\frac{1}{4}$ and $\frac{1}{5}$ respectively.

If they all fire simultaneously at the target, find the probability that:

(i) Paul misses it **(ii)** all three hit it

(iii) all three miss it **(iv)** at least one man hits it

(v) Eugene hits it, Paul misses it and Dave hits it

Solution:

Represent the information with a table:

	Eugene	Paul	Dave
P(hit)	$\frac{1}{3}$	$\frac{1}{4}$	$\frac{1}{5}$
P(miss)	$\frac{2}{3}$	$\frac{3}{4}$	$\frac{4}{5}$

P(hit) $+ P$(miss) $= 1$

Thus, P(miss) $= 1 - P$(hit)

(i) $P(\text{Paul misses}) = \frac{3}{4}$

(ii) $P(\text{all three hit it}) = P(\text{Eugene hits it}) \cdot P(\text{Paul hits it}) \cdot P(\text{Dave hits it})$

$$= \frac{1}{3} \cdot \frac{1}{4} \cdot \frac{1}{5} = \frac{1}{60}$$

(iii) $P(\text{all three miss}) = P(\text{Eugene misses}) \cdot P(\text{Paul misses}) \cdot P(\text{Dave misses})$

$$= \frac{2}{3} \cdot \frac{3}{4} \cdot \frac{4}{5} = \frac{2}{5}$$

(iv) $P(\text{at least one man hits it}) = 1 - P(\text{all three miss})$

$$= 1 - \frac{2}{5} = \frac{3}{5}$$

(v) $P(\text{Eugene hits it, Paul misses it and Dave hits it})$

$$= P(\text{Eugene hits it}) \cdot P(\text{Paul misses it}) \cdot P(\text{Dave hits it})$$

$$= \frac{1}{3} \cdot \frac{3}{4} \cdot \frac{1}{5} = \frac{1}{20}$$

Example

(a) A bag contained 8 red, 12 blue and an unknown number of green beads. In a random draw the probability of drawing a green bead was $\frac{1}{5}$. How many green beads were in the bag at the start?

(b) A drawer contains 5 red and x blue biros. One is drawn at random and not replaced. Another is then drawn at random. If the probability that both are blue is $\frac{1}{6}$, how many blue biros are in the drawer?

Solution:

(a) Let $x =$ the number of green beads.

Thus, the total number of beads is $(x + 20)$ [8 red, 12 blue and x green]

Given: $P(\text{green bead}) = \dfrac{1}{5}$

$\therefore \qquad \dfrac{x}{x + 20} = \dfrac{1}{5}$

$\Rightarrow \qquad 5x = x + 20$

$\Rightarrow \qquad 4x = 20$

$\Rightarrow \qquad x = 5$

Thus, there are 5 green beads.

(b) 5 red biros, x blue biros. Thus, the total number of biros $= (x+5)$.

Given: P(blue and then a blue) $= \dfrac{1}{6}$

$\therefore \quad P(\text{1st blue}) \cdot P(\text{2nd blue}) = \dfrac{1}{6}$

$\Rightarrow \qquad \dfrac{x}{x+5} \cdot \dfrac{x-1}{x+4} = \dfrac{1}{6}$ $\quad \left[\begin{array}{l} \text{one fewer blue is available, i.e.} \\ x-1, \text{ for the second selection} \\ \text{and the total is also reduced} \\ \text{by 1, i.e. } x+5-1 = x+4. \end{array} \right]$

$\Rightarrow \qquad \dfrac{x^2-x}{x^2+9x+20} = \dfrac{1}{6}$

$\Rightarrow \qquad 6x^2 - 6x = x^2 + 9x + 20$

$\Rightarrow \qquad x^2 - 3x - 4 = 0$

$\Rightarrow \qquad (x-4)(x+1) = 0$

$\Rightarrow \qquad x = 4 \text{ or } x = -1 \quad (\text{reject } x = -1)$

Thus, the number of blue biros $= 4$

Example

A die is loaded so that the probability of a particular number being thrown is proportional to that number, so that $P(1) = k$, $P(2) = 2k$, $P(3) = 3k$, etc.

Find the probability that:

(i) 1 is thrown   **(ii)** 3 or 4 is thrown.

Solution:

$$P(1 \text{ or } 2 \text{ or } 3 \text{ or } 4 \text{ or } 5 \text{ or } 6) = 1 \quad (\text{it must be one of these})$$

$\therefore \quad P(1) + P(2) + P(3) + P(4) + P(5) + P(6) = 1$

$\Rightarrow \qquad k + 2k + 3k + 4k + 5k + 6k = 1$

$\Rightarrow \qquad 21k = 1$

$\Rightarrow \qquad k = \frac{1}{21}$

(i) $P(1) = k = \frac{1}{21}$

(ii) $P(3 \text{ or } 4) = P(3) + P(4) = 3k + 4k = 7k = 7(\frac{1}{21}) = \frac{1}{3}$

Example

A box contains 6 white discs and 4 black discs. A disc is selected at random from the box and replaced by a disc of the other colour. A second disc is then randomly selected from the box.

Determine the probability that:

(i) the first disc selected is black and the second disc selected is white

(ii) both discs selected are white.

Assume that spare white and black discs are available.

Solution:

A table is very useful in solving this problem.

(i) P(black and then a white)

	White	Black	
1st selection	6	4	$P(\text{Black first}) = \frac{4}{10} = \frac{2}{5}$
2nd selection	7	3	$P(\text{White second}) = \frac{7}{10}$

(Black taken out is replaced with a white before the second selection)

$P(\text{Black and then a white}) = P(\text{Black first}) \cdot P(\text{White second}) = \frac{2}{5} \cdot \frac{7}{10} = \frac{14}{50} = \frac{7}{25}$

(ii) P(white and then a white)

	White	Black	
1st selection	6	4	$P(\text{White first}) = \frac{6}{10} = \frac{3}{5}$
2nd selection	5	5	$P(\text{White second}) = \frac{5}{10} = \frac{1}{2}$

(White taken out is replaced with a black before the second selection)

$P(\text{White and then a white}) = P(\text{White first}) \cdot P(\text{White second}) = \frac{3}{5} \cdot \frac{1}{2} = \frac{3}{10}$

Example

Box A contains 2 red balls and 5 black balls.

Box B contains 3 red balls and 2 black balls.

A box is chosen at random. A ball is drawn from this box and placed in the other box from which a ball is then drawn.

Find the probability that:

(i)   the first ball drawn is red

(ii) both balls drawn are the same colour, given that there is an equal probability of selecting box A or box B.

Solution:

$P(\text{box } A) = P(\text{box } B) = \frac{1}{2}$.

(i) $P(\text{first ball is red})$

$= P(\text{box } A \text{ and then a red}) \text{ or } P(\text{box } B \text{ and then a red})$

$= P(\text{box } A) \cdot P(\text{red}) + P(\text{box } B) \cdot P(\text{red})$

$= \frac{1}{2} \cdot \frac{2}{7} + \frac{1}{2} \cdot \frac{3}{5} = \frac{1}{7} + \frac{3}{10} = \frac{31}{70}$

(ii) $P(\text{both balls the same colour}) = P(\text{both red}) \text{ or } P(\text{both black})$

$P(\text{both red}) = P\left(\begin{array}{c} \text{box } A \text{ and then a red and} \\ \text{then a red from box } B \end{array} \right) \text{ or } P\left(\begin{array}{c} \text{box } B \text{ and then a red and} \\ \text{then a red from box } A \end{array} \right)$

$= \frac{1}{2} \cdot \frac{2}{7} \cdot \frac{4}{6} + \frac{1}{2} \cdot \frac{3}{5} \cdot \frac{3}{8} = \frac{2}{21} + \frac{9}{80} = \frac{349}{1680}$

↗   (red put into box B)   ↖   (red put into box A)

$P(\text{both black}) = P\left(\begin{array}{c} \text{box } A \text{ and then a black and} \\ \text{then a black from box } B \end{array} \right) \text{ or } P\left(\begin{array}{c} \text{box } B \text{ and then a black and} \\ \text{then a black from box } A \end{array} \right)$

$= \frac{1}{2} \cdot \frac{5}{7} \cdot \frac{3}{6} + \frac{1}{2} \cdot \frac{2}{5} \cdot \frac{6}{8} = \frac{5}{28} + \frac{3}{20} = \frac{23}{70}$

↗   (black put into box B)   ↖   (black put into box A)

Thus, $P(\text{both balls the same colour}) = \frac{349}{1680} + \frac{23}{70} = \frac{901}{1680}$

Example

Three students have their birthdays in the same week. What is the probability that:

(i) none have their birthday on a Sunday

(ii) all have their birthdays on a Tuesday or Wednesday

(iii) all have their birthdays on the same day

(iv) all the birthdays fall on different days

(v) at least two of them have their birthdays on the same day?

Solution:

(i) P(any one of them not having his or her birthday on a Sunday) $= \frac{6}{7}$

Thus, P(none has a birthday on a Sunday) $= \frac{6}{7} \cdot \frac{6}{7} \cdot \frac{6}{7} = \frac{216}{343}$

(ii) P(any one of them having their birthday on a Tuesday or Wednesday) $= \frac{2}{7}$

Thus, P(all have their birthday on Tuesday or Wednesday) $= \frac{2}{7} \cdot \frac{2}{7} \cdot \frac{2}{7} = \frac{8}{343}$

(iii) P(any one of them was born, say, on a Monday) $= \frac{1}{7}$

Thus, P(all have their birthdays on Monday) $= \frac{1}{7} \cdot \frac{1}{7} \cdot \frac{1}{7} = \frac{1}{343}$

But they could all have their birthdays on Monday or Tuesday or Wednesday or Thursday or Friday or Saturday or Sunday.

Thus, P(all have their birthday on the same day)

$= \frac{1}{343} + \frac{1}{343} + \frac{1}{343} + \frac{1}{343} + \frac{1}{343} + \frac{1}{343} + \frac{1}{343} = \frac{7}{343} = \frac{1}{49}$

(iv) P(their birthdays fall on three different days)

Any one of them could have his or her birthday on one of 7 days.

The first student has a choice of 7 out of 7.

The second student has a choice of 6 out of 7, to be different.

The third student has a choice of 5 out of 7, to be different.

Thus, P(their birthdays fall on three different days) $= \frac{7}{7} \cdot \frac{6}{7} \cdot \frac{5}{7} = \frac{30}{49}$

(v) P(at least two have their birthdays on the same day)

$= 1 - P$(their birthdays fall on three different days) $= 1 - \frac{30}{49} = \frac{19}{49}$

Difference Equations

A difference equation is an equation in which we can calculate a term of a sequence from preceding terms. For example, $u_{n+2} = 5u_{n+1} - 6u_n$ is a difference equation. To get a particular term, it is normally necessary to calculate **all** the previous terms.

Solving a difference equation means finding an expression for u_n in terms of n only. From this expression for u_n we can generate the sequence or find a particular term by substituting values for n. The general solution (expression for u_n) of a difference equation will be of the form:

$$u_n = la^n + mb^n$$

Where l and m are real numbers and a and b are the roots of the characteristic quadratic equation.

To solve a difference equation, do the following:

1. Solve the characteristic quadratic equation to get a and b.

2. Substitute the initial conditions and the values of a and b into $u_n = la^n + mb^n$.

3. Use simultaneous equations to find l and m.

Example

Solve the difference equation $u_{n+2} = 3u_{n+1} - 2u_n$, given $u_1 = 0$ and $u_2 = 1$. Find u_{10}.

Solution:

Step 1: $u_{n+2} - 3u_{n+1} + 2u_n = 0$

$x^2 - 3x + 2 = 0$ (characteristic quadratic equation)

$\Rightarrow \qquad (x - 2)(x - 1) = 0$

$\Rightarrow \qquad x = 2 \quad$ or $\quad x = 1$

$\therefore \qquad a = 2 \quad$ and $\quad b = 1$

Step 2: $u_n = la^n + mb^n = l(2)^n + m(1)^n$

Substitute, separately, $u_1 = 0$ and $u_2 = 1$

$u_1 = 0$	$u_2 = 1$
$\Rightarrow \quad l(2)^1 + m(1)^1 = 0$	$\Rightarrow \quad l(2)^2 + m(1)^2 = 1$
$\Rightarrow \qquad 2l + m = 0 \quad$ ①	$\Rightarrow \qquad 4l + m = 1 \quad$ ②

Step 3: Solving between ① and ② gives $l = \tfrac{1}{2}$ and $m = -1$

$u_n = la^n + mb^n$

$\therefore \quad u_n = \tfrac{1}{2}(2)^n - 1.1^n = 2^{n-1} - 1$

Thus, $u_{10} = 2^{10-1} - 1 = 2^9 - 1 = 512 - 1 = 511$

Example

Solve the difference equation $2u_{n+2} - 11u_{n+1} + 5u_n = 0$, $n \geq 0$, given $u_0 = 2$ and $u_1 = -8$. Find u_6.

Solution:

Step 1: $\quad 2u_{n+2} - 11u_{n+1} + 5u_n = 0$

$$2x^2 - 11x + 5 = 0 \quad \text{(characteristic equation)}$$
$$\Rightarrow \quad (2x - 1)(x - 5) = 0$$
$$\Rightarrow \quad x = \tfrac{1}{2} \quad \text{or} \quad x = 5$$
$$\therefore \quad a = \tfrac{1}{2} \quad \text{and} \quad b = 5$$

Step 2: $\quad u_n = la^n + mb^n = l(\tfrac{1}{2})^n + m(5)^n$

Substitute, separately, $u_0 = 2$ and $u_1 = -8$

$u_0 = 2$	$u_1 = -8$
$\Rightarrow \quad l(\tfrac{1}{2})^0 + m(5)^0 = 2$	$\Rightarrow \quad l(\tfrac{1}{2})^1 + m(5)^1 = -8$
$\Rightarrow \qquad l + m = 2 \ldots \text{①}$	$\Rightarrow \qquad \tfrac{1}{2}l + 5m = -8$
	$\Rightarrow \qquad l + 10m = -16 \ldots \text{②}$

Step 3: Solving between ① and ② gives $l = 4$ and $m = -2$

$$u_n = la^n + mb^n$$
$$\therefore \quad u_n = 4(\tfrac{1}{2})^n - 2(5)^n$$

Thus, $u_6 = 4(\tfrac{1}{2})^6 - 2(5)^6$

$$= 4(\tfrac{1}{64}) - 2(15\,625)$$
$$= \tfrac{1}{16} - 31\,250 = -31\,249\,\tfrac{15}{16}$$

Note: if the characteristic equation does not factorise then you have to use the '$-b$' formula. However, do not use your calculator. Leave your answers in surd form. It simplifies the work and avoids approximate answers.

Example

Solve the difference equation

$$u_{n+1} - 2u_n - 53u_{n-1} = 0, \ n \geq 1$$

when $u_0 = 0$ and $u_1 = 6$.

Solution:

Step 1: $\quad u_{n+1} - 2u_n - 53u_{n-1} = 0$

$$x^2 - 2x - 53 = 0 \quad \text{(characteristic equation)}$$

No factors, $\therefore$ use the '$-b$ formula', $a = 1$, $b = -2$, $c = -53$

$$x = \frac{2 \pm \sqrt{4 - 4(1)(-53)}}{2}$$

$$= \frac{2 \pm \sqrt{216}}{2} = \frac{2 \pm \sqrt{36.6}}{2} = \frac{2 \pm \sqrt{36}\sqrt{6}}{2} = \frac{2 \pm 6\sqrt{6}}{2} = 1 \pm 3\sqrt{6}$$

$$\therefore \quad a = 1 + 3\sqrt{6} \quad \text{and} \quad b = 1 - 3\sqrt{6}$$

Step 2: $\quad u_n = la^n = mb^n = l(1 + 3\sqrt{6})^n + m(1 - 3\sqrt{6})^n$

$u_0 = 0$	$u_1 = 6$
$\Rightarrow \quad l(1 + 3\sqrt{6})^0 - m(1 - 3\sqrt{6})^0 = 0$	$\Rightarrow \quad l(1 + 3\sqrt{6})^1 + m(1 - 3\sqrt{6})^1 = 6$
$l + m = 0$	$\Rightarrow \quad l + 3\sqrt{6}l + m - 3\sqrt{6}m = 6 \quad ②$
$l = -m \quad ①$	$\Rightarrow \quad -m - 3\sqrt{6}m + m - 3\sqrt{6}m = 6$
Put this into ②	(Replace l with $-m$)
	$\Rightarrow \qquad\qquad -6\sqrt{6}m = 6$
	$\Rightarrow \qquad\qquad -\sqrt{6}m = 1$
	$\Rightarrow \qquad\qquad m = -\frac{1}{\sqrt{6}}$
	$\Rightarrow \qquad\qquad l = \frac{1}{\sqrt{6}}$

$$u_n = la^n + mb^n$$

Thus, $u_n = \frac{1}{\sqrt{6}}(1 + 3\sqrt{6})^n - \frac{1}{\sqrt{6}}(1 - 3\sqrt{6})^n$

Example

Show that $u_n = \frac{1}{3}\{(1 + \sqrt{3})^n - (1 - \sqrt{3})^n\}$

is the solution of the difference equation

$$u_{n+2} - 2u_{n+1} - 2u_n = 0, \; n \geq 0$$

when $u_0 = 0$ and $u_1 = \frac{2\sqrt{3}}{3}$.

Solution:

We do not have to solve this difference equation.

All we have to do is test the solution given and the initial conditions.

$$u_n = \frac{1}{3}\{(1 + \sqrt{3})^n - (1 - \sqrt{3})^n\}$$

$$u_{n+1} = \frac{1}{3}\{(1 + \sqrt{3})^{n+1} - (1 - \sqrt{3})^{n+1}\}$$

$$u_{n+2} = \frac{1}{3}\{(1 + \sqrt{3})^{n+2} - (1 - \sqrt{3})^{n+2}\}$$

Thus, $u_{n+2} - 2u_{n+1} - 2u_n$

$= \frac{1}{3}[(1 + \sqrt{3})^{n+2} - (1 - \sqrt{3})^{n+2}] - 2 \cdot \frac{1}{3}[(1 + \sqrt{3})^{n+1} - (1 - \sqrt{3})^{n+1}] - 2 \cdot \frac{1}{3}[(1 + \sqrt{3})^n - (1 - \sqrt{3})^n]$

$= \frac{1}{3}[(1 + \sqrt{3})^{n+2} - (1 - \sqrt{3})^{n+2} - 2(1 + \sqrt{3})^{n+1} + 2(1 - \sqrt{3})^{n+1} - 2(1 + \sqrt{3})^n + 2(1 - \sqrt{3})^n]$

$= \frac{1}{3}[(1 + \sqrt{3})^{n+2} - 2(1 + \sqrt{3})^{n+1} - 2(1 + \sqrt{3})^n - (1 - \sqrt{3})^{n+2} + 2(1 - \sqrt{3})^{n+1} + 2(1 - \sqrt{3})^n]$

$= \frac{1}{3}[(1 + \sqrt{3})^n[(1 + \sqrt{3})^2 - 2(1 + \sqrt{3}) - 2] - (1 - \sqrt{3})^n[(1 - \sqrt{3})^2 - 2(1 - \sqrt{3}) - 2]]$

$= \frac{1}{3}\{(1 + \sqrt{3})^n[1 + 2\sqrt{3} + 3 - 2 - 2\sqrt{3} - 2] - (1 - \sqrt{3})^n[1 - 2\sqrt{3} + 3 - 2 + 2\sqrt{3} - 2]\}$

$= \frac{1}{3}[(1 + \sqrt{3})^n(0) - (1 - \sqrt{3})^n(0)] = \frac{1}{3}[0 + 0] = 0$

Also, $\quad u_0 = \frac{1}{3}[(1 + \sqrt{3})^0 - (1 - \sqrt{3})^0] = \frac{1}{3}[1 - 1] = \frac{1}{3}(0) = 0$

and $\quad u_1 = \frac{1}{3}[(1 + \sqrt{3})^1 - (1 - \sqrt{3})^1] = \frac{1}{3}[1 + \sqrt{3} - 1 + \sqrt{3}] = \frac{1}{3}[2\sqrt{3}] = \frac{2\sqrt{3}}{3}$

Thus, $\quad u_n = \frac{1}{3}[(1 + \sqrt{3})^n + (1 - \sqrt{3})^n]$ is the solution of the difference equation,

$$u_{n+2} - 2u_{n+1} - 2u_n = 0, \; n \geq 0$$

Note: we could have just solved the difference equation with the usual steps and showed that the solution is $u_n = \frac{1}{3}[(1 + \sqrt{3})^n - (1 - \sqrt{3})^n]$

Example

Solve $u_{n+2} + Au_{n+1} + Bu_n = 0$, $A, B \in \mathbf{Z}$ and $n \geq 0$, where $u_0 = 0$, $u_1 = 1$, $u_2 = 4$ and $u_3 = 37$.

Find u_{20}.

Solution:

We need to find the constants A and B.

$u_{n+2} + Au_{n+1} + Bu_n = 0$	$u_{n+2} + Au_{n+1} + Bu_n = 0$
Let $n = 0$.	Let $n = 1$.
$\implies \quad u_2 + Au_1 + Bu_0 = 0$	$\implies \quad u_3 + Au_2 + Bu_1 = 0$
$\implies \quad 4 + A(4) + B(0) = 0$	$\implies \quad 37 + (-4)(4) + B(1) = 0$
$\implies \quad 4 + A = 0$	$\implies \quad 37 - 16 + B = 0$
$\implies \quad A = -4$	$\implies \quad B = -21$

Step 1: $\quad u_{n+2} - 4u_{n+1} - 21u_n = 0$

$$x^2 - 4x - 21 = 0 \quad \text{(characteristic equation)}$$
$$\implies \quad (x - 7)(x + 3) = 0$$
$$\implies \quad x = 7 \quad \text{or} \quad x = -3$$

$\therefore \quad a = 7 \quad \text{and} \quad b = -3$

Step 2: $\quad u_n = la^n + mb^n = l(7)^n + m(-3)^n$

$u_0 = 0$	$u_1 = 1$
$\implies \quad l(7)^0 + m(-3)^0 = 0$	$\implies \quad l(7)^1 + m(-3)^1 = 1$
$\implies \quad l + m = 0 \quad \textcircled{1}$	$\implies \quad 7l - 3m = 1 \quad \textcircled{2}$

Step 3: Solving $\textcircled{1}$ and $\textcircled{2}$ gives $l = \frac{1}{10}$ and $m = -\frac{1}{10}$

$$u_n = la^n + mb^n$$

$\therefore \quad u_n = \frac{1}{10} 7^n - \frac{1}{10}(-3)^n = \frac{1}{10}[7^n - (-3)^n]$

Thus, $u_{20} = \frac{1}{10}[7^{20} - (-3)^{20}]$

Example

In a game played between two players, A and B, the first and second rounds consist of each drawing a ticket from a bag and subsequent rounds consist of finding the average of the previous two scores for that player. The game constines until it becomes obvious that one or other player will have the higher eventual score. If A drew tickets 1 and 100 in the first and second rounds, respectively, and B drew tickets 90 and 51, express each score in round n, i.e. u_n, as a function of n and hence determine the winner.

Solution:

Given: next score = average of two previous scores

$$\Rightarrow \quad \text{3rd score} = \frac{\text{2nd score} + \text{1st score}}{2} \quad \text{and} \quad \text{4th score} = \frac{\text{3rd score} + \text{2nd score}}{2}, \text{etc.}$$

i.e. $u_3 = \dfrac{u_2 + u_1}{2}, \quad u_4 = \dfrac{u_3 + u_2}{2}, \quad u_5 = \dfrac{u_4 + u_3}{2}, \text{etc.}$

Thus, $\qquad\qquad u_{n+2} = \dfrac{u_{n+1} + u_n}{2}$

$\Rightarrow \qquad\qquad 2u_{n+2} = u_{n+1} + u_n$

$\Rightarrow \qquad 2u_{n+2} - u_{n+1} - u_n = 0 \quad$ is the difference equation we have to solve.

$\qquad\qquad 2x^2 - x - 1 = 0 \quad$ (characteristic equation)

$\Rightarrow \qquad (2x + 1)(x - 1) = 0$

$\Rightarrow \qquad x = -\tfrac{1}{2} \quad \text{or} \quad x = 1$

$\therefore \qquad a = -\tfrac{1}{2} \quad \text{and} \quad b = 1$

$u_n = la^n + mb^n = l(-\tfrac{1}{2})^n - m(1)^n$

For A: $u_1 = 1$ and $u_2 = 100$

$u_1 = 1$

$\Rightarrow \quad l(-\tfrac{1}{2})^1 + m(1)^1 = 1$

$\Rightarrow \qquad\qquad -l + 2m = 2 \qquad ①$

$u_2 = 100$

$\Rightarrow \quad l(-\tfrac{1}{2})^2 + m(1)^2 = 100$

$\Rightarrow \qquad\qquad \tfrac{1}{4}l + m = 100$

$\Rightarrow \qquad\qquad l + 4m = 400 \qquad ②$

Solving ① and ② gives:

$l = 132 \quad \text{and} \quad m = 67$

$\therefore \quad u_n = 132(-\tfrac{1}{2})^n + 67(1)^n$ for A

For B: $u_1 = 90$ and $u_2 = 51$

$u_1 = 90$

$\Rightarrow \quad l(-\tfrac{1}{2})^1 + m(1)^1 = 90$

$\Rightarrow \qquad\qquad -l + 2m = 180 \qquad ③$

$u_2 = 51$

$\Rightarrow \quad l(-\tfrac{1}{2})^2 + m(1)^2 = 51$

$\Rightarrow \qquad\qquad \tfrac{1}{4}l + m = 51$

$\Rightarrow \qquad\qquad l + 4m = 204 \qquad ④$

Solving ③ and ④ gives:

$l = -52 \quad \text{and} \quad m = 64$

$\therefore \quad u_n = -52(-\tfrac{1}{2})^n + 64(1)^n$ for B

The eventual winner is the one where $\lim\limits_{n \to \infty} u_n$ is the greater.

For A: $u_n = 132(-\frac{1}{2})^n + 67(1)^n$

$\therefore \quad \lim\limits_{n \to \infty} u_n = [\lim\limits_{n \to \infty} 132(-\frac{1}{2})^n + 67(1)^n]$

$\qquad\qquad = 132(0) + 67$

$\qquad\qquad = 67$

For B: $u_n = -52(-\frac{1}{2})^n + 64(1)^n$

$\therefore \quad \lim\limits_{n \to \infty} u_n = [\lim\limits_{n \to \infty} -52(-\frac{1}{2})^n + 64(1)^n]$

$\qquad\qquad = -52(0) + 64$

$\qquad\qquad = 64$

Thus we conclude that A is the winner.

6. FURTHER CALCULUS AND SERIES

Maximum and Minimum Problems

There are usually 6 steps in solving maximum and minimum problems:

Step 1: Draw a diagram. Mark the variables on it.

Step 2: Write down an equation, in terms of the variables in the diagram, for the quantity to be maximised or minimised.

Step 3: If this equation is in terms of two variables, use the information in the question to express one variable in terms of the other variable. (Look for a link between the variables, usually something is constant.)

Step 4: Express the quantity to be maximised or minimised in terms of one variable.

Step 5: Differentiate the function obtained in Step 4.
Let this differentiated function = 0 and solve.

Step 6: Prove that it is a maximum or a minimum by finding the second derivative, i.e.

$$\frac{d^2y}{dx^2} < 0 \quad \text{(max. value)} \qquad \left| \qquad \frac{d^2y}{dx^2} > 0 \quad \text{(min. value)} \right.$$

Example

A rectangular area is enclosed by a three-sided fence using a ditch as the fourth side. What is the maximum area that can be enclosed by 100 m of fencing?

Solution:

Step 1:

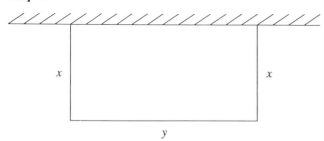

Step 2: Max: Area A

$$A = xy$$

(two variables, we need to link x and y)

Step 3 (link):

length of fence is constant

$\therefore \quad 2x + y = 100$ (given)

$\Rightarrow \quad y = (100 - 2x)$

Step 4:

$A = xy$

$A = x(100 - 2x)$

$A = 100x - 2x^2$

(one variable)

Step 5:

$$A = 100x - 2x^2$$

$$\frac{dA}{dx} = 100 - 4x = 0 \quad (\text{max/min})$$

$$\Rightarrow \quad -4x = -100$$

$$x = 25$$

$$y = 100 - 2x = 100 - 50 = 50$$

$$A = xy = 25 \times 50 = 1\,250 \text{ m}^2$$

$\therefore$ the maximum area is $1\,250$ m^2

Step 6:

$$\frac{dA}{dx} = 100 - 4x$$

$$\frac{d^2A}{dx^2} = -4 < 0$$

$\therefore$ max value

Example

A closed rectangular box is made of thin metal. The length of the box is three times its width. The volume of the box is 36 cm^3 and its width is x cm.

Show that the surface area is $(6x^2 + \dfrac{96}{x})$ cm^2

Find the dimensions of the box with least surface area.

Solution:

Step 1:

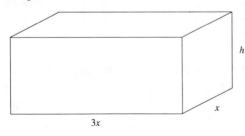

width = x

length = $3x$

height = h

Step 2: Min: surface area, A

$$A = 2(lw + lh + wh)$$

$$= 2(3x.x + 3x.h + x.h)$$

$$= 2(3x^2 + 4xh)$$

$$= 6x^2 + 8xh$$

(two variables, we need to link x and h)

Step 3 (link):

Volume is constant

$$lwh = V$$

$$\Rightarrow \quad 3x.x.h = 36 \quad (\text{given})$$

$$\Rightarrow \quad 3x^2h = 36$$

$$\Rightarrow \quad x^2h = 12$$

$$\Rightarrow \quad h = \frac{12}{x^2}$$

Step 4:

$$A = 6x^2 + 8xh$$

$$= 6x^2 + 8x.\frac{12}{x^2}$$

$$= 6x^2 + \frac{96}{x}$$

(answer to first part)

$$= 6x^2 + 96x^{-1}$$

Step 5:

$$A = 6x^2 + 96x^{-1}$$

$$\frac{dA}{dx} = 12x - 96x^{-2} = 0 \ (\text{max/min})$$

$$\Rightarrow \quad 12x = \frac{96}{x^2}$$

$$\Rightarrow \quad 12x^3 = 96$$

$$\Rightarrow \quad x^3 = 8$$

$$\Rightarrow \quad x = 2$$

Step 6:

$$\frac{dA}{dx} = 12x - 96x^{-2}$$

$$\frac{d^2A}{dx^2} = 12 + 192x^{-3}$$

$$= 12 + \frac{192}{x^3} > 0$$

when $x = 2$

$\therefore$ min value

Dimensions:

width $= x = 2\,\text{cm}$

length $= 3x = 6\,\text{cm}$

height $= \dfrac{12}{x^2} = \dfrac{12}{4} = 3\,\text{cm}$

Example

A rectangular sheet of cardboard is 24 cm long and 9 cm wide. Equal squares are cut out at the corners and the flaps are turned up to form an open box. Find its maximum volume.

Solution:

Step 1:

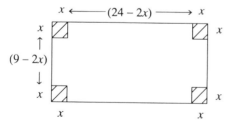 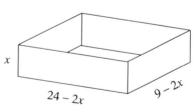

length $= 24 - 2x$,   breadth $= 9 - 2x$,   height $= x$

Step 2: Max: Volume

$$V = lbh$$

$$V = (24 - 2x)(9 - 2x)(x)$$

$$V = 4x^3 - 66x^2 + 216x$$

$\left(\begin{array}{c} \text{one variable} \\ \therefore \quad \text{steps 3 and 4 not needed} \end{array} \right)$

Step 5:

$$V = 4x^3 - 66x^2 + 216x$$

$$\frac{dV}{dx} = 12x^2 - 132x + 216 = 0 \ \text{(max/min)}$$

$$\Rightarrow \qquad x^2 - 11x + 18 = 0$$
$$\Rightarrow \qquad (x-9)(x-2) = 0$$
$$\Rightarrow \quad x - 9 = 0 \ \text{ or } \ x - 2 = 0$$
$$\Rightarrow \qquad x = 9 \ \text{ or } \ x = 2$$

$x = 9$ is rejected as the breadth of the cardboard is 9 cm and this would make the length of one side of the box negative.

Step 6:

$$\frac{dV}{dx} = 12x^2 - 132x + 216$$

$$\frac{d^2V}{dx^2} = 24x - 132$$

$$\left. \frac{d^2V}{dx^2} \right|_{x=2} = 24(2) - 132 = -84 < 0$$

$$\therefore \quad \text{a maximum}$$

length $= 24 - 2x = 24 - 4 = 20$
breadth $= 9 - 2x = 9 - 4 = 5$
height $= x = 2$

$V = lbh$
$V = 20 \times 5 \times 2 = 200 \, \text{cm}^3$

$\therefore \quad$ max volume $= 200 \, \text{cm}^3$

Example

The shape of a playing field is a rectangle with semicircular ends and its complete boundary is to be used as a running track 400 m in length. If the rectangular region is to have a maximum area, find the total length of the semicircular ends.

Solution:

Step 1:

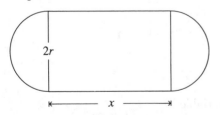

Let x = length of the rectangle and
let r = radius of the semicircular ends

Step 2:   Max: Area of rectangle

$$A = 2xr$$

(two variables, we need to link x and r)

Step 3 (link):

Boundary of track is a constant.

$$\therefore \quad 2x + 2\pi r = 400$$

$$x + \pi r = 200$$

$$x = 200 - \pi r$$

Step 4:

$$A = 2xr$$

$$\searrow$$

$$A = 2(200 - \pi r)r$$

$$A = 400r - 2\pi r^2$$

Step 5:

$$A = 400r - 2\pi r^2$$

$$\frac{dA}{dr} = 400 - 4\pi r = 0 \quad \text{(max/min)}$$

$$\Rightarrow \quad 4\pi r = 400$$

$$\pi r = 100$$

$$r = \frac{100}{\pi} \text{ m}$$

Step 6:

$$\frac{dA}{dr} = 400 - 4\pi r$$

$$\frac{d^2 A}{dr^2} = -4\pi < 0$$

$$\therefore \quad \text{max value}$$

Length of semicircular ends is the circumference of a circle of radius r.

$$C = 2\pi r = 2\pi\left(\tfrac{100}{\pi}\right) = 200 \text{ m}$$

Example

An ambulance at the point a has to reach, as quickly as possible, the point c on the road bc. It travels at 80 km/h between a and any point on the road. Once on the road it travels at 100 km/h. If $|bc| = 9$ km, $|ba| = 3$ km and $|bp| = x$ km, derive in terms of x an expression for t, the time

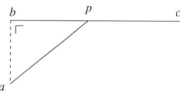

taken to reach c. Find the value of x for which the time is minimum and calculate this minimum time. (You need not test for the minimum.)

Solution:

Step 1:

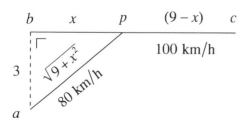

$$|ap| = \sqrt{9 + x^2} \quad \text{and} \quad |pc| = (9 - x)$$

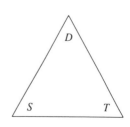

Dad's Silly Triangle

Step 2:

$$\text{Time} = \frac{\text{Distance}}{\text{Speed}}$$

$$T = \frac{|ap|}{80} + \frac{|pc|}{100}$$

$$T = \frac{\sqrt{9+x^2}}{80} + \frac{(9-x)}{100} \qquad \left(\begin{array}{c} \text{One variable,} \\ \therefore \quad \text{steps 3 and 4 not needed} \end{array} \right)$$

$$T = \frac{(9+x^2)^{\frac{1}{2}}}{80} + \frac{9}{100} - \frac{x}{100}$$

Step 5: (use chain rule)

$$\frac{dT}{dx} = \frac{\frac{1}{2}(9+x^2)^{-\frac{1}{2}}.2x}{80} + 0 - \frac{1}{100} = 0 \ (\text{max/min})$$

$$\frac{x}{80\sqrt{9+x^2}} = \frac{1}{100}$$

$$100x = 80\sqrt{9+x^2}$$

$$5x = 4\sqrt{9+x^2}$$

$$25x^2 = 16(9+x^2) \quad \text{(squaring both sides)}$$

$$25x^2 = 144 + 16x^2$$

$$9x^2 = 144$$

$$x^2 = 16$$

$$x = \pm 4$$

Thus, $x = 4$
($x = -4$ is rejected as distance cannot be negative)

$$\text{Time} = \frac{\text{Distance}}{\text{Speed}}$$

$$= \frac{\sqrt{9+x^2}}{80} + \frac{(9-x)}{100}$$

$$= \frac{\sqrt{9+16}}{80} + \frac{(9-4)}{100}$$

$$= \frac{\sqrt{25}}{80} + \frac{5}{100}$$

$$= \frac{5}{80} + \frac{1}{20}$$

$$= \frac{9}{80} \ \text{hours} \quad \text{(or 6.75 mins)}$$

Example

A company that manufactures dog food wishes to pack the food in closed cylindrical tins. What should be the dimensions of each tin if it is to have a volume of 128π cm^3 and the minimum possible surface area?

Solution:

Step 1:

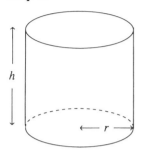

Step 2: Min: Surface Area, A

$$A = 2\pi r^2 + 2\pi rh$$

(two variables, we need to link r and h)

Step 4:

$$A = 2\pi r^2 + 2\pi rh$$

$$A = 2\pi r^2 + 2\pi r\left(\frac{128}{r^2}\right)$$

$$A = 2\pi r^2 + \frac{256\pi}{r}$$

$$A = 2\pi r^2 + 256\pi r^{-1}$$

Step 3 (link):

Volume is constant $= 128\pi$

Thus, $\pi r^2 h = 128\pi$

$$r^2 h = 128$$

$$h = \frac{128}{r^2}$$

Step 5:

$$A = 2\pi r^2 + 256\pi r^{-1}$$

$$\frac{dA}{dr} = 4\pi r - 256\pi r^{-2} = 0 \ \ \text{(max/min)}$$

$$4\pi r = \frac{256\pi}{r^2}$$

$$4r = \frac{256}{r^2}$$

$$4r^3 = 256$$

$$r^3 = 64$$

$$r = 4 \text{ cm}$$

$$h = \frac{128}{r^2} = \frac{128}{16} = 8 \text{ cm}$$

Step 6:

$$\frac{dA}{dr} = 4\pi r - 256\pi r^{-2}$$

$$\frac{d^2 A}{dr^2} = 4\pi + 512\pi r^{-3}$$

$$= 4\pi + \frac{512\pi}{r^3} > 0$$

when $r = 4$

$\therefore$ minimum

Each tin should have a radius of 4 cm and a height of 8 cm.

Example

The base of a solid prism is a right-angled triangle having sides of length $5t$, $4t$, $3t$ ($t \in \mathbf{R}$). The volume of the prism is a constant V.

If the height of the prism is x, express x in terms of V and t.

Show that when the total surface area of the prism is a minimum, the area of the two triangular ends is one-third the total area.

Solution:

Step 1:

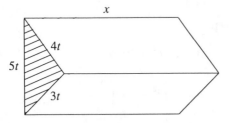

Step 2: Min: Total surface area, A

$$A = 2\triangle s + 3 \boxed{} s$$

$$= 6t^2 + 6t^2 + 4tx + 3tx + 5tx$$

$$= 12t^2 + 12tx$$

(two variables, we need to link t and x)

Step 3 (link):

Volume is constant

$$(\text{area of } \triangle)x = V$$

$$6t^2 x = V$$

$$x = \frac{V}{6t^2}$$

Step 4:

$$A = 12t^2 + 12tx$$

$$A = 12t^2 + 12t\left(\frac{V}{6t^2}\right)$$

$$A = 12t^2 + \frac{2V}{t}$$

$$A = 12t^2 + 2Vt^{-1}$$

Step 5:

$$A = 12t^2 + 2Vt^{-1}$$

$$\frac{dA}{dt} = 24t - 2Vt^{-2} = 0 \ \ (\text{max/min})$$

$$24t = \frac{2V}{t^2}$$

$$24t^3 = 2V$$

$$24t^3 = 2(6t^2x)$$

$$24t^3 = 12t^2x$$

$$2t = x$$

Step 6:

$$\frac{dA}{dt} = 24t - 2Vt^{-2}$$

$$\frac{d^2A}{dt^2} = 24 + 4Vt^{-3}$$

$$= 24 + \frac{4V}{t^3} > 0 \ \ \text{for} \ \ t > 0$$

$\therefore$ a minimum

Total Surface Area

$$= 12t^2 + 12tx$$

$$= 12t^2 + 12t(2t)$$

$$= 12t^2 + 24t^2 = 36t^2$$

Surface area of $\triangle$ ends

$$= 6t^2 + 6t^2 = 12t^2$$

$$\frac{12t^2}{36t^2} = \frac{1}{3}$$

$\therefore$ area of $\triangle$ ends

$= \frac{1}{3}$ total surface area

Example

Find the volume of the largest cylinder that can be cut from a solid sphere of radius a.

Solution:

Step 1:

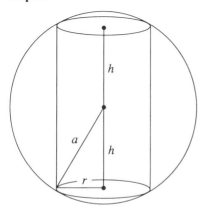

Let r = the radius of the cylinder and
let $2h$ = the height of the cylinder

Step 2:   Max: Volume of cylinder

$$V = \pi r^2(2h)$$

$$V = 2\pi r^2 h$$

(two variables, we need to link r and h)

Step 3 (link):

radius of sphere, a, is constant

$$r^2 + h^2 = a^2 \ \ (\text{Pythagoras})$$

$$\Rightarrow \ \ r^2 = (a^2 - h^2)$$

(Better to write this than $h^2 = a^2 - r^2$)

Step 5:

$$V = 2\pi a^2 h - 2\pi h^3$$

$$\frac{dV}{dh} = 2\pi a^2 - 6\pi h^2 = 0 \ \ (\text{max/min})$$

$$6\pi h^2 = 2\pi a^2$$
$$3h^2 = a^2$$
$$h^2 = \frac{a^2}{3}$$
$$h = \frac{a}{\sqrt{3}}$$

$$r^2 = a^2 - h^2 = a^2 - \frac{a^2}{3} = \frac{2a^2}{3}$$

$$V = 2\pi r^2 h$$
$$= 2\pi \frac{2a^2}{3} \cdot \frac{a}{\sqrt{3}}$$
$$= \frac{4}{3\sqrt{3}} \pi a^3$$

Step 4:

$$V = 2\pi r^2 h$$
$$\searrow$$
$$V = 2\pi (a^2 - h^2)h$$
$$V = 2\pi a^2 h - 2\pi h^3$$

Step 6:

$$\frac{dV}{dh} = 2\pi a^2 - 6\pi h^2$$

$$\frac{d^2V}{dh^2} = -12\pi h < 0$$

$$\text{for } h > 0$$

$$\therefore \quad \text{a maximum}$$

Example

The length of a radius of a circle is r. A rectangle is inscribed in the circle. Prove that the rectangle of maximum area is a square.

(You need not test for a maximum.)

Solution:

Step 1:

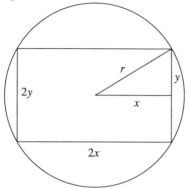

Let $2x$ = the length of the rectangle and let $2y$ = the breadth of the rectangle

Step 2:

Max: Area of rectangle, A

$A = l \times b = (2x)(2y) = 4xy$

(two variables, we need to link x and y)

> **Step 3 (link):**
>
> radius, r, of circle is constant
>
> $x^2 + y^2 = r^2$
>
> $\quad y^2 = r^2 - x^2$
>
> $\quad y = \sqrt{r^2 - x^2}$

Step 4:

$A = 4xy$

$A = 4x\sqrt{r^2 - x^2}$

$A = \sqrt{16x^2r^2 - 16x^4}$

(This makes the differentiation easier)

$A = (16x^2r^2 - 16x^4)^{\frac{1}{2}}$

Step 5:

$A = (16x^2r^2 - 16x^4)^{\frac{1}{2}}$

(use chain rule)

$\dfrac{dA}{dx} = \frac{1}{2}(16x^2r^2 - 16x^4)^{-\frac{1}{2}}(32xr^2 - 64x^3) = 0$ (max/min)

$\Rightarrow \dfrac{32xr^2 - 64x^3}{2\sqrt{16x^2r^2 - 16x^4}} = 0$

$\Rightarrow \quad 64x^3 = 32xr^2$ (fraction = 0, $\Rightarrow$ top = 0)

$\Rightarrow \quad 2x^2 = r^2$

(link) $\quad y^2 = r^2 - x^2 = 2x^2 - x^2 = x^2$

$\Rightarrow \quad y^2 = x^2$

$\Rightarrow \quad y = x$

$\therefore$ rectangle of maximum area is a square

Example

A right circular cone 11 cm in height and of base diameter 8 cm is to enclose a cylinder (see two-dimensional diagram).

Express the height (h) of the cylinder in terms of its radius (r).

Find the maximum volume of the cylinder in terms of π.

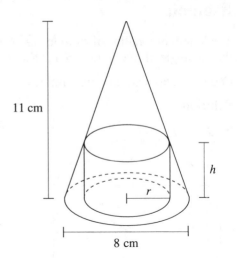

11 cm

8 cm

Solution:

Step 1:

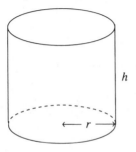

Step 2: Max: Volume of cylinder

$$V = \pi r^2 h$$

(two variables, we need to link r and h)

Step 3 (link):

(using similar triangles)

11

4

h

$4 - r$

$$\frac{h}{11} = \frac{4 - r}{4}$$

$$h = \frac{44 - 11r}{4}$$

Step 4:

$$V = \pi r^2 h$$

$$V = \pi r^2 \left(\frac{44 - 11r}{4} \right)$$

$$V = 11\pi r^2 - \tfrac{11}{4}\pi r^3$$

$$\frac{dV}{dr} = 22\pi r - \tfrac{33}{4}\pi r^2 = 0 \ \ (\text{max/min})$$

$$\Rightarrow \quad 88\pi r - 33\pi r^2 = 0$$

$$\Rightarrow \qquad\qquad 8 - 3r = 0 \ \ (r \neq 0)$$

$$\Rightarrow \qquad\qquad\qquad r = \tfrac{8}{3}$$

Step 5:

$$V = 11\pi r^2 - \tfrac{11}{4}\pi r^3$$

Max. volume, $r = \tfrac{8}{3}$

$$\text{Thus, } V_{\max} = 11\pi \left(\tfrac{8}{3}\right)^2 - \tfrac{11}{4}\pi \left(\tfrac{8}{3}\right)^3$$

$$= 11\pi \left(\tfrac{64}{9}\right) - \tfrac{11}{4}\pi \tfrac{512}{27}$$

$$= \tfrac{704}{9}\pi - \tfrac{1\,408}{27}\pi$$

$$= \tfrac{704}{27}\pi \ \text{cm}^3$$

Step 6:

$$\frac{dV}{dr} = 22\pi r - \tfrac{33}{4}\pi r^2$$

$$\frac{d^2V}{dr^2} = 22\pi - \tfrac{33}{2}\pi r$$

$$\left.\frac{d^2V}{dr^2}\right|_{r=\frac{8}{3}} = 22\pi - \tfrac{33}{2}\pi \left(\tfrac{8}{3}\right) = 22\pi - 44\pi = -22\pi < 0 \qquad \therefore \quad \text{max. volume}$$

Integration By Parts (Integration of Products)

$$\int u \, dv = uv - \int v \, du$$

(page 42 in the tables)

This is known as the formula for integration by parts, based on the product rule for differentiation. It is used to integrate products where neither function is related to the derivative of the other (i.e. substitution will not work), for example $\int x\,e^{2x}\,dx$. Our aim is to go from the given integral, $\int u \, dv$, to a new integral, $\int v \, du$, that is simpler.

We apply the formula with the following steps:

1. Let u = one part and dv = the other part.

2. Differentiate u and integrate dv.

3. Substitute into the formula.

4. Integrate the second part on the right-hand side.

Order of priority for u

The order of priority for u is:

Type	Examples	Memory Aid
1. Logs	$\ln x, (\ln x)^2$	L
2. Inverse trigonometric	$\sin^{-1} x, \tan^{-1} x$	IT
3. Algebraic	$x^2, \dfrac{1}{x^2}, \theta$	A
4. Exponential	e^x, e^{-x}, e^{3x}	E
5. Trigonometric	$\sin x, \cos 2\theta$	T

Whichever one of these we meet first, let this equal u and the other part equal dv.

Note: The order of 4 and 5, exponential and trigonometric, is not important, but if we have to integrate twice we must keep the order we started with.

Example

Find $\int x \ln x \, dx$

Solution:

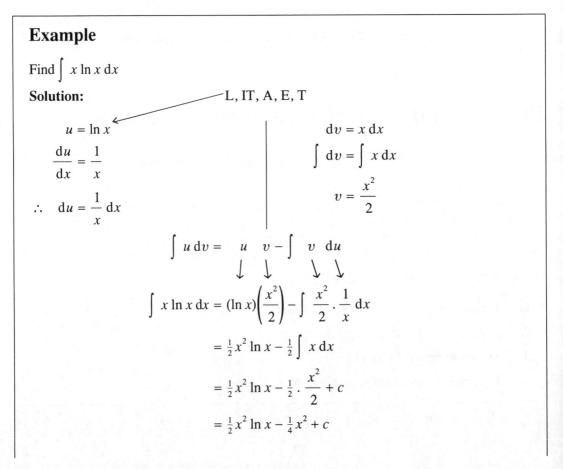

L, IT, A, E, T

$u = \ln x$

$\dfrac{du}{dx} = \dfrac{1}{x}$

$\therefore \quad du = \dfrac{1}{x} \, dx$

$dv = x \, dx$

$\int dv = \int x \, dx$

$v = \dfrac{x^2}{2}$

$$\int u \, dv = u \quad v - \int v \, du$$

$$\int x \ln x \, dx = (\ln x)\left(\frac{x^2}{2}\right) - \int \frac{x^2}{2} \cdot \frac{1}{x} \, dx$$

$$= \tfrac{1}{2}x^2 \ln x - \tfrac{1}{2}\int x \, dx$$

$$= \tfrac{1}{2}x^2 \ln x - \tfrac{1}{2} \cdot \frac{x^2}{2} + c$$

$$= \tfrac{1}{2}x^2 \ln x - \tfrac{1}{4}x^2 + c$$

Check by differentiating:

$$\tfrac{1}{2}x^2 \cdot \frac{1}{x} + (\ln x)(x) - \tfrac{1}{2}x = \tfrac{1}{2}x + x \ln x - \tfrac{1}{2}x = x \ln x$$

Example

Find $\int x\,e^{3x}\,dx$.

Solution:

L, IT, A, E, T

$$u = x$$

$$\frac{du}{dx} = 1$$

$$du = dx$$

$$dv = e^{3x}\,dx$$

$$\int dv = \int e^{3x}\,dx$$

$$v = \frac{e^{3x}}{3}$$

$$\int u\,dv = u \quad v - \int v\,du$$

$$\int x\,e^{3x}\,dx = (x)\left(\frac{e^{3x}}{3}\right) - \int \frac{e^{3x}}{3}\,dx$$

$$= \tfrac{1}{3}x\,e^{3x} - \tfrac{1}{3}\int e^{3x}\,dx$$

$$= \tfrac{1}{3}x\,e^{3x} - \tfrac{1}{3} \cdot \frac{e^{3x}}{3} + c$$

$$= \tfrac{1}{3}x\,e^{3x} - \tfrac{1}{9}e^{3x} + c$$

Check by differentiating:

$$\tfrac{1}{3}x \cdot 3\,e^{3x} + \tfrac{1}{3}e^{3x} - \tfrac{1}{3}e^{3x} = x\,e^{3x}$$

Some integrals don't look like a product, but can be turned into one easily.

Example

Find $\int \ln x \, dx$.

Solution:

We first write it as a product by inserting a factor of 1.

$$\int \ln x \, dx = \int 1 \cdot \ln x \, dx$$

L, IT, A, E, T

$u = \ln x$

$\dfrac{du}{dx} = \dfrac{1}{x}$

$du = \dfrac{1}{x} \, du$

$dv = 1 \, dx$

$\int dv = \int 1 \, dx$

$v = x$

$$\int u \, dv = u \quad v - \int v \, du$$

$$\int \ln x \, dx = (\ln x)x - \int x \, \frac{1}{x} \, dx$$

$$= x \ln x - \int 1 \, dx$$

$$= x \ln x - x + c$$

Sometimes a combination of methods is required.

Example

Find $\int \tan^{-1} x \, dx$.

Solution:

Again, write it as a product by inserting a factor of 1.

$$\int \tan^{-1} x \, dx = \int 1 \cdot \tan^{-1} x \, dx$$

L, IT, A, E, T

$u = \tan^{-1} x$

$\dfrac{du}{dx} = \dfrac{1}{1+x^2}$

$du = \dfrac{1}{1+x^2} \, dx$

$dv = 1 \, dx$

$\int dv = \int 1 \, dx$

$v = x$

$$\int u \, dv = \quad u \quad v \quad - \int v \quad du$$

$$\int \tan^{-1} x \, dx = (\tan^{-1} x)x - \int x\left(\frac{1}{1+x^2}\right) dx$$

$$= x \tan^{-1} x - \int \frac{x}{1+x^2} \, dx$$

We now have to use substitution to find $\int \frac{x}{1+x^2} \, dx$

$$u = 1 + x^2$$

$$\frac{du}{dx} = 2x$$

$$du = 2x \, dx$$

$$\tfrac{1}{2} du = x \, dx$$

$$\therefore \quad \int \frac{x}{1+x^2} \, dx = \tfrac{1}{2} \int \frac{1}{u} \, du$$

$$= \tfrac{1}{2} \ln u$$

$$= \tfrac{1}{2} \ln(1 + x^2)$$

$$\int \tan^{-1} x \, dx = x \tan^{-1} x - \int \frac{x}{1+x^2} \, dx$$

$$= x \tan^{-1} x - \tfrac{1}{2} \ln(1 + x^2) + c$$

Definite Integrals

For definite integrals, the formula is:

$$\int_a^b u \, dv = uv \Big|_a^b - \int_a^b v \, du$$

The uv part must also be evaluated between the limits. However, it is general practice to find an expression for the integral and then evaluate the whole expression between the limits (see the next two examples).

Example

Evaluate $\int_0^{\frac{\pi}{4}} \theta \cos 2\theta \, d\theta$

Solution: L, IT, A, E, T

$$u = \theta \leftarrow$$

$$\frac{du}{d\theta} = 1$$

$$du = d\theta$$

$$dv = \cos 2\theta \, d\theta$$

$$\int dv = \int \cos 2\theta \, d\theta$$

$$v = \tfrac{1}{2} \sin 2\theta$$

$$\int u \, dv = u \quad v \qquad - \int v \quad du$$

$$\int \theta \cos 2\theta \, d\theta = (\theta)(\tfrac{1}{2} \sin 2\theta) - \int \tfrac{1}{2} \sin 2\theta \, d\theta$$

$$= \tfrac{1}{2} \theta \sin 2\theta - \tfrac{1}{2} \int \sin 2\theta \, d\theta$$

$$= \tfrac{1}{2} \theta \sin 2\theta + \tfrac{1}{4} \cos 2\theta$$

$$\therefore \int_0^{\frac{\pi}{4}} \theta \cos 2\theta \, d\theta = \tfrac{1}{2} \theta \sin 2\theta + \tfrac{1}{4} \cos 2\theta \Big|_0^{\frac{\pi}{4}}$$

$$= [\tfrac{1}{2} \cdot \tfrac{\pi}{4} \sin \tfrac{\pi}{2} + \tfrac{1}{4} \cos \tfrac{\pi}{2}] - [\tfrac{1}{2}(0) \sin 0 + \tfrac{1}{4} \cos 0]$$

$$= [\tfrac{\pi}{8} + 0] - [0 + \tfrac{1}{4}]$$

$$= \tfrac{\pi}{8} - \tfrac{1}{4}$$

Sometimes we have to use 'integration by parts' twice.

Example

Evaluate $\int_1^e x(\ln x)^2 \, dx$.

Solution: L, IT, A, E, T

$$u = (\ln x)^2 \qquad\qquad\qquad dv = x \, dx$$

$$\frac{du}{dx} = 2 \ln x \cdot \frac{1}{x} \qquad\qquad \int dv = \int x \, dx$$

$$\qquad\qquad\qquad\qquad v = \tfrac{1}{2} x^2$$

$$du = 2 \ln x \cdot \frac{1}{x} \, dx$$

$$\int u \, dv = \quad u \quad v - \int v \quad du$$

$$\int x(\ln x)^2 \, dx = (\ln x)^2 (\tfrac{1}{2} x^2) - \int \tfrac{1}{2} x^2 . 2 \ln x . \frac{1}{x} \, dx$$

$$\int x(\ln x)^2 \, dx = \tfrac{1}{2} x^2 (\ln x)^2 - \int x \ln x \, dx \qquad ①$$

We now use 'integration by parts' again to find $\int x \ln x \, dx$

$$u = \ln x \qquad\qquad\qquad\qquad dv = x \, dx$$

$$\frac{du}{dx} = \frac{1}{x} \qquad\qquad\qquad\qquad \int dv = \int x \, dx$$

$$\qquad\qquad\qquad\qquad\qquad v = \tfrac{1}{2} x^2$$

$$du = \frac{1}{x} \, dx$$

216

$$\int u\, dv = \quad u \quad v \; - \int v \quad du$$

$$\int x \ln x\, dx = (\ln x)(\tfrac{1}{2}x^2) - \int \tfrac{1}{2}x^2 \cdot \frac{1}{x}\, dx$$

$$= \tfrac{1}{2}x^2 \ln x - \tfrac{1}{2}\int x\, dx$$

$$= \tfrac{1}{2}x^2 \ln x - \tfrac{1}{2} \cdot \frac{x^2}{2}$$

$$= \tfrac{1}{2}x^2 \ln x - \tfrac{1}{4}x^2 \qquad \qquad ②$$

We go back to the first result of 'integration by parts'.

$$\int x(\ln x)^2\, dx = \tfrac{1}{2}x^2(\ln x)^2 - \int x \ln x\, dx \qquad \qquad ①$$

$$= \tfrac{1}{2}x^2(\ln x)^2 - (\tfrac{1}{2}x^2 \ln x - \tfrac{1}{4}x^2) \qquad \text{(put ② into ①)}$$

$$= \tfrac{1}{2}x^2(\ln x)^2 - \tfrac{1}{2}x^2 \ln x + \tfrac{1}{4}x^2$$

$$\therefore \quad \int_1^e x(\ln x)^2\, dx = [\tfrac{1}{2}x^2(\ln x)^2 - \tfrac{1}{2}x^2 \ln x + \tfrac{1}{4}x^2]_1^e$$

$$= [\tfrac{1}{2}e^2(\ln e)^2 - \tfrac{1}{2}e^2 \ln e + \tfrac{1}{4}e^2] - [\tfrac{1}{2} \cdot 1^2(\ln 1)^2 - \tfrac{1}{2} \cdot 1^2(\ln 1) + \tfrac{1}{4} \cdot 1^2]$$

$$= [\tfrac{1}{2}e^2(1)^2 - \tfrac{1}{2}e^2(1) + \tfrac{1}{4}e^2] - [\tfrac{1}{2}(0) - \tfrac{1}{2}(0) + \tfrac{1}{4}]$$

$$= [\tfrac{1}{2}e^2 - \tfrac{1}{2}e^2 + \tfrac{1}{4}e^2] - [0 - 0 + \tfrac{1}{4}]$$

$$= \tfrac{1}{4}e^2 - \tfrac{1}{4} = \tfrac{1}{4}(e^2 - 1)$$

In some special cases when we integrate twice we end up with the *original* integral on *both* sides. When this happens we use algebra to get the required result.

Example

Find $\int e^{-x} \cos x\, dx$

Solution: L, IT, A, E, T

$$u = e^{-x}$$

$$\frac{du}{dx} = -e^{-x}$$

$$du = -e^{-x}\, dx$$

$$dv = \cos x\, dx$$

$$\int dv = \int \cos x\, dx$$

$$v = \sin x$$

$$\int u \, dv = uv - \int v \, du$$

$$\int e^{-x} \cos x \, dx = e^{-x} \sin x - \int \sin x (-e^{-x}) \, dx$$

$$\int e^{-x} \cos x \, dx = e^{-x} \sin x + \int e^{-x} \sin x \, dx \qquad \textcircled{1}$$

We now use 'integration by parts' again to find $\int e^{-x} \sin x \, dx$

$$u = e^{-x} \qquad\qquad\qquad\qquad dv = \sin x \, dx$$

$$\frac{du}{dx} = -e^{-x} \qquad\qquad\qquad \int dv = \int \sin x \, dx$$

$$\qquad\qquad\qquad\qquad\qquad v = -\cos x$$

$$du = -e^{-x} \, dx$$

$$\int u \, dv = uv - \int v \, du$$

$$\int e^{-x} \sin x \, dx = e^{-x}(-\cos x) - \int -\cos x \, . - e^{-x} \, dx$$

$$= -e^{-x} \cos x - \int e^{-x} \cos x \, dx \qquad \textcircled{2}$$

(back to where we started)

We now go back to the first result, $\textcircled{1}$, of 'integration by parts' and substitute $\textcircled{2}$ into $\textcircled{1}$.

$$\int e^{-x} \cos x \, dx = e^{-x} \sin x + \int e^{-x} \sin x \, dx \qquad \textcircled{1}$$

$$\int e^{-x} \cos x \, dx = e^{-x} \sin x + \left[-e^{-x} \cos x - \int e^{-x} \cos x \, dx \right]$$

$$\int e^{-x} \cos x \, dx = e^{-x} \sin x - e^{-x} \cos x - \int e^{-x} \cos x \, dx$$

$$\left[\int e^{-x} \cos x \, dx \text{ on both sides} \right]$$

$$\Rightarrow \quad 2\int e^{-x} \cos x \, dx = e^{-x} \sin x - e^{-x} \cos x$$

$$\Rightarrow \quad 2\int e^{-x} \cos x \, dx = e^{-x}(\sin x - \cos x)$$

$$\Rightarrow \quad \int e^{-x} \cos x \, dx = \tfrac{1}{2} e^{-x}(\sin x - \cos x) + c$$

Example

Find $\int e^{5x} \sin 3x \, dx$.

Solution: L, IT, A, E, T

$u = e^{5x}$ ← $dv = \sin 3x \, dx$

$\dfrac{du}{dx} = 5\,e^{5x}$ $\int dv = \int \sin 3x \, dx$

$du = 5\,e^{5x}\,dx$ $v = -\tfrac{1}{3}\cos 3x$

$\int u \, dv = u \quad v \quad - \int v \quad du$

$\int e^{5x} \sin 3x \, dx = e^{5x}(-\tfrac{1}{3}\cos 3x) - \int -\tfrac{1}{3}\cos 3x \cdot 5\,e^{5x}\,dx$

$\int e^{5x} \sin 3x \, dx = -\tfrac{1}{3}\,e^{5x}\cos 3x + \tfrac{5}{3}\int e^{5x}\cos 3x \, dx$ ①

We now use 'integration by parts' again to find $\int e^{5x}\cos 3x \, dx$

$u = e^{5x}$ $dv = \cos 3x \, dx$

$\dfrac{du}{dx} = 5\,e^{5x}$ $\int dv = \int \cos 3x \, dx$

$du = 5\,e^{5x}\,dx$ $v = \tfrac{1}{3}\sin 3x$

$\int u \, dv = u \quad v \quad - \int v \quad du$

$\int e^{5x} \cos 3x \, dx = e^{5x}(\tfrac{1}{3}\sin 3x) - \int \tfrac{1}{3}\sin 3x \cdot 5\,e^{5x}\,dx$

$\qquad\qquad = \tfrac{1}{3}\,e^{5x}\sin 3x - \tfrac{5}{3}\int e^{5x}\sin 3x \, dx$ ②

(back to where we started)

We now go back to the first result, ①, of 'integration of parts' and substitute ② into ①.

$\int e^{5x} \sin 3x \, dx = -\tfrac{1}{3}\,e^{5x}\cos 3x + \tfrac{5}{3}\int e^{5x}\cos 3x \, dx$ ①

$\int e^{5x} \sin 3x \, dx = -\tfrac{1}{3}\,e^{5x}\cos 3x + \tfrac{5}{3}\left[\tfrac{1}{3}\,e^{5x}\sin 3x - \tfrac{5}{3}\int e^{5x}\sin 3x \, dx\right]$ (put ② into ①)

$\int e^{5x} \sin 3x \, dx = -\tfrac{1}{3}\,e^{5x}\cos 3x + \tfrac{5}{9}\,e^{5x}\sin 3x - \tfrac{25}{9}\int e^{5x}\sin 3x \, dx$

$\left[\int e^{5x} \sin 3x \, dx \text{ on both sides}\right]$

$$\Rightarrow \quad \tfrac{34}{9} \int e^{5x} \sin 3x \, dx = \tfrac{5}{9} e^{5x} \sin 3x - \tfrac{1}{3} e^{5x} \cos 3x$$

$$\Rightarrow \quad \int e^{5x} \sin 3x \, dx = \tfrac{9}{34} \left(\tfrac{5}{9} e^{5x} \sin 3x - \tfrac{1}{3} e^{5x} \cos 3x \right)$$

$$= \tfrac{5}{34} e^{5x} \sin 3x - \tfrac{3}{34} e^{5x} \cos 3x$$

$$= \frac{e^{5x}}{34} (5 \sin 3x - 3 \cos 3x) + c$$

Whenever we integrate functions of the form $e^{kx} \sin nx$ or $e^{kx} \cos nx$, we end up with the original integral on both sides.

Ratio Test

There are many series which are not geometric, but become more like a geometric series as $n \longrightarrow \infty$, i.e.

the ratio $\quad \dfrac{\text{any term}}{\text{previous term}} = \dfrac{u_{n+1}}{u_n} \neq$ a constant

but as $n \longrightarrow \infty$, this ratio approaches a constant R. Such series, like geometric series,

converge   if $-1 < R < 1$

and **diverge**   if $R < -1$ or $R > 1$

Sometimes they are convergent or divergent when $R = \pm 1$.

The test we use to determine whether or not a power series is convergent, or to find the interval of convergence, is called **the ratio test**. The ratio test compares the general term, u_n, to the next term, u_{n+1}, of the same series by considering what happens to the ratio

$\dfrac{u_{n+1}}{u_n}$ as $n \longrightarrow \infty$, i.e. we find $\lim\limits_{n \to \infty} \dfrac{u_{n+1}}{u_n}$.

Suppose $\displaystyle\sum_{n=0}^{\infty} u_n = u_0 + u_1 + u_2 + u_3 + u_4 + u_5 + \cdots$

is a series such that

$$\lim_{n \to \infty} \frac{u_{n+1}}{u_n} = R$$

Then:

1. If $-1 < R < 1$, the series converges

2. If $R < -1$ or $R > 1$, the series diverges

3. If $R = -1$ or $R = 1$, the test is inconclusive

Think about geometric series.

Note:

Consider the power series $\sum_{n=0}^{\infty} a_n x^n = a_0 + a_1 x + a_2 x^2 + \cdots$

If we apply the ratio test and obtain:

1. $R = 0$, the series is convergent for all x
2. $R = \infty$, the series is convergent only for $x = 0$.

Example

Test for convergence $\displaystyle\sum_{n=0}^{\infty} \frac{2^n}{n(n+1)}$

Solution:

$$[\text{replace } n \text{ with } (n+1)]$$

$$u_n = \frac{2^n}{n(n+1)} \implies u_{n+1} = \frac{2^{n+1}}{(n+1)(n+2)}$$

$$\frac{u_{n+1}}{u_n} = \frac{2^{n+1}}{(n+1)(n+2)} \cdot \frac{n(n+1)}{2^n} = \frac{2^{n+1}}{2^n} \cdot \frac{n(n+1)}{(n+1)(n+2)} = \frac{2n}{n+2}$$

To find R, take the limit
(divide each part by n)

$$R = \lim_{n\to\infty} \frac{u_{n+1}}{u_n} = \lim_{n\to\infty} \frac{2n}{n+2} = \lim_{n\to\infty} \frac{2}{1+\dfrac{2}{n}} = \frac{2}{1+0} = 2$$

$$R > 1$$

∴ by the ratio test the series diverges.

Example

Using the ratio test, test for convergence the series $\displaystyle\sum_{n=1}^{\infty} n\left(\tfrac{1}{2}\right)^n$

Solution:

$$[\text{replace } n \text{ with } (n+1)]$$

$$u_n = n\left(\tfrac{1}{2}\right)^n \implies u_{n+1} = (n+1)\left(\tfrac{1}{2}\right)^{n+1}$$

$$\frac{u_{n+1}}{u_n} = \frac{(n+1)\left(\tfrac{1}{2}\right)^{n+1}}{n\left(\tfrac{1}{2}\right)^n} = \frac{(n+1)}{n} \cdot \frac{1}{2} = \frac{n+1}{2n}$$

To find R, take the limit

(divide each part by n)

$$R = \lim_{n \to \infty} \frac{u_{n+1}}{u_n} = \lim_{n \to \infty} \frac{n+1}{2n} = \lim_{n \to \infty} \frac{1 + \dfrac{1}{n}}{2} = \frac{1+0}{2} = \frac{1}{2}$$

$$-1 < R < 1$$

$\therefore$ by the ratio test, the series converges.

Example

Test for convergence the series $\displaystyle\sum_{n=1}^{\infty} \frac{3^n}{n!}$

Solution:

$$u_n = \frac{3^n}{n!} \qquad \Rightarrow \qquad u_{n+1} = \frac{3^{n+1}}{(n+1)!}$$

$$\frac{u_{n+1}}{u_n} = \frac{\dfrac{3^{n+1}}{(n+1)!}}{\dfrac{3^n}{n!}} = \frac{3^{n+1}}{(n+1)!} \cdot \frac{n!}{3^n} = \frac{3^{n+1}}{3^n} \cdot \frac{n!}{(n+1)n!} = \frac{3}{n+1}$$

To find R, take the limit

(divide each part by n)

$$R = \lim_{n \to \infty} \frac{u_{n+1}}{u_n} = \lim_{n \to \infty} \frac{3}{n+1} = \lim_{n \to \infty} \frac{\dfrac{3}{n}}{1 + \dfrac{1}{n}} = \frac{0}{1+0} = \frac{0}{1} = 0$$

$$-1 < R < 1$$

$\therefore$ by the ratio test, the series converges.

Example

Show that the series $\sum\limits_{n=1}^{\infty} \dfrac{x^{2n}}{(2n)!}$ converges for all $x \in \mathbf{R}$.

Solution:

$$u_n = \frac{x^{2n}}{(2n)!} \quad \Longrightarrow \quad u_{n+1} = \frac{x^{2(n+1)}}{[2(n+1)]!} = \frac{x^{2n+2}}{(2n+2)!}$$

$$\frac{u_{n+1}}{u_n} = \frac{x^{2n+2}}{(2n+2)!} \cdot \frac{(2n)!}{x^{2n}} = \frac{x^{2n+2}}{x^{2n}} \cdot \frac{(2n)!}{(2n+2)!} = x^2 \cdot \frac{(2n)!}{(2n+2)(2n+1)(2n)!} = x^2 \cdot \frac{1}{4n^2+6n+2}$$

To find R, take the limit.   (divide each part by n^2)

$$R = \lim_{n \to \infty} \frac{u_{n+1}}{u_n} = \lim_{n \to \infty} x^2 \cdot \frac{1}{4n^2+6n+2} = x^2 \lim_{n \to \infty} \frac{\dfrac{1}{n^2}}{4 + \dfrac{6}{n} + \dfrac{2}{n^2}}$$

$$= x^2 \cdot \frac{0}{4+0+0} = x^2 \cdot \tfrac{0}{4} = x^2 \cdot 0 = 0$$

$\therefore$ by the ratio test, $\sum\limits_{n=1}^{\infty} \dfrac{x^{2n}}{2n!}$ is convergent for all $x \in \mathbf{R}$.

Example

Find the range of values of x for which the series

$\sum\limits_{n=1}^{\infty} \dfrac{x^n}{n \cdot 3^n}$ is **(i)** convergent   **(ii)** divergent.

Solution:

$$u_n = \frac{x^n}{n \cdot 3^n} \quad \Longrightarrow \quad u_{n+1} = \frac{x^{n+1}}{(n+1) \cdot 3^{n+1}}$$

$$\frac{u_{n+1}}{u_n} = \frac{\dfrac{x^{n+1}}{(n+1) \cdot 3^{n+1}}}{\dfrac{x^n}{n \cdot 3^n}} = \frac{x^{n+1}}{(n+1) \cdot 3^{n+1}} \cdot \frac{n \cdot 3^n}{x^n}$$

$$= x \cdot \frac{n}{(n+1)3} = x \cdot \frac{n}{3n+3}$$

To find R, take the limit.

223

$$R = \lim_{n \to \infty} \frac{u_{n+1}}{u_n} = \lim_{n \to \infty} x \cdot \frac{n}{3n+3} = x \lim \frac{1}{3 + \dfrac{3}{n}} \quad \text{(divide each part by } n\text{)}$$

$$= x \cdot \frac{1}{3+0} = x \cdot \frac{1}{3} = \frac{x}{3}$$

Convergent	Divergent
$-1 < R < 1$	$R < -1$ or $R > 1$
$-1 < \frac{x}{3} < 1$	$\frac{x}{3} < -1$ or $\frac{x}{3} > 1$
$-3 < x < 3$	$x < -3$ or $x > 3$

When $x = \pm 3$, $R = \pm 1$ and the ratio test fails, so we cannot determine by methods on our syllabus whether or not the series is convergent for $x = \pm 3$.

Example

Test the series for convergence:

$$\frac{\sqrt{2}}{5} + \frac{\sqrt{3}}{5^2} + \frac{\sqrt{4}}{5^3} + \frac{\sqrt{5}}{5^4} + \cdots$$

Solution:

$$u_n = \frac{\sqrt{n+1}}{5^n} \qquad \Rightarrow \qquad u_{n+1} = \frac{\sqrt{n+2}}{5^{n+1}}$$

$$\frac{u_{n+1}}{u_n} = \frac{\dfrac{\sqrt{n+2}}{5^{n+1}}}{\dfrac{\sqrt{n+1}}{5n}} = \frac{\sqrt{n+2}}{5^{n+1}} \cdot \frac{5^n}{\sqrt{n+1}} = \frac{1}{5} \frac{\sqrt{n+2}}{\sqrt{n+1}} = \frac{1}{5} \sqrt{\frac{n+2}{n+1}}$$

To find R, take the limit.

$$R = \lim_{n \to \infty} \frac{u_{n+1}}{u_n} = \lim_{n \to \infty} \frac{1}{5} \sqrt{\frac{n+2}{n+1}} = \frac{1}{5} \sqrt{\lim_{n \to \infty} \frac{n+2}{n+1}}$$

$$= \frac{1}{5} \sqrt{\lim_{n \to \infty} \frac{1 + \frac{2}{n}}{1 + \frac{1}{n}}} = \frac{1}{5} \sqrt{\frac{1+0}{1+0}} = \frac{1}{5} \sqrt{1} = \frac{1}{5}$$

$$-1 < R < 1$$

$\therefore$ by the ratio test, the series is convergent.

Note: The series is $\displaystyle\sum_{n=1}^{\infty} \frac{\sqrt{n+1}}{5^n}$

Example

Test the series for convergence:

$$1 - \frac{1}{2}\left(\frac{1}{3}\right) + \frac{1}{3}\left(\frac{1}{3}\right)^2 - \frac{1}{4}\left(\frac{1}{3}\right)^3 + \frac{1}{5}\left(\frac{1}{3}\right)^4 - \frac{1}{6}\left(\frac{1}{3}\right)^5 + \cdots$$

Solution:

$$u_n = \frac{(-1)^{n+1}}{n}\left(\frac{1}{3}\right)^{n-1} \qquad \Rightarrow \qquad u_{n+1} = \frac{(-1)^{n+2}}{n+1}\left(\frac{1}{3}\right)^n$$

$$\frac{u_{n+1}}{u_n} = \frac{\dfrac{(-1)^{n+2}}{(n+1)}\left(\dfrac{1}{3}\right)^n}{\dfrac{(-1)^{n+1}}{n}\left(\dfrac{1}{3}\right)^{n-1}} = \frac{(-1)^{n+2}}{(-1)^{n+1}} \cdot \frac{n}{n+1} \cdot \frac{\left(\dfrac{1}{3}\right)^n}{\left(\dfrac{1}{3}\right)^{n-1}} = -1 \cdot \frac{n}{n+1} \cdot \frac{1}{3} = \frac{-n}{3n+3}$$

To find R, take the limit.

$$R = \lim_{n \to \infty} \frac{u_{n+1}}{u_n} = \lim_{n \to \infty} \frac{-n}{3n+3} = \lim_{n \to \infty} \frac{-1}{3 + \dfrac{3}{n}} = \frac{-1}{3+0} = -\frac{1}{3}$$

$$-1 < R < 1$$

$\therefore$ by the ratio test, the series is convergent.

Note: The series is $\displaystyle\sum_{n=1}^{\infty} \frac{(-1)^{n+1}}{n}\left(\frac{1}{3}\right)^{n-1}$

Maclaurin Series

A function may be expanded as an infinite power series, i.e.

$$f(x) = a_0 + a_1 x + a_2 x^2 + a_3 x^3 + a_4 x^4 + \cdots + a_r x^r + \cdots$$

Our task is to evaluate the constants $a_0, a_1, a_2, a_3, a_4, \ldots$

Method:

1. Substitute $x = 0$ on both sides to find a_0.

   To find $a_1, a_2, a_3, a_4, \ldots, a_r, \ldots$ do the following:

2. Differentiate both sides with respect to x.

3. Then substitute $x = 0$ on both sides.

   Repeat steps 2 and 3 to find the required number of terms.

Let $f(x) = a_0 + a_1x + a_2x^2 + a_3x^3 + a_4x^4 + \cdots + a_rx^r + \cdots$

1.	$f(0) = a_0$	$a_0 = \dfrac{f(0)}{0!}$
2.	$f'(x) = a_1 + 2a_2x + 3a_3x^2 + 4a_4x^3 + \cdots$ $f'(0) = a_1$	$a_1 = \dfrac{f'(0)}{1!}$
3.	$f''(x) = 2a_2 + 6a_3x + 12a_4x^2 + \cdots$ $f''(0) = 2a_2$	$a_2 = \dfrac{f''(0)}{2!}$
4.	$f^{(3)}(x) = 6a_3 + 24a_4x + \cdots$ $f^{(3)}(0) = 6a_3$	$a_3 = \dfrac{f^{(3)}(0)}{3!}$
5.	$f^{(4)}(x) = 24a_4 + \cdots$ $f^{(4)}(0) = 24a_4$	$a_4 = \dfrac{f^{(4)}(0)}{4!}$

By continuing this process we can show that:

$$a_r = \frac{f^{(r)}(0)}{r!}$$

By comparing with our original series:

$$f(x) = \quad a_0 \quad + \quad a_1x \quad + \quad a_2x^2 \quad + \quad a_3x^3 \quad + \quad a_4x^4 \quad + \cdots$$
$$\downarrow \qquad \downarrow \qquad \downarrow \qquad \downarrow \qquad \downarrow$$
$$f(x) = \frac{f(0)}{0!} + \frac{f'(0)}{1!}x + \frac{f''(0)}{2!}x^2 + \frac{f^{(3)}(0)}{3!}x^3 + \frac{f^{(4)}(0)}{4!}x^4 + \cdots$$

This is known as *Maclaurin's Theorem* and the series is called the Maclaurin expansion of $f(x)$.

Notice how tidy each term is:

The term with x is multiplied by $f'(0)$ and divided by 1!

The term with x^2 is multiplied by $f''(0)$ and divided by 2!

The term with x^3 is multiplied by $f^{(3)}(0)$ and divided by 3!

The term with x^4 is multiplied by $f^{(4)}(0)$ and divided by 4!

The term with x^{r-1} is multiplied by $f^{(r-1)}(0)$ and divided by $(r-1)!$

The term with x^r is multiplied by $f^{(r)}(0)$ and divided by $r!$

$$f(x) = f(0) + f'(0)x + \frac{f''(0)}{2!}x^2 + \frac{f^{(3)}(0)}{3!}x^3 + \frac{f^{(4)}(0)}{4!}x^4 + \cdots$$

Exponential Series

Example

Find the first five terms in the Maclaurin series for e^x.

Use these first five terms to find an approximate value for:

    (i) e   **(ii)** $e^{0.5}$

Solution:

Let $\;f(x) = e^x = f(0) + f'(0)x + \dfrac{f''(0)}{2!}x^2 + \dfrac{f^{(3)}(0)}{3!}x^3 + \dfrac{f^{(4)}(0)}{4!}x^4 + \cdots$

$f(x) = e^x \qquad\Longrightarrow\qquad f(0) = e^0 = 1$

$f'(x) = e^x \qquad\Longrightarrow\qquad f'(0) = e^0 = 1$

$f''(x) = e^x \qquad\Longrightarrow\qquad f''(0) = e^0 = 1$

$f^{(3)}(x) = e^x \qquad\Longrightarrow\qquad f^{(3)}(0) = e^0 = 1$

$f^{(4)}(x) = e^x \qquad\Longrightarrow\qquad f^{(4)}(0) = e^0 = 1$

(In general: $\;f^r(x) = e^x\;$ and $\;\therefore\;\; f^r(0) = e^0 = 1$)

$\therefore\;\; e^x = 1 + x + \dfrac{x^2}{2!} + \dfrac{x^3}{3!} + \dfrac{x^4}{4!}\;$ (5 terms)

$e = e^1$, replace x with 1.

Thus, $e = e^1 = 1 + 1 + \dfrac{1}{2!} + \dfrac{1}{3!} + \dfrac{1}{4!} = 2.7083333$

$e^{0.5}$, replace x with 0.5

Thus, $e^{0.5} = 1 + 0.5 + \dfrac{(0.5)^2}{2!} + \dfrac{(0.5)^3}{3!} + \dfrac{(0.5)^4}{4!} = 1.6484375$

$$e^x = 1 + x + \frac{x^2}{2!} + \frac{x^3}{3!} + \frac{x^4}{4!} + \cdots + \frac{x^r}{r!} + \cdots$$

This is known as the exponential series in which $u_r = \dfrac{x^{r-1}}{(r-1)!}$

and can be shown by the ratio test to be convergent for all $x \in R$.

To find a series for e^{-x}, replace x with $-x$.

$$e^{-x} = 1 - x + \frac{x^2}{2!} - \frac{x^3}{3!} + \frac{x^4}{4!} - \frac{x^5}{5!} + \frac{x^6}{6!} - \frac{x^7}{7!} + \cdots$$

or go through the same procedure as above for e^x.

Logarithm Series

The function $f(x) = \ln x$ is not defined for $x = 0$ because $f(0) = \ln 0$ is not defined and therefore has no Maclaurin series.

However, we can obtain a Maclaurin series for $\ln(1 + x)$.

Example

Find the Maclaurin series for $\ln(1 + x)$ up to the term containing x^5.

Deduce a Maclaurin series for $\ln(1 - x)$ and hence write down the first 3 non-zero terms

in the expansion of $\ln\left(\dfrac{1+x}{1-x}\right)$.

Use these 3 terms to find an approximate value for $\ln 3$.

Solution:

Let $f(x) = \ln(1 + x) = f(0) + f'(0)x + \dfrac{f''(0)}{2!}x^2 + \dfrac{f^{(3)}(0)}{3!}x^3 + \dfrac{f^{(4)}(0)}{4!}x^4 + \dfrac{f^{(5)}(0)}{5!}$

$\begin{aligned}
f(x) &= \ln(1 + x) & \Longrightarrow \quad & f(0) = \ln 1 = 0 \\
f'(x) &= \frac{1}{1+x} = (1+x)^{-1} & \Longrightarrow \quad & f'(0) = \frac{1}{1} = 1 \\
f''(x) &= -(1+x)^{-2} & \Longrightarrow \quad & f''(0) = -(1)^{-2} = -1 \\
f^{(3)}(x) &= 2(1+x)^{-3} & \Longrightarrow \quad & f^{(3)}(0) = 2(1)^{-3} = 2 = 2! \\
f^{(4)}(x) &= -6(1+x)^{-4} & \Longrightarrow \quad & f^{(4)}(0) = -6(1)^{-4} = -6 = -3! \\
f^{(5)}(x) &= 24(1+x)^{-5} & \Longrightarrow \quad & f^{(5)}(0) = 24(1)^{-5} = 24 = 4!
\end{aligned}$

228

$$\therefore \quad \ln(1 + x) = 0 + 1.x + \frac{(-1)}{2!}x^2 + \frac{2!}{3!}x^3 + \frac{(-3!)}{4!}x^4 + \frac{4!}{5!}x^5$$

$$\therefore \quad \ln(1 + x) = x - \frac{x^2}{2} + \frac{x^3}{3} - \frac{x^4}{4} + \frac{x^5}{5}$$

To find the Maclaurin series for $\ln(1 - x)$, we replace x with $-x$ in the Maclaurin series of $\ln(1 + x)$.

$$\therefore \quad \ln(1 - x) = -x - \frac{x^2}{2} - \frac{x^3}{3} - \frac{x^4}{4} - \frac{x^5}{5}$$

$$\ln\left(\frac{1 + x}{1 - x}\right) = \ln(1 + x) - \ln(1 - x)$$

$$= \left(x - \frac{x^2}{2} + \frac{x^3}{3} - \frac{x^4}{4} + \frac{x^5}{5}\right) - \left(-x - \frac{x^2}{2} - \frac{x^3}{3} - \frac{x^4}{4} - \frac{x^5}{5}\right)$$

(using the series above)

$$= x - \frac{x^2}{2} + \frac{x^3}{3} - \frac{x^4}{4} + \frac{x^5}{5} + x + \frac{x^2}{2} + \frac{x^3}{3} + \frac{x^4}{4} + \frac{x^5}{5}$$

$$= 2x + \frac{2}{3}x^3 + \frac{2}{5}x^5$$

Let $\quad \ln\left(\frac{1 + x}{1 - x}\right) = \ln 3$

$$\implies \quad \frac{1 + x}{1 - x} = 3$$

$$\implies \quad 1 + x = 3 - 3x$$

$$\implies \quad 4x = 2$$

$$\implies \quad x = \tfrac{1}{2}$$

$\therefore$ to evaluate $\ln 3$, replace x with $\frac{1}{2}$ in the first three terms of $\ln\left(\frac{1 + x}{1 - x}\right)$.

$$\therefore \quad \ln 3 = 2(\tfrac{1}{2}) + \tfrac{2}{3}(\tfrac{1}{2})^3 + \tfrac{2}{5}(\tfrac{1}{2})^5 = 1.0958333$$

Trigonometric Series

Example

Use Maclaurin's Theorem to derive a series for $\sin x$ and $\cos x$. Use the ratio test to show that the Maclaurin series for $\cos x$ is convergent for all $x \in \mathbf{R}$.

Use the first five terms to find an approximate value for $\cos(0.2)$.

Note: x is measured in radians.

Solution:

$$f(x) = \sin x = f(0) + f'(0)x + \frac{f''(0)}{2!}x^2 + \frac{f^{(3)}(0)}{3!}x^3 + \cdots$$

$$
\begin{aligned}
f(x) &= \sin x &\Rightarrow&\quad f(0) = \sin 0 = 0 \\
f'(x) &= \cos x &\Rightarrow&\quad f'(0) = \cos 0 = 1 \\
f''(x) &= -\sin x &\Rightarrow&\quad f''(0) = -\sin 0 = 0 \\
f^{(3)}(x) &= -\cos x &\Rightarrow&\quad f^{(3)}(0) = -\cos 0 = -1 \\
f^{(4)}(x) &= \sin x &\Rightarrow&\quad f^{(4)}(0) = \sin 0 = 0 \\
f^{(5)}(x) &= \cos x &\Rightarrow&\quad f^{(5)}(0) = \cos 0 = 1
\end{aligned}
$$

etc.

$$\therefore \quad \sin x = \cancel{0} + (1)x + \frac{\cancel{0}}{\cancel{2!}}x^2 + \frac{(-1)}{3!}x^3 + \frac{\cancel{(0)}}{\cancel{4!}}x^4 + \frac{1}{5!}x^5$$

$$\therefore \quad \sin x = x - \frac{x^3}{3!} + \frac{x^5}{5!} \quad \text{(first three terms)}$$

By completing the pattern:

$$\boxed{\sin x = x - \frac{x^3}{3!} + \frac{x^5}{5!} - \frac{x^7}{7!} + \frac{x^9}{9!} - \frac{x^{11}}{11!} + \cdots}$$

To find the Maclaurin series for $\cos x$, differentiate both sides w.r.t. x.

$$\cos x = 1 - \frac{3x^2}{3!} + \frac{5x^4}{5!} - \frac{7x^6}{7!} + \frac{9x^8}{9!} - \frac{11x^{10}}{11!} + \cdots$$

$$\boxed{\cos x = 1 - \frac{x^2}{2!} + \frac{x^4}{4!} - \frac{x^6}{6!} + \frac{x^8}{8!} - \frac{x^{10}}{10!} + \cdots}$$

$$\left(\textbf{Note:} \quad \frac{3}{3!} = \frac{3}{3.2!} = \frac{1}{2!} \qquad \frac{9}{9!} = \frac{9}{9.8!} = \frac{1}{8!} \quad \text{etc.}\right)$$

From this we can see that the series consists of even powers only.

Terms containing x^2, x^6, x^{10}, ... are negative and
terms containing x^0, x^4, x^8 are positive.

$$\therefore \quad u_n = (-1)^n \frac{x^{2n}}{(2n)!}$$

$$\therefore \quad \cos x = 1 - \frac{x^2}{2!} + \frac{x^4}{4!} - \frac{x^6}{6!} + \frac{x^8}{8!} - \cdots = \sum_{n=0}^{\infty} (-1)^n \frac{x^{2n}}{(2n)!}$$

$$u_n = (-1)^n \frac{x^{2n}}{(2n!)} \quad \Rightarrow \quad u_{n+1} = (-1)^{n+1} \frac{x^{2(n+1)}}{[2(n+1)!]} = (-1)^{n+1} \frac{x^{2n+2}}{(2n+2)!}$$

$$\frac{u_{n+1}}{u_n} = \frac{(-1)^{n+1} x^{2n+2}}{(2n+2)!} \cdot \frac{(2n)!}{(-1)^n x^{2n}}$$

$$= \frac{(-1)^{n+1}}{(-1)^n} \cdot \frac{x^{2n+2}}{x^{2n}} \cdot \frac{\cancel{(2n)!}}{(2n+2)(2n+1)\cancel{(2n)!}}$$

$$= \frac{-x^2}{4n^2 + 6n + 2} = -x^2 \cdot \frac{1}{4n^2 + 6n + 2}$$

To find R, take the limit.

$$R = \lim_{n \to \infty} \frac{u_{n+1}}{u_n} = \lim_{n \to \infty} -x^2 \cdot \frac{1}{4n^2 + 6n + 2}$$

$$= -x^2 \lim_{n \to \infty} \frac{\dfrac{1}{n^2}}{4 + \dfrac{6}{n} + \dfrac{2}{n^2}} = -x^2 \cdot \frac{0}{4 + 0 + 0} = x^2 \cdot 0 = 0$$

$\therefore$ By the ratio test,

$$\cos x = 1 - \frac{x^2}{2!} + \frac{x^4}{4!} - \frac{x^6}{6!} + \frac{x^8}{8!} - \cdots = \sum_{n=0}^{\infty} (-1)^n \frac{x^{2n}}{(2n)!}$$

is convergent for all $x \in \mathbf{R}$.

$$\cos x = 1 - \frac{x^2}{2!} + \frac{x^4}{4!} - \frac{x^6}{6!} + \frac{x^8}{8!}$$

$$\cos(0.2) = 1 - \frac{(0.2)^2}{2!} + \frac{(0.2)^4}{4!} - \frac{(0.2)^6}{6!} + \frac{(0.2)^8}{8!}$$

$$= 0.9800665$$

Example

Use Maclaurin's theorem to find the first 3 non-zero terms in the expansion of $\sin^2 x$.

Solution:

Let $f(x) = \sin^2 x = f(0) + f'(0)x + \dfrac{f''(0)}{2!}x^2 + \dfrac{f^{(3)}(0)}{3!}x^3 + \cdots$

$$
\begin{aligned}
f(x) &= \sin^2 x & &\Rightarrow & f(0) &= 0 \\
f'(x) &= 2\sin x \cos x = \sin 2x & &\Rightarrow & f'(0) &= 0 \\
f''(x) &= 2\cos 2x & &\Rightarrow & f''(0) &= 2 \\
f^{(3)}(x) &= -4\sin 2x & &\Rightarrow & f^{(3)}(0) &= 0 \\
f^{(4)}(x) &= -8\cos 2x & &\Rightarrow & f^{(4)}(0) &= -8 \\
f^{(5)}(x) &= 16\sin 2x & &\Rightarrow & f^{(5)}(0) &= 0 \\
f^{(6)}(x) &= 32\cos 2x & &\Rightarrow & f^{(6)}(0) &= 32
\end{aligned}
$$

$\therefore \quad \sin^2 x = \cancel{0} + \cancel{0}.x + \dfrac{2}{2!}x^2 + \dfrac{\cancel{0}}{\cancel{3!}}x^3 + \dfrac{-8}{4!}x^4 + \dfrac{\cancel{0}}{\cancel{5!}}x^5 + \dfrac{32}{6!}x^6$

$\therefore \quad \sin^2 x = x^2 - \dfrac{x^4}{3} + \dfrac{2x^6}{45} \qquad$ (first three terms)

Binomial Series

Example

Find $f(0), f'(0), f''(0), f'''(0)$ for

$\qquad f(x) = (1+x)^m.$

Hence write the first four terms and the $(r+1)$th term of the Maclaurin series for $f(x) = (1+x)^m$.

Test the series for convergence when $m \ \varepsilon \ Q \backslash N$.

Solution:

Let $f(x) = (1+x)^m = f(0) + f'(0)x + f''(0)x^2 + f'''(0)x^3 + \cdots$

$$
\begin{aligned}
f(x) &= (1+x)^m & &\Rightarrow & f(0) &= 1 \\
f'(x) &= m(1+x)^{m-1} & &\Rightarrow & f'(0) &= m \\
f''(x) &= m(m-1)(1+x)^{m-2} & &\Rightarrow & f''(0) &= m(m-1) \\
f'''(x) &= m(m-1)(m-2)(1+x)^{m-3} & &\Rightarrow & f'''(0) &= m(m-1)(m-2)
\end{aligned}
$$

Thus, $f(x) = (1 + x)^m$

$$= 1 + mx + \frac{m(m-1)}{2!}x^2 + \frac{m(m-1)(m-2)}{3!}x^3$$

$$+ \cdots \frac{m(m-1)(m-2)\ldots(m-r)(m+1-r)}{r!}x^r + \cdots$$

Thus, $\quad u_{r+1} = \dfrac{m(m-1)(m-2)\ldots(m-r)(m+1-r)}{r!}x^r$

and $\quad u_r = \dfrac{m(m-1)(m-2)\ldots(m-r)}{(r-1)!}x^{r-1}$

Ratio test:

$$\frac{u_{r+1}}{u_r} = \frac{m(m-1)(m-2)\ldots(m-r)(m+1-r)}{m(m-1)(m-2)\ldots(m-r)} \cdot \frac{(r-1)!}{r!} \cdot \frac{x^r}{x^{r-1}} = \frac{m+1-r}{r}x$$

$$R = \lim_{r \to \infty} \frac{u_{r+1}}{u_r} = \lim_{r \to \infty} \left(\frac{m+1-r}{r}\right)x = \lim_{r \to \infty}\left(\frac{m}{r} + \frac{1}{r} - 1\right)x = (-1)(x) = -x$$

Convergent for $-1 < R < 1$,

Thus, convergent for $-1 < -x < 1$, i.e. $-1 < x < 1$

Example

Use Maclaurin's theorem to obtain the first four terms in the series for $\sqrt{1+3x}$ and use these four terms to find an approximate value for $\sqrt{1.06}$.

Solution:

Let $\quad f(x) = (1+3x)^{\frac{1}{2}} = f(0) + f'(0)x + \dfrac{f''(0)}{2!}x^2 + \dfrac{f^{(3)}(0)}{3!}x^3 + \cdots$

$f(x) = (1+3x)^{\frac{1}{2}} \qquad\qquad\qquad\qquad \Rightarrow \qquad f(0) = 1$

$f'(x) = \frac{1}{2}(1+3x)^{-\frac{1}{2}} \cdot 3 = \frac{3}{2}(1+3x)^{-\frac{1}{2}} \qquad \Rightarrow \qquad f'(0) = \frac{3}{2}$

$f''(x) = -\frac{1}{2} \cdot \frac{3}{2}(1+3x)^{-\frac{3}{2}} \cdot 3 = -\frac{9}{4}(1+3x)^{-\frac{3}{2}} \qquad \Rightarrow \qquad f''(0) = -\frac{9}{4}$

$f^{(3)}(x) = -\frac{3}{2} \cdot -\frac{9}{4}(1+3x)^{-\frac{5}{2}} \cdot 3 = \frac{81}{8}(1+3x)^{-\frac{5}{2}} \qquad \Rightarrow \qquad f^{(3)}(0) = \frac{81}{8}$

$\therefore \quad (1+3x)^{\frac{1}{2}} = 1 + \frac{3}{2}x - \dfrac{\frac{9}{4}}{2!}x^2 + \dfrac{\frac{81}{8}}{3!}x^3$

$(1+3x)^{\frac{1}{2}} = 1 + \frac{3}{2}x - \frac{9}{8}x^2 + \frac{27}{16}x^3 \qquad$ (first 4 terms)

$$\text{let} \quad \sqrt{1 + 3x} = \sqrt{1.06}$$
$$\Rightarrow \quad 1 + 3x = 1.06$$
$$3x = 0.06$$
$$x = 0.02$$

∴ Substitute $x = 0.02$ into the series to find $\sqrt{1.06}$

∴ $\sqrt{1.06} = 1 + \frac{3}{2}(0.02) - \frac{9}{8}(0.02)^2 + \frac{27}{16}(0.02)^3 = 1.0295635$

Approximating π

We use the power series for $\tan^{-1} x$ to approximate π.

Example

Find the Maclaurin series for $\tan^{-1} x$ and use the first eight terms to find an approximate value for π.

Solution:

Let $f(x) = \tan^{-1} x = f(0) + f'(0)x + \dfrac{f''(0)}{2!}x^2 + \dfrac{f^{(3)}(0)}{3!}x^3 + \cdots$

$f(x) = \tan^{-1} x$ $\Rightarrow$ $f(0) = 0$

$f'(x) = \dfrac{1}{1 + x^2} = (1 + x^2)^{-1}$ $\Rightarrow$ $f'(0) = 1$

$f''(x) = -1(1 + x^2)^{-2} \cdot 2x = \dfrac{-2x}{(1 + x^2)^2}$ $\Rightarrow$ $f''(0) = 0$

$f^{(3)}(x) = \dfrac{6x^2 - 2}{(1 + x^2)^3}$ $\Rightarrow$ $f^{(3)}(0) = -2$

∴ $\tan^{-1} x = 0 + 1 \cdot x + \dfrac{0}{2!}x^2 + \dfrac{-2}{3!}x^3 + \cdots$

∴ $\tan^{-1} x - \dfrac{x^3}{3} + \dfrac{x^5}{5} - \dfrac{x^7}{7} + \dfrac{x^9}{9} - \dfrac{x^{11}}{11} + \dfrac{x^{13}}{13} - \dfrac{x^{15}}{15}$

let $x = 1$ on both sides

∴ $\tan^{-1} 1 = 1 - \frac{1}{3} + \frac{1}{5} - \frac{1}{7} + \frac{1}{9} - \frac{1}{11} + \frac{1}{13} - \frac{1}{15}$

$\Rightarrow \dfrac{\pi}{4} = 0.754267954$

$\Rightarrow \pi = 4(0.754267954) = 3.017071817$

(not a good approximation to 3.141592654 after 8 terms)

Finding a Maclaurin series for $\tan^{-1}x$ involves a lot of tedious work. To overcome this we find a series for

$$\frac{1}{1+x^2}$$

and then use the fact that

$$\int \frac{1}{1+x^2}\,dx = \tan^{-1}x$$

These are a few different ways to find a series for $\dfrac{1}{1+x^2}$.

Here are two:

1. Use previous Maclaurin series.
2. Long division.

1. Previous Maclaurin series

Earlier we showed that:

$$\ln(1+x) = x - \frac{x^2}{2} + \frac{x^3}{3} - \frac{x^4}{4} + \frac{x^5}{5} - \frac{x^6}{6} + \frac{x^7}{7} - \cdots$$

(differentiate both sides w.r.t. x)

$$\implies \frac{1}{1+x} = 1 - x + x^2 - x^3 + x^4 - x^5 + x^6 - x^7 + \cdots$$

(replace x with x^2 on both sides)

$$\implies \frac{1}{1+x^2} = 1 - x^2 + x^4 - x^6 + x^8 - x^{10} + x^{12} - x^{14} + \cdots$$

(integrate both sides w.r.t. x)

$$\implies \tan^{-1}x = x - \frac{x^3}{3} + \frac{x^5}{5} - \frac{x^7}{7} + \frac{x^9}{9} - \frac{x^{11}}{11} + \frac{x^{13}}{13} - \frac{x^{15}}{15} + \cdots$$

2. Long division

$$
\begin{array}{r}
1 - x^2 + x^4 - x^6 + x^8 - x^{10} + x^{12} - \cdots \\[2pt]
\hline
\end{array}
$$

$1 + x^2 \,\big)\, 1$

$$
\begin{aligned}
&\underline{1 + x^2} \\
&\;-x^2 + 0 \\
&\;\underline{-x^2 - x^4} \\
&\qquad x^4 + 0 \\
&\qquad \underline{x^4 + x^6} \\
&\qquad\;\; -x^6 + 0 \\
&\qquad\;\; \underline{-x^6 - x^8} \\
&\qquad\qquad x^8 + 0 \\
&\qquad\qquad \underline{x^8 + x^{10}} \\
&\qquad\qquad\;\; -x^{10} + 0 \\
&\qquad\qquad\;\; \underline{-x^{10} - x^{12}} \\
&\qquad\qquad\qquad x^{12} + \cdots
\end{aligned}
$$

$$
\therefore \quad \frac{1}{1+x^2} = 1 - x^2 + x^4 - x^6 + x^8 - x^{10} + x^{12} - x^{14} + \cdots
$$

(integrate both sides w.r.t. x)

$$
\Rightarrow \quad \tan^{-1} x = x - \frac{x^3}{3} + \frac{x^5}{5} - \frac{x^7}{7} + \frac{x^9}{9} - \frac{x^{11}}{11} + \frac{x^{13}}{13} - \frac{x^{15}}{15} + \cdots
$$

The Maclaurin series for $\tan^{-1} x$ converges very slowly. To overcome this we use the following result:

$$
\boxed{\; \tan^{-1} x + \tan^{-1} y = \tan^{-1} \frac{x+y}{1-xy}, \quad \text{for } xy < 1 \;}
$$

The basic idea is to find two fractions x and y such that

$$
\tan^{-1} x + \tan^{-1} y = \tan^{-1} 1 = \tfrac{\pi}{4}
$$

and by combining two series into one we will get a series that converges far more rapidly. Consider the next example.

Example

Find the Maclaurin series for $\tan^{-1} x$, indicating the general term.

Show that $\tan^{-1}\frac{1}{2} + \tan^{-1}\frac{1}{3} = \frac{\pi}{4}$ and deduce an infinite series for π, indicating the first few terms with non-zero coefficients. Use the first four terms to find an approximation for π.

Solution:

Using long division on $\dfrac{1}{1+x^2}$

$$
\begin{array}{r}
1 - x^2 + x^4 - x^6 + \cdots \\
1 + x^2 \,\overline{\big)\, 1 + 0 + 0 + 0} \\
\underline{1 + x^2} \\
-x^2 + 0 \\
\underline{-x^2 - x^4} \\
x^4 + 0 \\
\underline{x^4 + x^6} \\
-x^6 + 0 \cdots
\end{array}
$$

$\therefore$ By long division

$$\frac{1}{1+x^2} = 1 - x^2 + x^4 - x^6 + x^8 - x^{10} + x^{12} - \cdots$$

$$\Rightarrow \quad \tan^{-1} x = x - \frac{x^3}{3} + \frac{x^5}{5} - \frac{x^7}{7} + \frac{x^9}{9} - \frac{x^{11}}{11} + \frac{x^{13}}{13} - \cdots$$

integrating both sides w.r.t. x

$$\tan^{-1}\frac{1}{2} + \tan^{-1}\frac{1}{3} = \tan^{-1}\frac{\frac{1}{2} + \frac{1}{3}}{1 - \frac{1}{2} \times \frac{1}{3}} = \tan^{-1} 1 = \frac{\pi}{4}$$

$$\tan^{-1} x = x - \frac{x^3}{3} + \frac{x^5}{5} - \frac{x^7}{7} + \cdots$$

$$\tan^{-1}\frac{1}{2} = \frac{1}{2} - \frac{\left(\frac{1}{2}\right)^3}{3} + \frac{\left(\frac{1}{2}\right)^5}{5} - \frac{\left(\frac{1}{2}\right)^7}{7} + \cdots$$

$$\tan^{-1}\frac{1}{3} = \frac{1}{3} - \frac{\left(\frac{1}{3}\right)^3}{3} + \frac{\left(\frac{1}{3}\right)^5}{5} - \frac{\left(\frac{1}{3}\right)^7}{7} + \cdots$$

Thus, $\tan^{-1}\frac{1}{2} + \tan^{-1}\frac{1}{3}$

$$= \left[\frac{1}{2} + \frac{1}{3}\right] - \frac{1}{3}\left[\left(\frac{1}{2}\right)^3 + \left(\frac{1}{3}\right)^3\right] + \frac{1}{5}\left[\left(\frac{1}{2}\right)^5 + \left(\frac{1}{3}\right)^5\right] - \frac{1}{7}\left[\left(\frac{1}{2}\right)^7 + \left(\frac{1}{3}\right)^7\right] + \cdots$$

but $\tan^{-1}\frac{1}{2} + \tan^{-1}\frac{1}{3} = \frac{\pi}{4}$

$$\therefore \quad \frac{\pi}{4} = [\tfrac{1}{2} + \tfrac{1}{3}] - \tfrac{1}{3}[(\tfrac{1}{2})^3 + (\tfrac{1}{3})^3] + \tfrac{1}{5}[(\tfrac{1}{2})^5 + (\tfrac{1}{3})^5] - \tfrac{1}{7}[(\tfrac{1}{2})^7 + (\tfrac{1}{3})^7] + \cdots$$

$$\therefore \quad \pi = 4\{[\tfrac{1}{2} + \tfrac{1}{3}] - \tfrac{1}{3}[(\tfrac{1}{2})^3 + (\tfrac{1}{3})^3] + \tfrac{1}{5}[(\tfrac{1}{2})^5 + (\tfrac{1}{3})^5] - \tfrac{1}{7}[(\tfrac{1}{2})^7 + (\tfrac{1}{3})^7] + \cdots$$

$$\pi = 4(0.78521264) = 3.140850562 \quad \text{(using four terms)}$$

$$u_n = 4\left[\frac{(-1)^{n+1}}{2n-1} [(\tfrac{1}{2})^{2n-1} + (\tfrac{1}{3})^{2n-1}] \right]$$

$$\pi = 4 \sum_{n=1}^{\infty} \frac{(-1)^{n+1}}{2n-1} [x^{2n-1} + y^{2n-1}]$$

provided $\tan^{-1} x + \tan^{-1} y = \tan^{-1} 1$, $xy < 1$

7. PROOFS

Equation of a Tangent to a Circle

The equation of the tangent to the circle $x^2 + y^2 = r^2$ at the point (x_1, y_1) on the circle is: $x_1 x + y_1 y = r^2$

Proof:

From the diagram:

Slope of radius $R = \dfrac{y_1 - 0}{x_1 - 0} = \dfrac{y_1}{x_1}$

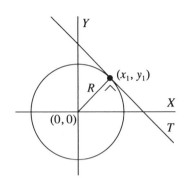

Thus, slope of the tangent T is $-\dfrac{x_1}{y_1}$, as $R \perp T$.

Equation of the tangent, T:

$$(y - y_1) = m(x - x_1)$$

$$\implies \quad (y - y_1) = -\frac{x_1}{y_1}(x - x_1)$$

$$\implies \quad y_1 y - y_1^2 = -x_1 x + x_1^2$$

$$\implies \quad x_1 x + y_1 y = x_1^2 + y_1^2$$

$$\implies \quad x_1 x + y_1 y = r^2 \quad \text{(since } (x_1, y_1) \text{ is on the circle, } x_1^2 + y_1^2 = r^2\text{)}$$

Thus, the equation of the tangent T is $x_1 x + y_1 y = r^2$

Angle between Two Lines

If θ is the angle between two lines with slopes m_1 and m_2, then:

$$\tan \theta = \frac{m_1 - m_2}{1 + m_1 m_2}$$

Proof:

Let $L_1: y = m_1x + c_1$ and $L_2: y = m_2x + c_2$
be two lines making angles α and β,
respectively, with the X-axis. Let θ be
one of the angles made by the
intersection of the lines.

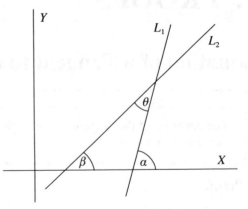

The slope of $L_1 = m_1 = \tan \alpha$

The slope of $L_2 = m_2 = \tan \beta$

From the diagram, $\alpha = \theta + \beta$ (exterior angle)

$\Rightarrow \qquad \theta = \alpha - \beta$

$\Rightarrow \qquad \tan \theta = \tan(\alpha - \beta)$

$$= \frac{\tan \alpha - \tan \beta}{1 + \tan \alpha \tan \beta} = \frac{m_1 - m_2}{1 + m_1m_2}$$

Perpendicular Distance from a Point to a Line

> The perpendicular distance, d, from the point (x_1, y_1) to the line $ax + by + c = 0$ is
> given by:
>
> $$\frac{|ax_1 + by_1 + c|}{\sqrt{a^2 + b^2}}$$

Proof:

Let L be the line $ax + by + c = 0$,
intersecting the X-axis at q and the Y-axis
at r. Let p be the point (x_1, y_1) and let d
be the perpendicular distance from p to L.

The coordinates of q are $\left(-\dfrac{c}{a}, 0\right)$ and

the coordinates of r are $\left(0, -\dfrac{c}{b}\right)$.

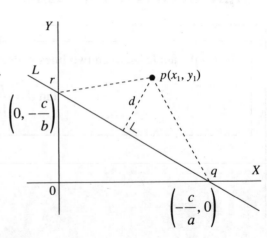

Method: We find the area of Δpqr by
two different methods and equate them.

1. By formula.

Area of Δpqr

$= \frac{1}{2}|\text{base}|.|\text{perpendicular height}|$

$= \frac{1}{2}|qr|.d$

$= \frac{1}{2}d\sqrt{\left(\frac{c}{a}\right)^2 + \left(-\frac{c}{b}\right)^2}$

$= \frac{1}{2}d\sqrt{\frac{c^2}{a^2} + \frac{c^2}{b^2}}$

$= \frac{1}{2}d\sqrt{\frac{a^2c^2 + b^2c^2}{a^2b^2}}$

$= \frac{1}{2}d\sqrt{\frac{c^2}{a^2b^2}(a^2 + b^2)}$

$= \frac{1}{2}d.\frac{c}{ab}\sqrt{a^2 + b^2}$

2. By the translation $\left(0, -\dfrac{c}{b}\right) \to (0, 0)$.

$\left(0, -\dfrac{c}{b}\right) \to (0, 0)$, thus

$\left(-\dfrac{c}{a}, 0\right) \to \left(-\dfrac{c}{a}, \dfrac{c}{b}\right)$, and

$(x_1, y_1) \to \left(x_1, y_1 + \dfrac{c}{b}\right)$

Area of $\Delta pqr = \frac{1}{2}|x_1 y_2 - x_2 y_1|$

$= \frac{1}{2}\left|x_1\left(\frac{c}{b}\right) - \left(-\frac{c}{a}\right)\left(y_1 + \frac{c}{b}\right)\right|$

$= \frac{1}{2}\left|\frac{cx_1}{b} + \frac{cy_1}{a} + \frac{c^2}{ab}\right|$

$= \frac{1}{2}\left|\frac{acx_1 + bcy_1 + c^2}{ab}\right|$

$= \frac{1}{2}\frac{c}{ab}|ax_1 + by_1 + c|$

Area of Δpqr = Area of Δpqr

$\Rightarrow \quad \frac{1}{2}d\,\dfrac{c}{ab}\,\sqrt{a^2+b^2} = \frac{1}{2}\,\dfrac{c}{ab}\,|ax_1 + by_1 + c|$

$\Rightarrow \quad d\,\sqrt{a^2+b^2} = |ax_1 + by_1 + c|$

$\Rightarrow \quad d = \dfrac{|ax_1 + by_1 + c|}{\sqrt{a^2+b^2}}$

Cosine Rule

$$\text{In } \Delta abc, \quad a^2 = b^2 + c^2 - 2bc\cos A$$

Proof:

In Δabc, let $|cd|$ be the length of the perpendicular from c to $[ab]$. Let $|cd| = h$ and $|ad| = x$, thus, $|db| = c - x$

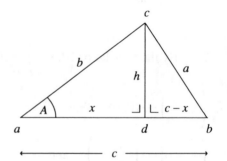

Using Pythagoras' Theorem:

On Δacd: $\quad h^2 + x^2 = b^2 \Rightarrow h^2 = b^2 - x^2$

On Δbcd: $\quad h^2 + (c-x)^2 = a^2 \Rightarrow h^2 = a^2 - (c-x)^2$

Thus, $\quad a^2 - (c-x)^2 = b^2 - x^2 \quad (h^2 = h^2)$

$\Rightarrow \quad a^2 - c^2 + 2cx - x^2 = b^2 - x^2$

$\Rightarrow \quad\quad\quad a^2 = b^2 + c^2 - 2cx$

$\Rightarrow \quad\quad\quad a^2 = b^2 + c^2 - 2bc\cos A \quad$ (replace x with $b\cos A$)

In Δacd,

$$\cos A = \frac{x}{b}$$

$\Rightarrow \quad b\cos A = x$

Cos (A + B)

$$\cos(A + B) = \cos A \cos B - \sin A \sin B$$

Proof:

Let $p(\cos A, \sin A)$ and $q(\cos B, \sin B)$ be two points on the unit circle.

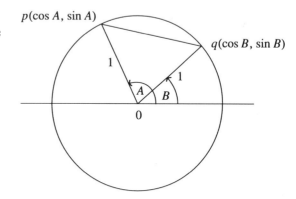

Using the distance formula:

$$|pq|^2 = (\cos A - \cos B)^2 + (\sin A - \sin B)^2$$
$$= \cos^2 A - 2\cos A \cos B + \cos^2 B + \sin^2 A - 2\sin A \sin B + \sin^2 B$$
$$= (\cos^2 A + \sin^2 A) + (\cos^2 B + \sin^2 B) - 2(\cos A \cos B + \sin A \sin B)$$
$$= 1 + 1 - 2(\cos A \cos B + \sin A \sin B)$$
$$= 2 - 2(\cos A \cos B + \sin A \sin B) \qquad ①$$

Using the cosine rule on $\triangle opq$:

$$|pq|^2 = 1 + 1 - 2\cos(A - B)$$
$$= 2 - 2\cos(A - B) \qquad ②$$

Equating ① and ② gives:

$$2 - 2\cos(A - B) = 2 - 2(\cos A \cos B + \sin A \sin B)$$
$$\Rightarrow \qquad \cos(A - B) = \cos A \cos B + \sin A \sin B$$

Replace B with $-B$ on both sides.

$$\Rightarrow \quad \cos[A - (-B)] = \cos A \cos(-B) + \sin A \sin(-B)$$
$$\Rightarrow \qquad \cos(A + B) = \cos A \cos B - \sin A \sin B$$

$[\cos(-B) = \cos B \text{ and } \sin(-B) = -\sin B]$

Difference Equations: Theorem

If α and β are the roots of the quadratic equation $px^2 + qx + r = 0$ and $u_n = l\alpha^n + m\beta^n$ for all n, then:

$pu_{n+2} + qu_{n+1} + ru_n = 0$ for all n.

Proof:

$$u_n = l\alpha^n + m\beta^n$$

$$\Rightarrow \quad u_{n+1} = l\alpha^{n+1} + m\beta^{n+1} = \alpha l\alpha^n + \beta m\beta^n$$

$$\Rightarrow \quad u_{n+2} = l\alpha^{n+2} + m\beta^{n+2} = \alpha^2 l\alpha^n + \beta^2 m\beta^n$$

If α and β are the roots of $px^2 + qx + r = 0$, then:

$$p\alpha^2 + q\alpha + r = 0 \quad \text{and} \quad p\beta^2 + q\beta + r = 0$$

Thus, $pu_{n+2} + qu_{n+1} + ru_n$

$$= p(\alpha^2 l\alpha^n + \beta^2 m\beta^n) + q(\alpha l\alpha^n + \beta m\beta^n) + r(l\alpha^n + m\beta^n)$$

$$= p\alpha^2 l\alpha^n + p\beta^2 m\beta^n + q\alpha l\alpha^n + q\beta m\beta^n + rl\alpha^n + rm\beta^n$$

$$= l\alpha^n(p\alpha^2 + q\alpha + r) + m\beta^n(p\beta^2 + q\beta + r)$$

$$= l\alpha^n(0) + m\beta^n(0)$$

$$= 0$$

Attempt **FIVE** questions from Section **A** and **ONE** question from Section **B**.

Each qestions carries 50 marks.

WARNING: Marks may be lost if all necessary work is not clearly shown.

SECTION A

Answer FIVE questions from this section.

---

1. **(a)** A circle with centre $(-3, 7)$ passes through the point $(5, -8)$.
Find the equation of the circle.

(b) The equation of a circle is $(x + 1)^2 + (y - 8)^2 = 160$.

The line $x - 3y + 25 = 0$ intersects the circle at the points p and q.

(i) Find the co-ordinates of p and the co-ordinates of q.

(ii) Investigate if $[pq]$ is a diameter of the circle.

(c) The circle $x^2 + y^2 + 2gx + 2fy + c = 0$ passes through the points $(3, 3)$ and $(4, 1)$.

The line $3x - y - 6 = 0$ is a tangent to the circle at $(3, 3)$.

(i) Find the real numbers g, f and c.

(ii) Find the co-ordinates of the point on the circle at which the tangent parallel to $3x - y - 6 = 0$ touches the circle.

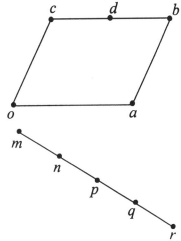

2. **(a)** *oabc* is a parallelogram where o is the origin.
d is the midpoint of $[cb]$.

(i) Express $\vec{b}$ in terms of $\vec{a}$ and $\vec{c}$.

(ii) Express $\vec{d}$ in terms of $\vec{a}$ and $\vec{c}$.

(b) $[mr]$ is divided into four line segments of equal length by the points n, p and q.

Given that $\vec{m} = -2\vec{i} + 3\vec{j}$ and $\vec{q} = 7\vec{i} - 9\vec{j}$, express

(i) $\vec{p}$ in terms of $\vec{i}$ and $\vec{j}$

(ii) $\vec{r}$ in terms of $\vec{i}$ and $\vec{j}$.

(c) rst is a triangle where $\vec{r} = -\vec{i} + 2\vec{j}$, $\vec{s} = -4\vec{i} - 2\vec{j}$ and $\vec{t} = 3\vec{i} - \vec{j}$.

    (i) Express $\vec{rs}$, $\vec{st}$ and $\vec{tr}$ in terms of $\vec{i}$ and $\vec{j}$.

    (ii) Show that the triangle rst is right-angled at r.

    (iii) Find the measure of $\angle rst$.

3. **(a)** The line B contains the points $(6, -2)$ and $(-4, 10)$.

    The line A with equation $ax + 6y + 21 = 0$ is perpendicular to B.

    Find the value of the real number a.

(b) f is the transformation $(x, y) \rightarrow (x', y')$ where

$$x' = -5x - 6y$$
$$y' = 4x + 3y.$$

    L is the line $x - 9y = 2$.

    (i) Find the equation of $f(L)$, the image of L under f:

    M is a line containing the point $(1, k)$ where $k \in \mathbf{Z}$.

    (ii) Given that $f(M)$ is $5x' - 2y' + 3k = 0$, find the value of k.

(c) N is the line $tx + (t - 2)y + 4 = 0$ where $t \in \mathbf{R}$.

    (i) Write down the slope of N in terms of t.

    (ii) Given that the angle between N and the line $x - 3y + 1 = 0$ is $45°$, find the two possible values of t.

4. **(a)** The length of an arc of a circle is 10 cm. The radius of the circle is 4 cm. The measure of the angle at the centre of the circle subtended by the arc is θ.

    (i) Find θ in radians.

    (ii) Find θ in degrees, correct to the nearest degree.

(b) **(i)** Write $\cos 2x$ in terms of $\sin x$.

    (ii) Hence, find all the solutions of the equation

$$\cos 2x - \sin x = 1$$

    in the domain $0° \leqslant x \leqslant 360°$.

(c) A triangle has sides a, b and c.

    The angles opposite a, b and c are A, B and C, respectively.

    (i) Prove that $a^2 = b^2 + c^2 - 2bc \cos A$.

    (ii) Show that $c(b \cos A - a \cos B) = b^2 - a^2$.

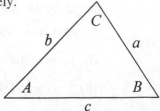

5. **(a)** Evaluate $\displaystyle\lim_{\theta \to 0} \frac{\sin 7\theta}{\sin 2\theta}$.

(b) xyz is a triangle where $|xy| = 8$ cm and $|yz| = 6$ cm.

Given that the area of triangle xyz is 12 cm^2, find

(i) the two possible values of $|\angle xyz|$.

(ii) the two possible values of $|xz|$, correct to one decimal place.

(c) A is an obtuse angle such that

$$\sin\left(A + \frac{\pi}{6}\right) + \sin\left(A - \frac{\pi}{6}\right) = \frac{4\sqrt{3}}{5}.$$

(i) Find $\sin A$ and $\tan A$.

(ii) Given that $\tan(A + B) = \frac{1}{2}$, find $\tan B$ and express your answer in the form $\dfrac{p}{q}$ where $p, q \in \mathbf{Z}$ and $q \neq 0$.

6. **(a)** **(i)** How many different sets of three books or of four books can be selected from six different books?

(ii) How many of the above sets contain one particular book?

(b) Solve the difference equation

$$u_{n+2} - 8u_{n+1} + 11u_n = 0, \qquad \text{where } n \geqslant 0,$$

given that $u_0 = 0$ and $u_1 = 2\sqrt{15}$.

(c) A box contains four silver coins, two gold coins and x copper coins.

Two coins are picked at random, and without replacement, from the box.

(i) Write down an expression in x for the probability that the two coins are copper.

If it is known that the probability of picking two copper coins is $\frac{4}{13}$,

(ii) how many coins are in the box and

(iii) what is the probability that neither of the two coins picked is copper?

7. **(a)** **(i)** How many different four-letter arrangements can be made from the letters of the word FRIDAY if each letter is used no more than once in each arrangement?

(ii) How many of the above arrangements begin with the letter D and also end with a vowel?

(b) To play a game a player spins a wheel.

The wheel is fixed to a wall. It spins freely around its centre point. Its rim is divided equally into twelve regions. Three of the regions are coloured red. Four are coloured blue. Five are coloured green.

When the wheel stops an arrow fixed to the wall points to one of the regions. All the regions are equally likely to stop at the arrow. The colour of the region to which the arrow points is the outcome of the game.

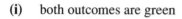

arrow

When the game is played twice, calculate the probability that

(i) both outcomes are green

(ii) both outcomes are the same colour

(iii) the first outcome is red and the second outcome is green

(iv) one outcome is green and the other outcome is blue.

(c) Consider the numbers

$$1, \quad k, \quad 3k-2, \quad 9$$

where $k \in \mathbf{Z}$.

The mean of these numbers is $\bar{x}$. The standard deviation is σ.

(i) Express $\bar{x}$ in terms of k.

(ii) Given that $\sigma = \sqrt{20}$, find the value of k.

SECTION B

Answer ONE question from this section.

---

8. **(a)** Use integration by parts to find $\displaystyle\int x \cos x \, dx$

(b) $f(x) = f(0) + \dfrac{f'(0)x}{1!} + \dfrac{f''(0)x^2}{2!} + \dfrac{f'''(0)x^3}{3!} + \dots$ is the Maclaurin series for $f(x)$.

(i) Derive the Maclaurin series for $f(x) = \sin x$ up to and including the term containing x^7.

(ii) Write down the general term and use the Ratio Test to show that the series converges for all $x \in \mathbf{R}$.

(c) o is the origin, $(0, 0)$.

$p(x, y)$ is a point on the curve $y = \dfrac{9}{x}$, where $x > 0$.

$|op|$ is the distance from the origin to p.

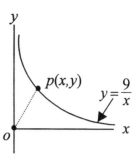

(i) Express $|op|$ in terms of x.

(ii) Given that there is one value of x for which $|op|$ is a minimum, find this value of x.

(iii) Hence, find the minimum value of $|op|$.

---

9. **(a)** Two fair dice are thrown.

(i) What is the probability of getting a four on both dice?

(ii) What is the probability of getting a four on at least one die?

(b) The probability of passing a driving test is $\frac{2}{3}$. Six students take the test.

Use a binomial distribution to find

(i) the probability that none of the students passes the test

(ii) the probability that half of the students pass the test.

(c) A particular drug gives relief from pain. The period of pain relief reported by people who are treated with the drug is normally distributed with mean 50 hours and standard deviation 16 hours.

In a random sample of 64 people who have been treated with the drug, what is the probability that the mean period of pain relief reported is between 48 hours and 53 hours?

---

10. **(a)** A binary operation $\circ$ is defined by $a \circ b = \dfrac{a + b}{2}$ where $a, b \in \mathbf{R}$.

Investigate if $(a \circ b) \circ c = a \circ (b \circ c)$.

(b) The group G, $*$ is defined by the following Cayley table:

$*$	e	a	b	c	d	f	g	h
e	e	a	b	c	d	f	g	h
a	a	b	d	h	e	c	f	g
b	b	d	e	g	a	h	c	f
c	c	h	g	b	f	a	e	d
d	d	e	a	f	b	g	h	c
f	f	c	h	a	g	e	d	b
g	g	f	c	e	h	d	b	a
h	h	g	f	d	c	b	a	e

(i)   Find the order of each element.

(ii) Write down three subgroups of order two.

(iii) $H = \{e, c, x, y\}$ is a subgroup of G. What elements of G do x and y represent?

(iv) Show that $K = \{e, b, f, h\}$ is a subgroup of G and explain why H and K are not isomorphic.

11. **(a)** h is the transformation $(x, y) \rightarrow (x', y')$ where $x' = 5x$ and $y' = 3y$.

    (i)   Find the image of the circle $x^2 + y^2 = 4$ under h.

    (ii) Show that the image is an ellipse and find its eccentricity.

(b) Let g be a similarity transformation.

    (i)   The angle $\angle pqr$ is mapped to the angle $\angle p'q'r'$ under g.
        Given that the line qs bisects $\angle pqr$, show that $q's'$ bisects $\angle p'q'r'$.

    (ii) Hence, prove that if h is the incentre of the triangle pqr, $g(h)$ is the incentre of the triangle $p'q'r'$.

(c) f is the transformation $(x, y) \rightarrow (x', y')$ where $x' = ax$ and $y' = by$ for $a > b > 0$.

    (i)   Given that $f(C)$ is the ellipse $\dfrac{x'^2}{a^2} + \dfrac{y'^2}{b^2} = 1$, show that C is the circle $x^2 + y^2 = 1$.

    (ii) Hence, show that the locus of midpoints of parallel chords of the ellipse $f(C)$ is a diameter (less its endpoints) of $f(C)$.

ANSWERS

2001 Paper 2

1. **(a)** $(x+3)^2 + (y-7)^2 = 289$ or $x^2 + y^2 + 6x - 14y - 231 = 0$

   (b) (i) $p(-13, 4)$, $q(11, 12)$ **(ii)** yes, $[pq]$ is a diameter

   (c) (i) $g = -\frac{9}{2}$, $f = -\frac{5}{2}$, $c = 24$ **(ii)** $(6, 2)$

2. **(a) (i)** $\vec{a} + \vec{c}$ **(ii)** $\frac{1}{2}\vec{a} + \vec{c}$ **(b) (i)** $4\vec{i} - 5\vec{j}$ **(ii)** $10\vec{i} - 13\vec{j}$

   (c) (i) $-3\vec{i} - 4\vec{j}$; $7\vec{i} + \vec{j}$; $-4\vec{i} + 3\vec{j}$ **(iii)** $45°$ or $\dfrac{\pi}{4}$

3. **(a)** $a = -5$ **(b) (i)** $13x' + 17y' - 6 = 0$ **(ii)** $k = -1$

   (c) (i) $-\dfrac{t}{t-2}$ or $\dfrac{t}{2-t}$ **(ii)** $t = \frac{4}{3}$ or $t = -2$

4. **(a) (i)** $\frac{5}{2}$ radians   **(ii)** $143°$ **(b) (i)** $1 - 2\sin^2 x$ **(ii)** $0°, 180°, 210°, 330°, 360°$

5. **(a)** $\frac{7}{2}$ **(b) (i)** $30°$; $150°$ **(ii)** 4.1; 13.5 **(c) (i)** $\sin A = \frac{4}{5}$, $\tan A = -\frac{4}{3}$ **(ii)** $\frac{11}{2}$

6. **(a) (i)** 35 **(ii)** 20 **(b)** $\sqrt{3}(4+\sqrt{5})^n - \sqrt{3}(4-\sqrt{5})^n$ **(c) (i)** $\dfrac{x(x-1)}{(x+6)(x+5)}$ **(ii)** 14 **(iii)** $\frac{15}{91}$

7. **(a) (i)** 360 **(ii)** 24 **(b) (i)** $\frac{25}{144}$ **(ii)** $\frac{25}{72}$ **(iii)** $\frac{5}{48}$ **(iv)** $\frac{5}{18}$ **(c) (i)** $k + 2$ **(ii)** 5

8. **(a)** $x \sin x - \cos x + c$ **(b) (i)** $x - \dfrac{x^3}{3!} + \dfrac{x^5}{5!} - \dfrac{x^7}{7!}$ **(ii)** $(-1)^{n-1} \dfrac{x^{2n-1}}{(2n-1)!}$

   (c) (i) $\sqrt{x^2 + \dfrac{81}{x^2}}$ **(ii)** 3 **(iii)** $\sqrt{18}$ or $3\sqrt{2}$

9 **(a) (i)** $\frac{1}{36}$ **(ii)** $\frac{11}{36}$ **(b) (i)** $\frac{1}{729}$ **(ii)** $\frac{160}{729}$ **(c)** 0.7745

10. **(a)** $(a \circ b) \circ c \neq a \circ (b \circ c)$

    (b) (i) order $(e) = 1$; order $(a) = 4$; order $(b) = 2$; order $(c) = 4$; order $(d) = 4$; order $(f) = 2$; order $(g) = 4$; order (h) 2

    (ii) $\{e, b\}, \{e, f\}, \{e, h\}$ **(iii)** $x = b$; $y = g$

11. **(a) (i)** $\dfrac{(x')^2}{100} + \dfrac{(y')^2}{36} = 1$ **(ii)** $\frac{4}{5}$

EXAM PAPERS

AN ROINN OIDEACHAIS AGUS EOLAÍOCHTA

LEAVING CERTIFICATE EXAMINATION, 2002

MATHEMATICS – HIGHER LEVEL – PAPER 2 (300 marks)

MONDAY, 10 JUNE – MORNING, 9.30 to 12.00

Attempt **FIVE** Questions from Section **A** and **ONE** Question from Section **B**.
Each question carries 50 marks.

WARNING: Marks may be lost if all necessary work is not clearly shown.

SECTION A

Answer FIVE questions from this section.

1. **(a)** The following parametric equations define a circle:

$$x = 4 + 3 \cos \theta, \quad y = -2 + 3 \sin \theta, \quad \text{where } \theta \in \mathbf{R}.$$

What is the Cartesian equation of the circle?

(b) The points $a(-2, 4)$, $b(0, -10)$ and $c(6, -2)$ are the vertices of a triangle.

   (i) Verify that the triangle is right-angled at c.

   (ii) Hence, or otherwise, find the equation of the circle that passes through the points a, b and c.

(c) The circle C has equation $x^2 + y^2 - 4x + 6y - 12 = 0$.

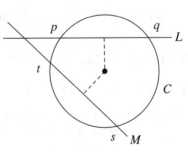

   L intersects C at the points p and q.
   M intersects C at the points t and s.
   $|pq| = |ts| = 8$.

   (i) Find the radius of C and hence show that the
   distance from the centre of C to each
   of the lines L and M is 3.

   (ii) Given that L and M intersect at the point $(-4, 0)$,
   find the equations of L and M.

2. (a) $\vec{s} = 4\vec{i} - 3\vec{j}$, and $\vec{t} = 2\vec{i} - 5\vec{j}$.

Find $|\vec{st}|$.

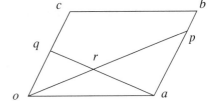

(b) *oabc* is a parallelogram, where *o* is the origin.

$p \in [ab]$ such that $|ap| : |pb| = 3 : 1$.

q is the midpoint of $[oc]$.

(i) Using equiangular triangles, or otherwise, find the ratio $|or| : |rp|$.

(ii) Express $\vec{p}$, and hence $\vec{r}$, in terms of $\vec{a}$ and $\vec{b}$.

(c) $\vec{k} = \vec{i} + 3\vec{j}$, $\vec{n} = 4\vec{i} - 2\vec{j}$, $\vec{u} = 2\vec{i} + \vec{j}$ and $\vec{v} = x\vec{i} + y\vec{j}$ where $x, y \in \mathbf{R}$.

(i) Express the value of $\vec{kn}.\vec{kv}$ in the form $ax + by + c$ where $a, b, c \in \mathbf{R}$.

(ii) Prove that if $\vec{kn}.\vec{kv} = \vec{kn}.\vec{ku}$, and $\vec{u} \neq \vec{v}$, then $\vec{kn} \perp \vec{uv}$.

3. (a) $a(-1, 4)$ and $b(5, -4)$ are two points.

Find the equation of the perpendicular bisector of $[ab]$.

(b) *f* is the transformation $(x, y) \rightarrow (x', y')$ where $x' = 3x + y$ and $y' = x - 2y$.

S is the square whose vertices are $(0, 0)$, $(1, 0)$, $(1, 1)$ and $(0, 1)$.

(i) Find the image under *f* of each of the four vertices of *S*.

(ii) Express *x* and y in terms of x' and y'.

(iii) By considering the lines $ax + by + c = 0$ and $ax + by + d = 0$, or otherwise, prove that *f* maps every pair of parallel lines to a pair of parallel lines. (You may assume that *f* maps every line to a line.)

(iv) Show both *S* and $f(S)$ on a diagram.

(v) Find the area of $f(S)$.

4. (a) Find the value of θ for which $\cos \theta = -\dfrac{\sqrt{3}}{2}$, $0° \le \theta \le 180°$.

(b) (i) Use the formula $\sin^2 A = \dfrac{1}{2}(1 - \cos 2A)$ to express $\sin^2 \dfrac{1}{2} x$ in terms of $\cos x$.

(ii) Hence, or otherwise, find all the solutions of the equation

$$\sin^2 \dfrac{1}{2} x - \cos^2 x = 0$$

in the domain $0° \le x \le 360°$.

(c) A chain passes around two circular wheels as shown. One wheel has radius 75 cm and the other has radius 15 cm. The centres, e and f, of the wheels are 120 cm apart.

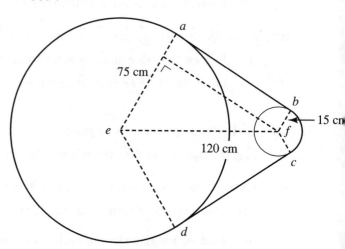

The chain consists of the common tangent $[ab]$, the minor arc bc, the common tangent $[cd]$ and the major arc da.

(i) Find the measure of $\angle aef$.

(ii) Find $|ab|$ in surd form.

(iii) Find the length of the chain, giving your answer in the form $k\pi + l\sqrt{3}$ where $k, l \in \mathbf{Z}$.

5. (a) The area of triangle abc is 12 cm².

$|ab| = 8$ cm and $|\angle abc| = 30°$.

Find $|bc|$.

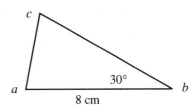

(b) (i) Prove that $\tan(A + B) = \dfrac{\tan A + \tan B}{1 - \tan A \tan B}$.

(ii) Hence, or otherwise, prove that $\tan 22\frac{1}{2}° = \sqrt{2} - 1$.

(c) A vertical radio mast $[pq]$ stands on flat horizontal ground. It is supported by three cables that join the top of the mast, q, to the points a, b, and c on the ground. The foot of the mast, p, lies inside the triangle abc.

Each cable is 52 m long and the mast is 48 m high.

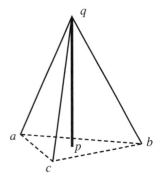

(i) Find the (common) distance from p to each of the points a, b and c.

(ii) Given that $|ac| = 38$ m and $|ab| = 34$ m, find $|bc|$ correct to one decimal place.

6. (a) Nine friends wish to travel in a car. Only two of them, John and Mary, have licences to drive. Only five people can fit in the car (i.e. the driver and four others).

In how many ways can the group of five people be selected if

(i) both John and Mary are included

(ii) either John or Mary is included, but not both?

Later, another one of the nine friends, Anne, gets a driving licence.

(iii) The next time the journey is made, in how many ways can the group of five be chosen, given that at least one licensed driver must be included?

(b) (i) Solve the difference equation $6u_{n+2} - 5u_{n+1} + u_n = 0$, where $n \geqslant 0$, given that $u_0 = 5$ and $u_1 = 2$.

(ii) Find an expression in n for the sum of the terms $u_0 + u_1 + u_2 + \cdots + u_n$. (Hint: it is the sum of two geometric series.)

(iii) Evaluate the sum to infinity of this series $\left(\text{that is: } \displaystyle\sum_{n=0}^{\infty} u_n\right)$.

7. (a) Two unbiased dice, each with faces numbered from 1 to 6, are thrown.

    (i) What is the probability of getting a total equal to 8?

    (ii) What is the probability of getting a total less than 8?

(b) The table below shows the prices of various commodities in the year 2000, as a percentage of their prices in 1999. These are called *price relatives*. (For example, the price relative for *Food, Drink & Other Goods* is 105, indicating that the cost of these items was 5% greater in 2000 than in 1999.)

The table also shows the weight assigned to each commodity. The weight represents the importance of the commodity to the average consumer.

Commodity	Weight	Price in 2000 as % of price in 1999
Housing	8	110
Fuel and Transport	19	108
Tobacco	5	116
Services	16	105
Clothing & Durable Goods	10	97
Food, Drink & Other Goods	42	105

    (i) Calculate the weighted mean of the price relatives in the table.

    (ii) Calculate, correct to two decimal places, the change in the weighted mean if *Tobacco* is removed from consideration.

(c) A palindromic number is one that reads the same backwards as forwards, such as 727 or 38183.

    (i) This year, 2002, is a palindromic year. When is the next palindromic year?

    (ii) How many palindromic years are there from 1000 to 9999 inclusive.

    (iii) A whole number, greater than 9 and less than 10 000, is selected at random. What is the probability that the number is palindromic?

SECTION B

Answer ONE question from this section.

8. **(a)** Use integration by parts to find $\int x \ln x \, dx$.

(b) The perimeter of a sector of a circle of radius r is 8 metres.

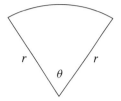

(i) Express θ in terms of r, where θ is the angle of the sector in radians, as shown.

(ii) Hence, show that the area of the sector, in square metres, is $4r - r^2$.

(iii) Find the maximum possible area of the sector.

(c) The Maclaurin series for $\tan^{-1} x$ is $x - \dfrac{x^3}{3} + \dfrac{x^5}{5} - \dfrac{x^7}{7} + \cdots$

The series is convergent when $|x| < 1$.

(i) Write down the first four terms in the series expansion for $\tan^{-1} \frac{1}{2}$.

(ii) Use the fact that $\tan^{-1} \dfrac{1}{2} + \tan^{-1} \dfrac{1}{3} = \dfrac{\pi}{4}$ to derive a series expansion for π, giving the terms up to and including seventh powers.

(iii) Use these terms to find an approximation for π.
Give your answer correct to four decimal places.

9. **(a)** z is a random variable with standard normal distribution. Find $P(z < -0.46)$.

(b) A certain player takes 25 penalty shots during this year's season. Each penalty shot is independent of all others. Experience from previous seasons indicates that on each occasion the probability that this player scores is $\dfrac{3}{5}$.

(i) Find the probability that she scores exactly 15 of the 25 times.

(ii) Use the normal approximation to the binomial distribution to estimate the probability that she scores at least 18 times.

(c) **(i)** $P(E \mid F)$ denotes the conditional probability of "E given F".
Write down an equation to express the relationship between $P(F)$, $P(E \mid F)$ and $P(E \cap F)$.

(ii) E and F are events such that $P(E \mid F) = \dfrac{1}{2}$, $P(F \mid E) = \dfrac{1}{3}$, and $P(E \cap F) = \dfrac{1}{7}$.

Find $P(E \cup F)$.

(iii) Are the events E and F in part **(ii)** independent? Give a reason for your answer.

10. (a) The set $\{0, 2, 4, 6\}$ is a group under addition modulo 8.

Draw up its Cayley table and write down the inverse of each element.

(b) The incomplete table shown is the Cayley table for the group $\{a, b, c, d\}, *$.

*	a	b	c	d
a	c			
b				
c			b	
d				c

    (i) Explain why b must be the identity element.

    (ii) Copy and complete the table.

    (iii) List all of the subgroups of $\{a, b, c, d\}, *$.

(c) (i) $G, *$ is a group and H is a non-empty subset of G.
Give a set of conditions that must be verified in order to show that $H, *$ is a subgroup of $G, *$?

    (ii) G is a group and $g \in G$. Prove that the set $H = \{g^n \mid n \in \mathbf{Z}\}$ is a subgroup of G.

    (iii) C is a cyclic group of order 10 and x is a generator of C.
Describe all the subgroups of C in terms of x.

11. (a) The equation of an ellipse is $\dfrac{x^2}{25} + \dfrac{y^2}{9} = 1$.
Calculate the eccentricity of the ellipse.

(b) Let f be the transformation $(x, y) \rightarrow (x', y')$, where

$$x' = 3x + 4y + 1$$
$$y' = 4x - 3y + 2.$$

Let $p(x_1, y_1)$ and $q(x_2, y_2)$ be two distinct points.

    (i) Find the distance between $f(p)$ and $f(q)$ in terms of x_1, x_2, y_1 and y_2.

    (ii) Hence, or otherwise, prove that f is a similarity transformation.

(c) $[u'v']$ is a chord of the ellipse $E : \dfrac{x^2}{100} + \dfrac{y^2}{25} = 1$.

The midpoint of $[u'v']$ is $p'(8, 2)$.

    (i) Write down a linear transformation f that maps the unit circle $S : x^2 + y^2 = 1$ onto E.

    (ii) Write down the co-ordinates of p, where $f(p) = p'$.

    (iii) Noting that, in a circle, the line joining the centre to the midpoint of a chord is perpendicular to the chord, find the equation of uv, where $f(u) = u'$ and $f(v) = v'$.

    (iv) Find the co-ordinates of u and v, and hence the co-ordinates of u' and v'.

ANSWERS

2002 Paper 2

1. (a) $x^2 + y^2 - 8x + 4y + 11 = 0$ (b) (ii) $x^2 + y^2 + 2x + 6y - 40 = 0$

     (c) (i) 5   (ii) $L : y = 0;\ M : 4x + 3y + 16 = 0$

2. (a) $\sqrt{8}$ or $2\sqrt{2}$ (b) (i) $2 : 3$ (ii) $\vec{p} = \frac{1}{4}\vec{a} + \frac{3}{4}\vec{b};\ \ \vec{r} = \frac{1}{10}\vec{a} + \frac{3}{10}\vec{b}$

     (c) (i) $3x - 5y + 12$

3. (a) $3x - 4y - 6 = 0$ (b) (i) $(0, 0), (3, 1), (4, -1), (1, -2)$

     (ii) $x = \dfrac{2x^1 + y^1}{7}$ $y = \dfrac{x^1 - 3y^1}{7}$ (v) 7

4. (a) $150°$ or $\dfrac{5\pi}{6}$ (b) (i) $\frac{1}{2}(1 - \cos x)$ (ii) $60°, 180°, 300°$

     (c) (i) $60°$ (ii) $60\sqrt{3}$ (iii) $110\pi + 120\sqrt{3}$

5. (a) 6 cm   (c) (i) 20 m   (ii) 30.6 m

6. (a) (i) 35   (ii) 70   (iii) 120   (b) (i) $u_n = 2(\frac{1}{2})^n + 3(\frac{1}{3})^n$

     (ii) $4\left[1 - \dfrac{1}{2^{n+1}}\right] + \dfrac{9}{2}\left[1 - \dfrac{1}{3^{n+1}}\right]$ (iii) $\dfrac{17}{2}$

7. (a) (i) $\frac{5}{36}$ (ii) $\frac{7}{12}$ (b) (i) 105.72   (ii) mean decreases by 0.54

     (c) (i) 2112   (ii) 90   (iii) $\dfrac{7}{370}$

8. (a) $\frac{1}{2}x^2 \ln x - \frac{1}{4}x^2 + c$ (b) (i) $\dfrac{8 - 2R}{R}$ or $\dfrac{8}{R} - 2$ (iii) 4 m^2

     (c) (i) $\frac{1}{2} - \frac{1}{24} + \frac{1}{160} - \frac{1}{896}$ (ii) $\pi = 4[\frac{1}{2} - \frac{1}{24} + \frac{1}{160} - \frac{1}{896} + \frac{1}{3} - \frac{1}{81} + \frac{1}{1215} - \frac{1}{15309}]$ (iii) 3.1409

9. (a) 0.3228   (b) (i) 0.161   (ii) 0.1539

     (c) (i) $p(E \mid F) = \dfrac{p(E \cap F)}{p(F)}$ or $p(E \cap F) = p(F) \cdot p(E \mid F)$ (ii) $\frac{4}{7}$

     (iii) No: $p(E \cap F) \neq p(E).p(E \mid F)$, i.e. $\frac{1}{7} \neq \frac{3}{7} \times \frac{2}{7}$

10. (a)

+ mod 8	0	2	4	6	
0	0	2	4	6	$0^{-1} = 0$
2	2	4	6	0	$2^{-1} = 6$
4	4	6	0	2	$4^{-1} = 4$
6	6	0	2	4	$6^{-1} = 2$

(b) (i)
$a * a = c \Rightarrow a$ not the identity
$c * c = b \Rightarrow c$ not the identity
$d * d = c \Rightarrow d$ not the identity
$\therefore b$ is the identity

(ii)

*	a	b	c	d
a	c	a	d	b
b	a	b	c	d
c	d	c	b	a
d	b	d	a	c

(iii) Subgroups are:
$\{b\}, \{b, c\}, \{a, b, c, d\}$

(c) (i)   **1.** $a, b \in H$, then $a * b \in H$ Closure, no new elements.
and   **2.** $a \in H$, then $a^{-1} \in H$ Inverses, each element has an inverse.
Alternatively
     1. $a, b \in H$, then $a * b^{-1} \in H$ Closure and inverses.

(iii) C is of order 10.
$\therefore$ By Lagrange's Theorem, order of subgroup is a factor of 10,
i.e., of order 1, 2, 5, 10
Thus, the four subgroups are generated by x, x^2, x^5, and x^{10}.

11.   **(a)** $e = \frac{4}{5}$ **(b) (i)** $\sqrt{[(3x_2 + 4y_2) - (3x_1 + 4y_1)]^2 + [(4x_2 - 3y_2) - (4x_1 - 3y_1)]^2}$

(ii) $|f(p) f(q)| = 5 |pq| \; \therefore f$ is a similarity transformation.

Note: f is a linear transformation if $\dfrac{|f(p) f(q)|}{|pq|} = k$.

(c)   **(i)** $f : (x, y) \rightarrow (10x, 5y)$ or in matrix form, $f = \begin{pmatrix} 10 & 0 \\ 0 & 5 \end{pmatrix}$

(ii) $p(\frac{4}{5}, \frac{2}{5})$ **(iii)** $uv : 2x + y - 2 = 0$

(iv) $u(1, 0)$, $v(\frac{3}{5}, \frac{4}{5})$, $u'(10, 0)$, $v'(6, 4)$.